THEORY OF QUANTUM FLUIDS

This is Volume 31 in
PURE AND APPLIED PHYSICS
A Series of Monographs and Textbooks
Consulting Editors: H. S. W. MASSEY AND KEITH A. BRUECKNER
A complete list of titles in this series appears at the end of this volume

THEORY OF QUANTUM FLUIDS

EUGENE FEENBERG

Washington University
St. Louis, Missouri

ACADEMIC PRESS New York and London 1969

ACADEMIC PRESS, INC.
111 Fifth Avenue, New York, New York 10003

United Kingdom Edition published by
ACADEMIC PRESS, INC. (LONDON) LTD.
Berkeley Square House, London W1X 6BA

LIBRARY OF CONGRESS CATALOG CARD NUMBER: 75-84249

PRINTED IN THE UNITED STATES OF AMERICA

Preface

A considerable literature has developed around the method of correlated basis functions with semiquantitative results emerging in problems of nuclear matter and the helium liquids. Clearly a comprehensive review of the field would be useful. The present monograph is not that review; instead it is a severely limited and selective report with emphasis on the microscopic description of liquid ^{4}He and liquid ^{3}He in the physical density range using simple (but essentially realistic) forms of the potential function between pairs of neutral atoms and covering the properties of the ground states and limited ranges of low excited states.

Several omissions may be noted. I have not discussed the relation between the reaction operator formalism of Brueckner and the method of correlated basis functions. The reason is simple—to my knowledge no progress has been made on this fundamental problem. The formalism and applications of the thermodynamic Green's functions fall outside the narrow scope of this monograph. The same reason is offered for other significant omissions, in particular the two-fluid hydrodynamics and the theory of quantized vortex motion (for ^{4}He) and the possibility of a pairing type phase transition at very low temperatures (for ^{3}He).

EUGENE FEENBERG

2

Introduction

All theories of the helium liquids treat the neutral atoms as elementary particles in the sense that excited states of the atoms need not appear explicitly in an adequate theoretical description of the liquid state. Energy quantities characteristic of the liquids fall in the range 1–10°K/atom; excitation energies are greater by factors 10^4–10^5. Thus the vaporization energy of 10^4 atoms is actually smaller than the excitation energy of a single atom. Potentials between pairs (and also among triples) of atoms are adequate substitutes for the dynamical quantum structure of the interacting electronic systems.

A brief sketch of the contents follows. The radial distribution function and the three-particle distribution function generated by an N-particle correlation function are basic mathematical tools in the theory. The ground state solution of the N-particle Schroedinger equation supplies a convenient and nearly optimum choice of correlation function yielding simple formulas for diagonal and off-diagonal matrix elements of the identity and the Hamiltonian operator. In the boson problem this function does indeed describe the ground state; the same function in the fermion problem describes the ground state of a hypothetical boson system with the same particle mass and mutual spin-independent interactions as the actual fermions. Numerical results are derived ultimately from a product-type approximation for the ground state eigenfunction (product of two particle factors).

The Fourier transform $\rho_{\mathbf{k}}$ of the N-particle density operator provides the building material for model states representing systems of free phonons moving through the ground substrate. In the boson problem the representation of the Hamiltonian operator in the paired phonon function space is brought to diagonal form by a sequence of explicit linear transformations, the last of these having exactly the structure of the Bogoliubov transformation as employed in the theory of the low density weakly interacting boson system. Here, however, the creation and annihilation operators do not act on the occupation numbers of single particle states but on the excitation levels of free phonon states, and the ground state trial function serves as the active substrate which supports, emits, and adsorbs free phonons. The analysis starts with a product-type trial function to describe the ground state and yields an improved ground state trial function still of the same product type (ultimately the optimum function of this type) and a lowered estimate of the ground state energy.

Two corrections to the usual estimates of ground state energy are individually of the same order of magnitude as the actual discrepancy between theory and experiment. These are the three-particle polarization energy (a positive quantity) and a second order energy correction (a negative quantity) generated by virtual processes in which three free phonons emerge together from the substrate and are reabsorbed together back into the substrate. For ^{4}He these corrections nearly cancel over the entire density range of the liquid state. A second type of three-phonon vertex, the virtual splitting of a phonon into two and the coalescence of two phonons into one, occurs in the theory of the dispersion relation connecting the energy and wave number of the physical phonon.

Available numerical results on the properties of the ^{4}He system may be characterized as close to or within the 10–20% range of agreement with measured values. This includes the ground state energy, pressure, compressibility, radial distribution function and liquid structure function, and the dispersion relation for the elementary excitations. The theory of excitations is not yet adequate to describe the phase transition from He II to He I.

The artificial problem of the charged boson system at high densities provides a relaxed interlude between the rigors of the real boson system (liquid ^{4}He) and the real fermion system (liquid ^{3}He). Here interest was concentrated for some time on the evaluation of a second term in the formula for the ground state energy as a function of density, competing calculations giving on the one hand a constant independent of density and on the other a term in the logarithm of the density. This conflict, not without dramatic and comic overtones, was finally resolved in favor of the constant.

A variety of cluster expansion techniques is available for the treatment of the fermion problem. These are adapted to realistic conditions of high density and strong interaction by expressing all cluster integrals directly in terms of the distribution functions generated by the N-particle correlation function. Expansions in terms of two-particle correlation factors do not occur.

The major computational difficulty in determining the energy spectrum is the nonorthogonality of the correlated basis. Linear transformations are found which produce an orthonormal basis in a narrow range of low states and simultaneously generate a nearly diagonal representation of the Hamiltonian operator in the same narrow range. A correction to the diagonal elements of H has the form of the standard second order Schroedinger perturbation energy. Destructive interference between direct and orthogonalizaton components in the interaction matrix element reduces the second order energy to a small correction to the diagonal matrix elements. From this foundation numerical results are derived for the ground state energy, first and zeroth sound, effective mass of quasi-particles, thermal coefficient of expansion, magnetic susceptibility, the quasi-particle interaction function and forward scattering amplitudes, and coefficients of thermal conductivity, viscosity, and spin diffusion in the range of nearly complete degeneracy ($T < 0.05°K$). These results include microscopic realizations of all the physical quantities occurring in Landau's phenomenological quasi-particle formalism.

A final chapter is devoted to the microscopic theory of a single ^3He atom in the ^4He liquid.

Contents

THEORY OF QUANTUM FLUIDS

CHAPTER 1

Properties of the Radial Distribution Function

1.1. DEFINITION AND GENERAL PROPERTIES OF DISTRIBUTION FUNCTIONS*

A useful description of a uniform quantum fluid is contained in the set of n-particle distribution functions $p^{(n)}(1, 2, \ldots, n)$ for $n = 1, 2, \ldots, N$. For a system in a pure state these functions are defined by the integrals

$$p^{(n)}(1, 2, \ldots, n) = N(N-1) \cdots (N-n+1) \int |\psi(1, 2, \ldots, N)|^2 \, dv_{n+1, \ldots, N} \tag{1.1}$$

Here $\psi(1, 2, \ldots, N)$ is normalized in the volume Ω and the integration includes summation over the discrete (spin–isospin) coordinates of *all* the particles. When needed, particular types of spin–isospin correlation can be selected by introducing suitable projection operators between ψ^* and ψ in Eq. (1.1). The conventional normalization determined by the factor $N(N-1)\cdots(N-n+1)$ proves convenient in the applications.

All surface effects are neglected in the following discussion. Thus we consider here only the limiting condition $N \to \infty$ while $\rho = N/\Omega$ remains constant. At any value of N, surface effects may be minimized by imposing the nonphysical, but mathematically convenient, periodic boundary condition on the state functions. In a cube of side L ($\Omega = L^3$) this condition determines a discrete set of plane wave orbitals $\exp(i\mathbf{k} \cdot \mathbf{r})$, with $\mathbf{k} = (2\pi/L) \times (\nu_1, \nu_2, \nu_2)$ and $\nu_i = 0, \pm 1, \pm 2, \ldots$. If $\psi(1, 2, \ldots, N)$ is an eigenfunction

* See Green [1]; also Hill [2].

of the total momentum operator $\mathbf{P}$, it can be expressed as a product of two factors

$$\psi = (\exp i\mathbf{k} \cdot \mathbf{r}_{\text{cm}})\varphi \tag{1.2}$$

in which $\mathbf{r}_{\text{cm}} = (1/N) \sum \mathbf{r}_l$, and $\mathbf{P}' = \hbar\mathbf{k}$ is the momentum eigenvalue. Also, and most important, φ depends only on coordinate differences (thus $\mathbf{P}\varphi = 0$). In this context

$$p^{(n)}(1, 2, \ldots, n) = \frac{N(N-1)\cdots(N-n+1)}{\Omega^n}$$

$$\times \sum_{\mathbf{k}_1, \ldots, \mathbf{k}_n} C^{(n)}(\mathbf{k}_1, \ldots, \mathbf{k}_n) \prod_1^n \exp i\mathbf{k}_l \cdot \mathbf{r}_l \tag{1.3}$$

subject to the constraint

$$C^{(n)}(\mathbf{k}_1, \ldots, \mathbf{k}_n) = 0 \qquad \text{if } \sum_1^n \mathbf{k}_l \neq 0 \tag{1.4}$$

A partial characterization of the distribution functions can be drawn from fairly general physical considerations:

(a) $p^{(n)}(1, 2, \ldots, n) 0 \geq$ [by Eq. (1.1)].

(b) $p^{(n)}(1, \ldots, i, \ldots, j, \ldots, n) = p^{(n)}(1, \ldots, j, \ldots, i, \ldots, n)$; the property of complete symmetry (a consequence of the symmetry or antisymmetry of ψ for systems of identical particles).

(c) $p^{(n)}(\mathbf{r}_1 + \mathbf{a}, \ldots, \mathbf{r}_n + \mathbf{a}) = p^{(n)}(\mathbf{r}_1, \ldots, r_m)$, with $\mathbf{a}$ an arbitrary displacement [consequence of the periodic boundary condition in conjunction with Eqs. (1.2)–(1.4)]. In particular, for $n = 2$, $p^{(2)}(1, 2)$ is a function of r_{12} only.

(d) $p^{(n)}(1, \ldots, i, \ldots, j, \ldots, n) = 0$ if $r_{ij} = 0$ (consequence of strong, eventually infinite, repulsive forces acting between two particles when they approach closely). This behavior may be characterized by introducing a length r_0 such that the range $r_{ij} < r_0$ is unimportant in evaluating matrix elements involving $p^{(n)}(1, \ldots, i, \ldots, j, \ldots, n)$. In particular, if the two-particle interaction involves a hard core of range r_0, the condition becomes $p^{(n)}(1, \ldots, i, \ldots, j, \ldots, n) = 0, r_{ij} \leq r_0, 1 \leq i \leq j \leq n.$

(e) If one space point is far removed from all the others ($r_{ni} \gg \rho^{-1/3}, i = 1, 2, \ldots, n-1$), $p^{(n)}(1, 2, \ldots, n-1, n) = \rho p^{(n-1)}(1, 2, \ldots, n-1)\,[1 + O(1/N)]$.

(f) Repeated applications of (*e*) yield, finally, $p^{(n)}(1, 2, \ldots, n) = \rho^n[1 + O(1/N)]$ if $r_{ij} \gg \rho^{-1/3}$, $1 \leq i < j \leq n \ll N$. Properties (e) and (f) result from the finite range of the interparticle interactions and the absence of long-range-order.

Equation (1.1) implies a sequential relation,

$$p^{n-1}(1, \ldots, n-1) = [1/(N-n+1)] \int p^n(1, \ldots, n-1, n)\, d\mathbf{r}_n \tag{1.5}$$

and this, in combination with Eqs. (1.3)–(1.4), requires

$$C^{n-1}(\mathbf{k}_1, \ldots, \mathbf{k}_{n-1}) = C^n(\mathbf{k}_1, \ldots, \mathbf{k}_{n-1}, 0) \tag{1.6}$$

For $n = 2$

$$p^{(1)} = [1/(N-1)] \int p^{(2)}(1, 2)\, d\mathbf{r}_2 = \rho \tag{1.7}$$

since $C^{(1)}(\mathbf{k}_1)$ vanishes unless $\mathbf{k}_1 = 0$. Thus Eqs. (1.2) leads to a constant one-particle density (with no trace of a surface effect). A statement equivalent to Eq. (1.7).

$$(1/\rho) \int [p^{(2)}(1, 2) - \rho^2]\, d\mathbf{r}_2 = -1 \tag{1.8}$$

provides a measure of the extent to which $(1/\rho)p^{(2)}(1, 2)$ departs from the mean density ρ. The superscript 2 on $p^{(2)}(1, 2)$ will be dropped hereafter.

1.2. RADIAL DISTRIBUTION FUNCTION AND LIQUID STRUCTURE FUNCTION

It is customary to write $p(1, 2) = \rho^2 g(r_{12})$ and furthermore to neglect the slight dependence of $g(r)$ on the direction of r. Since $p(1, 2)$ depends only on $\mathbf{r}_{12}$, both points $\mathbf{r}_1$ and $\mathbf{r}_2$ may be taken near the center of the box (assuming $r_{12} \ll L$), where the angular dependence is surely negligible. But then the angular dependence is negligible everywhere. The function $g(r)$ is called the radial distribution function. In terms of $g(r)$ and its asymptotic value $g(\infty)$, Eq. (1.8) becomes

$$4\pi\rho \int_0^\infty [g(r) - g(\infty)] r^2\, dr + N[g(\infty) - 1] = -1 \tag{1.9}$$

The observable quantity most closely related to $g(r)$ is the liquid structure function defined (for $k \neq 0$) by

$$\begin{aligned} S(k) &= (1/N) \int |\psi|^2 \rho_{\mathbf{k}} \rho_{-\mathbf{k}}\, dv_{1,2,\ldots,N} \\ \rho_{\mathbf{k}} &= \sum_1^N \exp i\mathbf{k} \cdot \mathbf{r}_l \\ &= \int \sum_1^N \delta(\mathbf{r} - \mathbf{r}_l)(\exp i\mathbf{k} \cdot \mathbf{r})\, d\mathbf{r} \end{aligned} \tag{1.10}$$

We recognize $\rho_{\mathbf{k}}$ as the Fourier transform of the density operator

$$\rho(\mathbf{r}) = \sum_{1}^{N} \rho(\mathbf{r} - \mathbf{r}_l) \tag{1.11}$$

In terms of $g(r)$ and $g(\infty)$, Eq. (1.10) becomes

$$\begin{aligned} S(k) &= 1 + (1/N) \int p(1, 2)(\exp i\mathbf{k} \cdot \mathbf{r}_{12})\, d\mathbf{r}_1\, d\mathbf{r}_2 \\ &= 1 + \rho \int [g(r) - g(\infty)](\exp i\mathbf{k} \cdot \mathbf{r})\, d\mathbf{r} \end{aligned} \tag{1.12}$$

The first line of Eq. (1.10) exhibits $S(k)$ as a direct measure of the scattering intensity associated with the transmission of a monochromatic plane-wave disturbance through the liquid [3] (with unit relative intensity from atom 1 and the associated coherent intensity from the distribution of particles about atom 1). In fact, $S(k)$ and $g(r)$ were first introduced in classical theoretical discussions of coherent X-ray scattering in liquids. The same functions occur in the theoretical cross section for inelastic scattering of slow neutrons. [4] The second line of Eq. (1.12) may be used to define $S(0) \equiv S(0+)$ (continuity at the origin); thus

$$\begin{aligned} S(0) &= 1 + \rho \int [g(r) - g(\infty)]\, d\mathbf{r} \\ &= N[1 - g(\infty)] \end{aligned} \tag{1.13}$$

by Eq. (1.9).

We show, by considering fluctuations in density, that $S(k) \ll 1$ for $k \ll 2\pi\rho^{1/3}$; consequently, $\lim_{N\to\infty} |N[1 - g(\infty)]| \ll 1$. A more precise statement.

$$\lim_{N\to\infty} S(2\pi\rho^{1/3}\nu/N^{1/3}) = 0 \qquad \text{with} \quad \nu = [\nu_1{}^2 + \nu_2{}^2 + \nu_3{}^2]^{1/2}$$

is then derived from rigorous sum rules involving matrix elements of $\rho_{\mathbf{k}}$ and the restriction that ψ is the exact ground-state eigenfunction ψ_0 of H.

For orientation first consider the behavior of $S(k)$ when k is large ($k \gg 2\pi\rho^{1/3}$) to establish the magnitude of "normal" density fluctuations. The individual exponentials in $\rho_{\mathbf{k}}$ can be treated as independent random variables taking on all values on the unit circle with equal probability. In a small volume element $dv_{1,2\ldots,N}$ the factor $\rho_{\mathbf{k}}\rho_{-\mathbf{k}}$ ranges over all possible values from 0 to N^2 with a distribution appropriate to a quadratic form in a set of independent random variables. Thus $\rho_{\mathbf{k}}\rho_{-\mathbf{k}}$ can be replaced by the average value over the statistical distribution, leaving $|\psi|^2$ as the only variable factor in the integrand of the matrix element defining $S(k)$ [Eq. (1.10)]. The statistical distribution [5]

$$J(Q)\,dQ = (2/N)[\exp(-Q^2/N)]Q\,dQ \tag{1.14}$$

gives the probability of finding $Q = (\rho_{\mathbf{k}}\rho_{-\mathbf{k}})^{1/2}$ in the range dQ. Then

$$\begin{aligned} S(k) &\approx \frac{2}{N}\int_0^\infty \exp\left(-\frac{Q^2}{N}\right)\frac{Q^2}{N}\,Q\,dQ \\ &= 1, \qquad k \gg 2\pi\rho^{1/3} \end{aligned} \tag{1.15}$$

in agreement with the obvious deduction from Eq. (1.12). Equations (1.14) and (1.15) imply that the mean-square number fluctuation in the half-space defined by $\cos(\mathbf{k}\cdot\mathbf{r}) > 0$ approaches the "normal" order of magnitude $O(N)$. The same statement holds with $\sin(\mathbf{k}\cdot\mathbf{r})$ substituted for $\cos(\mathbf{k}\cdot\mathbf{r}) > 0$.

At the opposite extreme of small k ($0 < k \ll 2\pi\rho^{1/3}$), a sufficient argument for $S(k) \ll 1$ can be developed for the ground state of a system with density appropriate to a condensed phase and strong repulsive forces acting between pairs of particles when they approach closely. The instantaneous distribution of particles in the ground state can be pictured as fairly regular, each particle more or less near the center of an elementary cell. Thus the important configurations (values of $\mathbf{r}_1, \mathbf{r}_2, \cdots, \mathbf{r}_N$ in the close neighborhood of peak values of $|\psi|^2$) are those with the particles spaced fairly uniformly so that the distribution in the neighborhood of any particle does not vary greatly from particle to particle. Any noticeable departure from this description means excess kinetic energy and excess positive contribution to the potential energy from the repulsive component of the interaction potential; consequently occurs with small probability in the ground state or in any ψ capable of giving a good description of the ground state.

Consider now $\mathbf{k} = (2\pi/L)\,(\nu_1, \nu_2, \nu_3)$ subject to $0 < k \ll 2\pi\rho^{1/3}$. Very nearly equal numbers of particles occur in the two regions characterized by $\cos(\mathbf{k}\cdot\mathbf{r}) > 0$ and $\cos(\mathbf{k}\cdot\mathbf{r}) < 0$. The statistical spread in the number of particles in each of these half spaces is small compared to $(N/2)^{1/2}$. A similar statement applies to $\sin(\mathbf{k}\cdot\mathbf{r})$. We conclude that $|\rho_{\mathbf{k}}| \ll N^{1/2}$ in the general neighborhood of peak values of ψ^2; consequently, $S(k) \ll 1$ and $\lim_{N\to\infty} |N[1 - g(\infty)]| \ll 1$.

This argument can be summarized in the statement that the mean-square number fluctuation in a volume element with linear dimensions all large compared to $\rho^{-1/3}$ is very small compared to the mean number of particles in the element (subnormal fluctuations); at the opposite extreme, when the volume element is a thin slab of thickness smaller than $\rho^{-1/3}$ the mean-square number fluctuation approaches the mean number of particles in the element (more precisely, one-half of this).

A word of caution is in place here. "Small compared to one" need not signify that the limit vanishes; depending on the presence or absence of the correct long-range correlations in ψ, it may mean this, or it may mean merely that the limit is a small constant, say, 1/10. The essential, perhaps trivial, point is that number fluctuations are substantially smaller than in a low-density gas.

The preceding argument is worthwhile because it emphasizes the physical meaning of $S(k)$ as a qualitative measure of number fluctuations in appropriately defined half spaces and does not require that ψ be the exact ground-state wave function. We turn now to the derivation of sum rules needed to obtain a stronger version of the same result, but in a more precise, formal, and abstract manner, limited, however, by the restriction that ψ is the exact ground-state wavefunction.

1.3. SUM RULES INVOLVING $\rho_{\mathbf{k}}$*

Let $|n\rangle$ denote the complete, normalized orthogonal set of eigenfunctions of the Hamiltonian operator H. In particular, $|0\rangle$ describes the ground state. These functions may be used to express $S(k)$ in terms of the matrix elements of $\rho_{\mathbf{k}}$ and $\rho_{-\mathbf{k}}$:

$$\begin{aligned} S(k) &= (1/N)\langle 0|\rho_{\mathbf{k}}\,\rho_{-\mathbf{k}}|0\rangle \\ &= (1/N)\sum_n |\langle 0|\rho_{\mathbf{k}}|n\rangle|^2 \end{aligned} \tag{1.16}$$

Equation (1.16) states the first sum rule. The second rule is generated directly by evaluating the second commutator of H, $\rho_{\mathbf{k}}$, and $\rho_{-\mathbf{k}}$:

$$\begin{aligned} \hbar^2 k^2/2m &= (1/2N)\langle 0|[\rho_{-\mathbf{k}}, [H, \rho_{\mathbf{k}}]]|0\rangle \\ &= (1/N)\sum_n (E_n - E_0)|\langle 0|\rho_{\mathbf{k}}|n\rangle|^2 \end{aligned} \tag{1.17}$$

Time-reversal invariance is used in deriving Eq. (1.17) in the form that the sum over all states does not distinguish **k** from −**k**.

* See Price [6].

The third (Onsager–Price) sum rule involves a subtle insight into the behavior of the fluid system in a weak, slowly varying external field. Let $V(\mathbf{r})$ denote the potential of the external field for a particle at position $\mathbf{r}$. The total external potential can be expressed simply in terms of $\rho_{\mathbf{k}}$:

$$\sum_{1}^{N} V(\mathbf{r}_l) = \sum_{1}^{N} \sum_{\mathbf{k}\neq 0} V_{\mathbf{k}} \exp i\mathbf{k}\cdot\mathbf{r}_l$$

$$= \sum_{\mathbf{k}\neq 0} V_{\mathbf{k}}\rho_{\mathbf{k}}, \qquad V_{\mathbf{k}} = V_{-\mathbf{k}}^{*} \tag{1.18}$$

A possible constant component V_0 is eliminated by suitable choice of the zero level from which $V(\mathbf{r})$ is measured $[\int V(\mathbf{r})\, d\mathbf{r} = 0]$. Under the restriction to a slowly varying field only small values of k are involved in the expansion of Eq. (1.18); $V_{\mathbf{k}}$ is assumed negligible unless $k \ll 2\pi\rho^{1/3}$.

The change in the ground-state energy produced by the external field can be computed by two independent procedures: (a) by equating it to the total energy (positional and elastic) stored in the system because of differential changes in density, and (b) by equating it to the Schrödinger second-order energy generated by the perturbing potential:

(a) Energy density, pressure, and compressibility coefficient are related through the defining equations

$$e(\rho) = E_0/\Omega = (1/N)\rho E_0$$

$$p = -dE_0/d\Omega = -e + \rho\, de/d\rho \tag{1.19}$$

$$K^{-1} = -\Omega\, dp/d\Omega = \Omega\, d^2E_0/d\Omega^2 = \rho^2\, d^2e/d\rho^2$$

In the external field the system acquires a nonuniform particle density $\rho + \delta\rho(\mathbf{r})$ subject to the conservation condition $\int \delta\rho(\mathbf{r})\, d\mathbf{r} = 0$. The corresponding total energy is

$$E + \delta E = \int V(\mathbf{r})[\rho + \delta\rho(\mathbf{r})]\, d\mathbf{r}$$

$$+ \int \left[e + \frac{\partial e}{\partial \rho}\, \delta\rho(\mathbf{r}) + \frac{1}{2}\frac{\delta^2 e}{\partial \rho^2}\, [\delta\rho(\mathbf{r})]^2 + \cdots \right] d\mathbf{r} + \cdots$$

a sum of a direct additional potential energy, the original total energy E, and the energy of the elastic distortion associated with $\delta\rho(\mathbf{r})$. Introducing the conditions $\int V(\mathbf{r})\, d\mathbf{r} = 0$, and $\int d\rho(\mathbf{r})\, d\mathbf{r} = 0$, the increment in total energy is

$$\delta E = \int V(\mathbf{r})\, \delta\rho(\mathbf{r})\, d\mathbf{r} + \frac{1}{2K\rho^2} \int [\delta\rho(\mathbf{r})]^2\, d\mathbf{r}$$

$$= \frac{1}{2K\rho^2} \int [\delta\rho(\mathbf{r}) + K\rho^2 V(\mathbf{r})]^2\, d\mathbf{r} - \frac{1}{2} K\rho^2 \int V(\mathbf{r})^2\, d\mathbf{r} \qquad (1.20)$$

Equilibrium requires the minimum value of δE with respect to variations in $\delta\rho(\mathbf{r})$; consequently,

$$\delta\rho(\mathbf{r}) = -K\rho^2 V(\mathbf{r}) \qquad (1.21)$$

Equation (1.21) balances the local increment in pressure against the potential energy per unit volume of the particles in the external field. The final result is

$$\delta E = -\tfrac{1}{2} K\rho^2 \int V^2(\mathbf{r})\, d\mathbf{r}$$

$$= -\tfrac{1}{2} K\rho N \sum_{\mathbf{k}} |V_{\mathbf{k}}|^2 \qquad (1.22)$$

(b) Equation (1.18) gives us the Schrödinger second-order energy in the form

$$\delta E = \sum_n{}' \frac{|\sum_{\mathbf{k}} V_{\mathbf{k}} \langle 0|\rho_{\mathbf{k}}|n\rangle|^2}{E_0 - E_n} \qquad (1.23)$$

Since the total momentum $\mathbf{P}$ is a constant of motion, the functions $|n\rangle$ may be chosen as simultaneous eigenfunctions of H and $\mathbf{P}$, with the consequence that the sum over $\mathbf{k}$ in Eq. (1.23) reduces to a single term (varying with n). Thus

$$\delta E = \sum_{\mathbf{k}} |V_{\mathbf{k}}|^2 \sum_n{}' \frac{|\langle 0|\rho_{\mathbf{k}}|n\rangle|^2}{E_0 - E_n} \qquad (1.24)$$

At this point the condition that $V(\mathbf{r})$ is slowly varying ($V_{\mathbf{k}}$ negligible except for $k \ll 2\pi\rho^{1/3}$) permits the replacement of the sum over n in Eq. (1.24) by its limiting value as $k \to 0$:

$$\delta E = -NX \sum_{\mathbf{k}} |V_{\mathbf{k}}|^2$$

$$X = \lim_{\mathbf{k}\to 0} \frac{1}{N} \sum_n{}' \frac{|\langle 0|\rho_{\mathbf{k}}|n\rangle|^2}{E_n - E_0} \qquad (1.25)$$

The required sum rule follows from equating our two forms of δE:

$$\frac{1}{2mc^2} = \tfrac{1}{2}\rho K = \lim_{\mathbf{k}\to 0} (1/N) \sum_n{}' \frac{|\langle 0|\rho_{\mathbf{k}}|n\rangle|^2}{E_n - E_0} \qquad (1.26)$$

Notice that the left-hand member of Eq. (1.26) involves properties of the ground state alone, while the right-hand member involves excited states and the spectrum of eigenvalues; c in Eq. (1.26) is the velocity of first sound.

A further consequence of this analysis is that Eq. (1.21) for $\delta\rho(\mathbf{r})$ can be expressed as

$$\delta\rho(\mathbf{r}) = -2X\rho V(\mathbf{r}) \tag{1.27}$$

The consistency of the procedure [equating δE from (a) and (b)] can be checked by a direct calculation of $\delta\rho(\mathbf{r})$ from the perturbed ground state wave function

$$\psi = \psi_0 + \sum_{n,\mathbf{k}}' \frac{V_{\mathbf{k}}\langle n|\rho_{-\mathbf{k}}|0\rangle}{E_0 - E_n}\psi_n \tag{1.28}$$

(writing $\psi_0 = |0\rangle$ and $\psi_n = |n\rangle$). The resulting formula

$$\delta\rho(\mathbf{r}_1) = \rho\Omega \sum_{n,\mathbf{k}}' \frac{1}{E_0 - E_n}\Big[V_{\mathbf{k}}\langle n|\rho_{-\mathbf{k}}|0\rangle \int \psi_0{}^*\psi_n \, dv_{2,3,\ldots,N} + V_{\mathbf{k}}{}^*\langle 0|\rho_{\mathbf{k}}|n\rangle \int \psi_0\psi_n{}^* \, dv_{2,3,\ldots,N}\Big] \tag{1.29}$$

can be reduced by using

$$\psi_n = \sum_{\ldots,\mathbf{k}_l,\ldots} C_n(\ldots,\mathbf{k}_l,\ldots)\prod_1^N [(\exp i\mathbf{k}_l\cdot\mathbf{r}_l)/\Omega^{1/2}] \tag{1.30}$$

subject to $\sum \mathbf{k}_l = \text{const}$. Thus

$$\langle n|\rho_{-\mathbf{k}}|0\rangle = N \sum_{\ldots,\mathbf{k}_l,\ldots} C_n{}^*(\mathbf{k}_1, \mathbf{k}_2, \ldots, \mathbf{k}_N) C_0(\mathbf{k}_1 - \mathbf{k}, \mathbf{k}_2, \ldots, \mathbf{k}_N) \tag{1.31}$$

if $\sum \mathbf{k}_l = \mathbf{k}$ and vanishes otherwise. Also

$$\int \psi_0{}^*\psi_n \, dv_{2,\ldots,N} = (1/\Omega N)\langle 0|\rho_{\mathbf{k}}|n\rangle \exp i\mathbf{k}\cdot\mathbf{r}_1 \tag{1.32}$$

These relations in Eq. (1.29) verify Eq. (1.27) for $\delta\rho(\mathbf{r})$.

The physical content of the sum rules emerges more clearly when they are expressed in terms of the dynamic form factor [4]

$$\begin{aligned} S(k,\omega) &= (1/N)\langle 0|\rho_{\mathbf{k}}\,\delta(H - E_0)\rho_{\mathbf{k}}|0\rangle \\ &= (1/N)\sum_n |\langle 0|\rho_{\mathbf{k}}|n\rangle|^2\,\delta(\omega_n - \omega) \end{aligned} \tag{1.33}$$

with $\omega_n = E_n - E_0$. This function occurs as an intensity factor in the scattering of slow neutrons by liquid ^{4}He generated by the interaction potential

$$V_{\nu\alpha} = a \sum_1^N \delta(\mathbf{r}_\nu - \mathbf{r}_l) \tag{1.34}$$

In Eq. (1.34) a is the low-energy scattering length and the delta-function provides an adequate representation of the short-range ($\sim 10^{-13}$ cm) interaction between a neutron and a ^{4}He atom. In the Born approximation the transition amplitude contains the matrix element of $V_{\nu\alpha}$ between initial and final states $(\exp i\mathbf{k}_{\nu i} \cdot \mathbf{r}_\nu)|0\rangle$ and $(\exp i\mathbf{k}_{\nu f} \cdot \mathbf{r}_\nu)|n\rangle$. Thus the transition probability for momentum transfer $\mathbf{k} = \mathbf{k}_{\nu i} - \mathbf{k}_{\nu f}$ and final state $|n\rangle$ of the fluid is proportional to $|\langle n|\rho_{\mathbf{k}}|0\rangle|^2$. The function $S(k, \omega)$ is proportional to the transition probability per unit energy range for energy loss ω and momentum transfer $\hbar\mathbf{k}$.

In terms of $S(k, \omega)$, Eqs. (1.16), (1.17), and (1.26) become

$$S(k) = \int_0^\infty S(k, \omega)\, d\omega \tag{1.35}$$

$$\frac{\hbar^2 k^2}{2m} = \int_0^\infty \omega S(k, \omega)\, d\omega \tag{1.36}$$

$$\frac{1}{2mc^2} = \lim_{k\to 0} \int_0^\infty \frac{S(k, \omega)}{\omega}\, d\omega \tag{1.37}$$

These relations place a constraint on the behaviour of $S(k)$ near the origin. Equations (1.36) and (1.37) yield

$$\begin{aligned}\left(\frac{\hbar k}{2mc}\right)^2 &= \lim_{k\to 0} \frac{1}{2} \int_0^\infty \int_0^\infty \left(\frac{\omega}{\omega'} + \frac{\omega'}{\omega}\right) S(k, \omega) S(k, \omega')\, d\omega\, d\omega' \\ &= \lim_{k\to 0} \int_0^\infty \int_0^\infty \left[1 + \frac{(\omega - \omega')^2}{2\omega\omega'}\right] S(k, \omega) Sk, \omega')\, d\omega\, d\omega' \end{aligned} \tag{1.38}$$

with the immediate consequences

$$\lim_{k\to 0} \frac{S(k)}{k} \leq \frac{\hbar}{2mc}, \qquad S(0) \equiv S(0+) = 0 \tag{1.39}$$

Equations (1.13) can now be converted into a precise statement of asymptotic behavior valid for the radial distribution function defined by the ground-state eigenfunction:

$$\lim_{N\to\infty} N[1-g(\infty)] = 0$$
$$g(\infty) = 1 + O_\nu(1/N), \qquad \nu > 1 \tag{1.40}$$

where $O_\nu(1/N)$ means simply

$$\lim_{N\to\infty} NO_\nu(1/N) = 0, \qquad \nu > 1$$
$$= \text{const}, \quad \nu = 1$$

Equation (1.9) reduces to the more familiar statement [7]

$$\rho \int [g(r) - 1]\, d\mathbf{r} = -1 \tag{1.41}$$

Equation (1.40) gives precision to the statement following Eq. (1.8) by limiting the range in which $g(r) - 1$ contributes effectively to the integral in Eq. (1.41).

Sum rules for ω^2 and ω^3 are derived in Appendix 4-A following the discussion of the three-particle distribution function and the spectrum of elementary excitations.

1.4. A FLUCTUATION THEOREM FOR THE GROUND STATE

The asymptotic behavior described by Eq. (1.40) can be used to derive a fluctuation theorem. Let

$$n(r) - 1, \qquad 0 \le x \le \tfrac{1}{2}L$$
$$= 0, \qquad \tfrac{1}{2}L < x \le L \tag{1.42}$$

The operator for the number of particles in the range $0 \le x \le L/2$ is then

$$\mathcal{N} = \sum_1^N n(\mathbf{r}_l) \tag{1.43}$$

with the mean and mean-square values

$$\begin{aligned}\bar{\mathcal{N}} &= \tfrac{1}{2}N \\ \overline{\mathcal{N}^2} &= \tfrac{1}{2}N + N(N-1)\overline{n_1\, n_2} \\ &= \tfrac{1}{2}N + \rho^2 \int g(r_{12}) n_1\, n_2\, d\mathbf{r}_1\, d\mathbf{r}_2 \end{aligned} \tag{1.44}$$

Equation (1.8) or (1.41) in the form

$$\rho^2 \int [g(r_{12}) - 1][n_1 + (1 - n_1)][n_2 + (1 - n_2)]\, d\mathbf{r}_1\, d\mathbf{r}_2 = -N \tag{1.45}$$

implies

$$\begin{aligned}\rho^2 \int g(r_{12}) n_1\, n_2\, dv_1\, dv_2 = &-\tfrac{1}{2}N + (N/2)^2 \\ &+ \rho^2 \int [1 - g(r_{12})](1 - n_1) n_2\, d\mathbf{r}_1\, d\mathbf{r}_2 \end{aligned} \tag{1.46}$$

and, together with Eq. (1.44),

$$\overline{(\mathcal{N} - \bar{\mathcal{N}})^2} = \rho^2 \int [1 - g(r_{12})](1 - n_1) n_2\, d\mathbf{r}_1\, d\mathbf{r}_2 \tag{1.47}$$

The derivation of Eq. (1.47) does not depend on the precise form of the two half-spaces into which Ω is resolved. In addition, the half-spaces may consist of any number of disconnected elements, with $n(\mathbf{r}) = 1$ in one half-space and $n(\mathbf{r}) = 0$ in the other. The remainder term in Eq. (1.40) leads to an estimate $N^2 O_v(1/N)$ for the integral in Eq. (1.47). Another and more interesting contribution comes from the region in which $g(r_{12})$ is small ($r_{12} \leq \rho^{-1/3}$). Equation (1.42) leads to the estimate

$$\rho^2 (L^2 \rho^{-1/3}) \rho^{-1} = N^{2/3}$$

in which ρ^{-1} comes from integrating over $\mathbf{r}_2$ for fixed $\mathbf{r}_1$ and $L^2\rho^{-1/3}$ comes from the final integration over $\mathbf{r}_1$. Thus

$$\overline{(\mathcal{N} - \bar{\mathcal{N}})^2} = N^2 O_v(1/N) + \gamma N^{2/3} \tag{1.48}$$

This estimate of the mean-square number fluctuation permits a more precise evaluation of the liquid structure function at $k = 2\pi/L$:

$$\begin{aligned} S(2\pi/L) &\sim (1/N)\overline{(\mathcal{N} - \bar{\mathcal{N}})^2} \\ &= N O_v(1/N) + (\gamma/N^{1/3}) \end{aligned} \tag{1.49}$$

To extend the result to the range $2\pi/L \leq k \ll 2\pi\rho^{1/3}$, observe that the factor γ in Eq. (1.49) is proportional to the internal surface area bounding the regions in which $\cos(\mathbf{k} \cdot \mathbf{r})$ is positive [or $\sin(\mathbf{k} \cdot \mathbf{r})$ is positive]. But this area is on the average proportional to k (proportional to the number of internal plane nodal surfaces). Consequently, Eq. (1.49) can be extended immediately to

$$S(k) \sim NO_\nu(1/N) + (\gamma'/2\pi\rho^{1/3})k \tag{1.50}$$

for $2\pi/L \leq k \ll 2\pi\rho^{1/3}$. In the limit $N \to \infty$, $\nu > 1$,

$$S(k) \sim (\gamma'/2\pi\rho^{1/3})k, \qquad 0 < k \ll 2\pi\rho^{1/3} \tag{1.51}$$

A more analytical approach to these relations is given in Appendix 1-B.

A concluding remark on Eq. (1.47): When the half-spaces consist of a large number of alternating thin slabs (thickness $\ll \rho^{-1/3}$) each factor $1 - n_1$ and n_2 can be replaced by the independent average value $\frac{1}{2}$. In this limiting case the mean-square number fluctuation attains the maximum value $\frac{1}{2}\mathcal{N} = \frac{1}{4}N$.

1.5. EXAMPLES: GROUND STATES OF NONINTERACTING BOSON AND FERMION SYSTEMS

A. Boson System

The ground-state eigenfunction ψ is a constant. With no forces acting to moderate fluctuations in coordinate space the argument leading to Eq. (1.40) fails. Thus the results

$$\begin{aligned} p(1, 2) &= N(N-1)/\Omega^2 \\ g(r) &= 1 - (1/N) \\ S(k) &= 1, \qquad k \neq 0 \end{aligned} \tag{1.52}$$

are peculiar to this problem.

B. Fermion System (Spinless Particles)

In this case

$$\psi = (N!\,\Omega^N)^{-1/2} \sum_\nu (\pm) P_\nu \prod_1^N \exp i\mathbf{k}_l \cdot \mathbf{r}_l \tag{1.53}$$

with k ranging over all discrete allowed wave vectors in a sphere of radius $k_F = (6\pi^2\rho)^{1/3}$. A simple calculation yields

$$p(1, 2) = \rho^2 g(r_{12}) = \frac{1}{\Omega^2} \sum_{\mathbf{k}', \mathbf{k}''} [1 - \exp i(\mathbf{k}' - \mathbf{k}'') \cdot \mathbf{r}_{12}] \tag{1.54}$$

or

$$g(r) = 1 - l^2(k_F r), \qquad l(x) = (3/x^3)(\sin x - x \cos x) \tag{1.55}$$

Observe that

$$\begin{aligned} g(r \sim L) &\sim 1 - 9/2(k_F L)^4 \\ &\sim 1 - O(N^{-4/3}) \end{aligned} \tag{1.56}$$

in agreement with Eq. (1.40). The liquid structure function is given by

$$\begin{aligned} S(k) &= 1 + (1/N) \int p(1, 2) \exp i\mathbf{k} \cdot \mathbf{r}_{12}\, d\mathbf{r}_1\, d\mathbf{r}_2 \\ &= 1 - \frac{1}{\Omega^2 N} \int \exp i\mathbf{k} \cdot \mathbf{r}_{12} \sum_{\mathbf{k}', \mathbf{k}''} \exp i(\mathbf{k}' - \mathbf{k}'') \cdot \mathbf{r}_{12}\, d\mathbf{r}_1\, d\mathbf{r}_2 \\ &= 1 - \frac{1}{N} \sum_{\mathbf{k}', \mathbf{k}''} \delta(\mathbf{k} + \mathbf{k}' - \mathbf{k}'') \end{aligned} \tag{1.57}$$

Here the sum over $\mathbf{k}'$ and $\mathbf{k}''$ includes all allowed wave vectors in the volume common to two spheres of radius k_F and distance k between centers. The geometrical picture leads easily to the formula

$$\begin{aligned} S(k) &= (3k/4k_F) - \tfrac{1}{2}(k/2k_F)^3, \qquad & k \le 2k_F \\ &= 1, & k > 2k_F \end{aligned} \tag{1.58}$$

Equation (1.58) conforms to the general property described by Eq. (1.51): $S(k)$ is a linear function of k in the range $k \ll 2\pi\rho^{1/3}$. Here this property can be traced back to the asymptotic behavior of $g(r)$: for $k \ll 2\pi\rho^{1/3}$

$$\begin{aligned} S(k) &\approx 4\pi\rho \int_0^\infty \left(1 - \frac{\sin kr}{kr}\right) \frac{9}{2(k_F r)^4}\, r^2\, dr \\ &= \frac{3k}{\pi k_F} \int_0^\infty \left(1 - \frac{\sin x}{x}\right) \frac{dx}{x^2} \end{aligned} \tag{1.59}$$

in agreement with the leading term of $S(k)$ in Eq. (1.58) [since the integral in the second line of Eq. (1.59) has the value $\pi/4$].

1.6. DISTRIBUTION FUNCTIONS UNDER EQUILIBRIUM CONDITIONS

Let $p_{Nl}(1, 2)$ denote the two particle distribution function for N particles in energy state E_{Nl}; $S_{Nl}(k)$ is the corresponding liquid structure function. In the canonical ensemble describing the N-particle system

$$p_N(1, 2; T) = \sum_l [\exp(-\beta E_{Nl})] p_{Nl}(1, 2) \left[\sum_l \exp(-\beta E_{Nl})\right]^{-1} \tag{1.60}$$

and, for $k \neq 0$,

$$\begin{aligned} S_N(k; T) &= \frac{1}{N} \frac{\sum_l \exp(-\beta E_{Nl}) \int |\psi_{Nl}|^2 \rho_{\mathbf{k}}^{(N)} \rho_{-\mathbf{k}}^{(N)} \, dv_{1, 2, \ldots, N}}{\sum_l \exp(-\beta E_{Nl})} \\ &= 1 + \frac{1}{N} \int p_N(1, 2; T) \exp i\mathbf{k} \cdot \mathbf{r}_{12} \, d\mathbf{r}_1 \, d\mathbf{r}_2 \end{aligned} \tag{1.61}$$

In the grand canonical ensemble with mean particle number N the corresponding definitions are

$$p(1, 2; T) = \frac{\sum_{N'l'} p_{N'}(1, 2; T) \exp \beta(\mu N' - E_{N'l'})}{\sum_{N''l''} \exp \beta(\mu N'' - E_{N''l''})} \tag{1.62}$$

and, for $k \neq 0$,

$$\begin{aligned} S(k; T) &= \frac{\sum_{N'l'} \int |\psi_{N'l'}|^2 \rho_{\mathbf{k}}^{(N')} \rho_{-\mathbf{k}}^{(N')} \, dv_{1, 2, \ldots, N'} \exp -\beta(E_{N'l'} - \mu N')}{N \sum_{N''l''} \exp -\beta(E_{N''l''} - \mu N'')} \\ &= 1 + \frac{1}{N} \int p(1, 2; T) \exp i\mathbf{k} \cdot \mathbf{r}_{12} \, d\mathbf{r}_1 \, d\mathbf{r}_2 \end{aligned} \tag{1.63}$$

Equation (1.62) and (1.63) generate the ground state distributions at $T = 0$ ($\beta = \infty$). To extend these definitions to $k = 0$ so that $S_N(0; T) = S_N(0+; T)$ and $S(0; T) = S(0+; T)$ requires only that $p_N(1, 2; T)$ and $p(1, 2; T)$ be replaced by $p_N(1, 2; T) - p_N(\infty)$ and $p(1, 2; T) - p(\infty)$, respectively. Here $p_N(\infty)$ and ($p(\infty)$ denote the asymptotic limiting values assumed by the distribution functions as $r_{12} \to \infty$. The definitions of $p_N(1, 2; T)$ and $p(1, 2; T)$ now lead to

$$p(\infty) = \sum_{N'l'} p_{N'}(\infty) \exp \beta(\mu N' - E_{N'l'}) \left[\sum_{N''l''} \exp \beta(\mu N'' - E_{N''l''})\right]^{-1} \tag{1.64}$$

If we assume

$$p_{N'}(\infty) = (N'^2/\Omega^2)[1 - (\alpha/N')] \tag{1.65}$$

Eq. (1.64) for $p(\infty)$ yields

$$\begin{aligned} p(\infty) &= (\overline{N'^2} - \alpha N)/\Omega^2 \\ &= \rho^2 + [\overline{(N' - N)^2} - \alpha N]/\Omega^2 \end{aligned} \tag{1.66}$$

where the bar denotes an average over the grand canonical ensemble. The mean-square number fluctuation is easily related to the volume integral of $p(1, 2)$. Observe that

$$(1/N) \int p(1, 2; T)\, d\mathbf{r}_1\, d\mathbf{r}_2 = \overline{N'(N' - 1)}/N \tag{1.67}$$

Thus

$$(1/N) \int [p(1, 2; T) - \rho^2]\, d\mathbf{r}_1\, d\mathbf{r}_2 = -1 + \overline{(N' - N)^2}/N \tag{1.68}$$

What makes these relations useful is the fact that the mean-square number fluctuation can also be expressed in terms of thermodynamic quantities through the properties of the chemical potential.

From

$$\rho = \frac{N}{\Omega} = \frac{1}{\Omega} \frac{\sum_{N'l'} N' \exp \beta(\mu N' - E_{N'l'})}{\sum_{N''l''} \exp \beta(\mu N'' - E_{N''l''})} \tag{1.69}$$

we obtain

$$\frac{1}{\beta}\left(\frac{\partial \rho}{\partial \mu}\right)_\beta = \frac{\rho \overline{(N' - N)^2}}{N} \tag{1.70}$$

Since μ can be identified with the Gibbs function per particle ($N\mu = G = U + P\Omega - TS$), we compute

$$\begin{aligned} \left(\frac{\partial \mu}{\partial \Omega}\right)_{TN} &= \frac{1}{N}\left(\frac{\partial G}{\partial \Omega}\right)_{TN} = -\frac{1}{\Omega}\left(\frac{\partial p}{\partial \rho}\right)_{TN} \\ &= -1/NK_T \end{aligned} \tag{1.71}$$

in which K_T is the isothermal compressibility. Thus

$$\begin{aligned} K_T &= -(1/N)(\partial \Omega/\partial \mu)_{TN} \\ &= (1/\rho^2)(\partial \rho/\partial \mu)_\beta \end{aligned} \tag{1.72}$$

The final result is [8], [9],

$$\overline{(N' - N)^2}/N = (1/\beta)\rho K_{\mathrm{T}} \tag{1.73}$$

and

$$(1/N) \int [p(1, 2; T) - \rho^2]\, d\mathbf{r}_1\, d\mathbf{r}_2 = -1 + (1/\beta)\rho K_{\mathrm{T}} \tag{1.74}$$

The corresponding relation for the canonical ensemble is

$$(1/N) \int [p_N(1, 2; T) - \rho^2]\, d\mathbf{r}_1\, d\mathbf{r}_2 = -1 \tag{1.75}$$

Equations (1.74) and (1.75) have consequences for $S(0; T)$ and $S_N(0; T)$:

$$\begin{aligned} S_N(0; T) &= 1 + (1/N) \int [p_N(1, 2; T) - p_N(\infty)]\, d\mathbf{r}_1\, d\mathbf{r}_2 \\ &= (\Omega/\rho)[\rho^2 - p_N(\infty)] \\ &= \alpha \end{aligned} \tag{1.76}$$

the last line following from Eq. (1.65). Similarly,

$$\begin{aligned} S(0; T) &= 1 + (1/N) \int [p(1, 2; T) - p(\infty)]\, d\mathbf{r}_1\, d\mathbf{r}_2 \\ &= (1/\beta)\rho K_{\mathrm{T}} + (\Omega/\rho)[\rho^2 - p(\infty)] \\ &= \alpha \end{aligned} \tag{1.77}$$

the last line a consequence of Eqs. (1.65), (1.66), and (1.73). Thus

$$S_N(0; T) = S(0; T) = \alpha \tag{1.78}$$

The identity of $S_N(k; T)$ and $S(k; T)$ can be inferred more directly by observing that the near-equality

$$p(1, 2; T) - p(\infty) \approx p_N(1, 2: T) - p_N(\infty) \tag{1.79}$$

appears to be a necessary consequence of the defining equations [(1.60) and (1.61)] and should be especially close when the dispersion over N' values in the grand canonical ensemble is small.

To evaluate α, we turn to an independent derivation of $S(k; T)$ in the long-wavelength region ($k\rho^{-1/3} \ll 2\pi$). The method is based on (1) constructing a quantized version of the classical isothermal sound field, and

(2) identifying $\rho_{\mathbf{k}}$ with the normal coordinates of the classical isothermal sound field (details are given in Chapter 3). We need the formula [7]

$$\begin{aligned} S(k;\,T) &= (\hbar k/2mc)\coth\tfrac{1}{2}\beta\hbar kc \\ &\to (\hbar k/2mc) \qquad \text{for}\quad \beta\hbar kc \gg 1 \gg k\rho^{-1/3} \\ &\to (1/\beta)K_{\mathrm{T}}\rho \qquad \text{for}\quad \beta\hbar kc \ll 1 \end{aligned} \tag{1.80}$$

where c is the velocity defined by $mc^2\rho K_{\mathrm{T}} = 1$. In liquid ^{4}He below the λ transition the large thermal conductivity permits the density fluctuations of ordinary sound to occur isothermally. In that case c is the velocity of ordinary (or first) sound. In other fluids the actual sound velocity is defined by $mc_s^{\,2}\rho K_s = 1$, where K_s is the compressibility under adiabatic conditions. Equations (1.80) and (1.77) imply $\alpha = (1/\beta)\rho K_{\mathrm{T}}$, and also that

$$p_N(\infty) = \rho^2[1 - (\rho K_{\mathrm{T}}/\beta N)], \qquad p(\infty) = \rho^2 \tag{1.81}$$

In terms of the radial distribution functions, these results require

$$g(\infty;\,T) = 1, \qquad g_N(\infty;\,T) = 1 - (\rho K_N/\beta N) \tag{1.82}$$

and

$$S(0;\,T) = S_N(0\,;T) = (1/\beta)\rho K_{\mathrm{T}} \tag{1.83}$$

Also, by Eq. (1.79),

$$S_N(k;\,T) \approx S(k;\,T) = 1 + \rho\int \exp(i\mathbf{k}\cdot\mathbf{r})[g(r;\,T) - 1]\,d\mathbf{r} \tag{1.84}$$

The corresponding ground-state formulas appear as the special case $T = 0$ ($\beta = \infty$) in the grand canonical formalism.

1.7. NECESSARY CONDITIONS ON THE RADIAL DISTRIBUTION AND LIQUID STRUCTURE FUNCTIONS

The discussion is limited to the ground-state functions $g(r)$ and $S(k)$, but can be extended easily to $g(r;\,T)$ and $S(k;\,T)$. The fundamental assumption involved in applications using trial functions for $g(r)$ is the existence of a many-particle normalized wave function ψ associated with $p(1, 2) = \rho^2 g(r_{12})$ through Eq. (1.1). What are the useful conditions on

$g(r)$ which follow necessarily from Eq. (1.1)? How closely do known necessary conditions approach sufficiency? These are the two basic questions when a given $g(r)$ is not generated directly and explicitly by a wave function. Discussions of these and related questions can be found in Refs. [10]–[13].

Conditions implied by the preceding discussion include:

$$g(r) \geq 0 \tag{1.85a}$$

$$S(k) \geq 0 \tag{1.85b}$$

$$\lim_{N\to\infty} N[1 - g(\infty)] = 0 \tag{1.85c}$$

$$\lim_{k\to 0} S(k)/k = \hbar/2mc \tag{1.85d}$$

$$4\pi\rho \int_0^\infty [g(r) - 1]r^2\, dr = -1 \tag{1.85e}$$

In practice (1.85a) and (1.85c) are imposed immediately on any trial function offered to serve as a radial distribution function. Condition (1.85e) is satisfied by introducing a suitable trial function $Z(s)$ and writing

$$g(r) = Z(\rho^{1/3} r/a) \tag{1.86}$$

The parameter a is determined by

$$4\pi a^3 \int_0^\infty (Z(s) - 1)s^2\, ds = -1 \tag{1.87}$$

One useful consequence of condition (1.85d) can be seen easily by writing

$$S(k) = \frac{4\pi\rho}{k^3} \int_0^\infty \left(\frac{\sin x}{x} - 1\right)\left[g\left(\frac{x}{k}\right) - 1\right] x^2\, dx \tag{1.88}$$

Condition (1.85d) is satisfied if and only if [14]

$$\lim_{r\to\infty} r^4 \overline{[g(r) - 1]} = \frac{-\hbar}{2\pi^2 m\rho c} \tag{1.89}$$

where the bar denotes an average over a range δr somewhat larger than $\rho^{-1/3}$ [compare with Eqs. (1.55)–(1.59)].

An additional condition on $g(r)$ can be derived from the existence of an absolute potential-energy minimum in a classical physical problem. This problem is the charged gas in a box filled with a fixed, uniform charge density of opposite sign and equal total amount of charge. Many years ago Wigner called attention to the fact that the classical potential energy of the charged system attains an absolute minimum value when the particles are located at the lattice points of a body-centered-cubic lattice [15]. This statement is equivalent to the inequality

$$\begin{aligned}\rho^{-1/3} V_{\text{coulomb}}(1, 2, \ldots, N) &\geq -N(1.792\, e^2/2r_s \rho^{1/3}) \\ &= -Ne^2 0.896(4\pi/3)^{1/3} \qquad (1.90)\end{aligned}$$

introducing the value at the minimum estimated by Wigner and Seitz [16] and by Fuchs [17]. In Eq. (1.90) r_s is the radius of a sphere of volume ρ^{-1}.

To obtain a functional inequality on $g(r)$ from Eq. (1.90), I use the (presumed existing) normalized ψ to compute the expectation value of the Coulomb potential energy. The result [18] is

$$\begin{aligned}\rho^{-1/3}\langle V_{\text{coulomb}}\rangle &= 2\pi N \rho^{2/3} \int_0^\infty [g(r)-1] \frac{e^2}{r} r^2\, dr \\ &\geq -Ne^2 0.896(4\pi/3)^{1/3} \qquad (1.91)\end{aligned}$$

or

$$\rho^{2/3} \int_0^\infty [1-g(r)] r\, dr \leq \frac{1.792}{4\pi} \left(\frac{4\pi}{3}\right)^{1/3} \qquad (1.92)$$

The normalization condition on $g(r)$ [condition (1.85e)] can be combined with Eq. (1.92) to yield

$$\frac{\int_0^\infty [1-g(r)] r\, dr}{\left[\int_0^\infty [1-g(r) r^2\, dr\right]^{2/3}} \leq \frac{1.792}{3^{1/3}} = 1.243 \qquad (1.93)$$

Equation (1.93) is the desired inequality.

Trial functions in the form $g(r) = Z(\rho^{1/3} r/a; \mu_1, \ldots, \mu_p)$ may be tested by Eq. (1.93). Failure of the inequality for physically interesting values of the parameters μ is sufficient reason to discard any proposed $g(r)$. The plain implication of such failure is that no ψ function exists capable of generating the given $g(r)$ by Eq. (1.1). Interesting values of $\boldsymbol{\mu}$ are determined by using $g(r)$ to compute the expectation value of the physical Hamiltonian (Chapters 6 and 7). The minimum value of $\langle H\rangle$ in the $\boldsymbol{\mu}$ space defines a point, $\boldsymbol{\mu} = \boldsymbol{\mu}^*(\rho)$, centrally located in the interesting region. In general, Eq. (1.93) imposes a strong constraint on the form of $Z(s; \boldsymbol{\mu})$ and on the allowed range of $\boldsymbol{\mu}$ values. Comparing integrands in the integrals occuring in condition (1.85e) and Eq. (1.92), we see that the latter gives relatively more weight to the region below the first rising slope of $g(r)$ and relatively less weight to the nearest-neighbor peak. The two statements together, as combined in Eq. (1.93), produce an effective constraint on the width of the region near the origin in which $g(r)$ is small, and on the magnitude and width of the nearest-neighbor peak [assuming that the oscillations in $g(r)$ are strongly damped after the nearest-neighbor peak].

The inequality of Eq. (1.90) has been generalized to the Yukawa potential and certain linear combinations of Yukawa potentials [19]. Each such inequality yields a necessary condition on $g(r)$. Equation (1.93) has proved useful in studies of nuclear matter and the formation of alpha-particle groups in the surface region of finite nuclei [20].

APPENDIX 1-A

Fourier Analysis of Fluctuations

The fluctuation analysis based on Eqs. (1.42) and (1.43) can be extended to the wave number $k=(2\pi/L)\nu$, ν a positive integer, by introducing a periodic function with fundamental period L/ν defined by the statement

$$\begin{aligned} \mathcal{N}_\nu(x) &= 1, \qquad 0 \le x \le L/2\nu \\ &= 0, \qquad L/2\nu < x < L/\nu \end{aligned} \tag{A.1}$$

The equivalent Fourier series for the interval $0 \le x \le L$ is

$$\begin{aligned} \mathcal{N}_\nu(x) &= \sum_{-\infty}^{\infty} \frac{1}{L} \int_0^L e^{-i2\pi m y/L} \mathcal{N}_\nu(y)\, dy\, e^{i2\pi m x/L} \\ &= \frac{1}{2} + \frac{1}{i\pi} \sum_{-\infty}^{\infty} \frac{1}{2p+1}\, e^{i(2p+1)kx} \end{aligned} \tag{A.2}$$

and the corresponding expansion for the associated total number operator [Eq. (1.43)] is

$$\mathcal{N} = \frac{1}{2} N + \frac{1}{i\pi} \sum_{-\infty}^{\infty} \frac{1}{2p+1}\, \rho_{(2p+1)k} \tag{A.3}$$

Equation (A.3) yields

$$\overline{(\mathcal{N}-\overline{\mathcal{N}})^2} = \frac{2N}{\pi^2} \sum_{0}^{\infty} \frac{1}{(2p+1)^2}\, S[(2p+1)k] \tag{A.4}$$

I treat k as a small fixed wave number [implying $\nu \sim O(N^{1/3})$]. Equation (A.4) establishes a rough correspondence between $S(k)$ and the mean-square number fluctuation similar, but not identical, to that assumed in Eq. (1.49). To see the dependence of the sum in Eq. (A.4) on k for $k \ll 2\pi\rho^{1/3}$, assume $S(x) \sim O(x)$, $x \to 0$ and use the relation

$$\frac{S[(2p+1)k]}{(2p+1)^2} \approx \frac{S(k)}{2p+1}, \qquad \text{with } (2p+1)k \ll 2\pi\rho^{1/3},$$

to separate off from the sum a component proportional to $S(k)$. The remainder of the sum can then be replaced by an integral. For example.

$$\sum_0^\infty \frac{1}{(2p+1)^2} S[(2p+1)k] \sim 2S(k) + \frac{1}{2} k \int_{15k}^\infty \frac{S(x)}{x^2}\, dx \tag{A.5}$$

in the range $15k \ll 2\pi\rho^{1/3}$. It is clear that the integral generates a term in $S(k) \ln(2\pi\rho^{1/3}/15k)^{1/2}$. The existence of the logarithmic term creates a difficulty for the intuitive physical argumentation employed to establish Eq. (1.51). However, the empirical and theoretical information on $S(k)$ for liquid ^{4}He can be used to show that the logarithmic term is unimportant for $k > (2\pi/100)\rho^{1/3} \sim 0.02\text{Å}^{-1}$ (in liquid ^{4}He). Thus the correspondence between $\overline{(\mathcal{N} - \bar{\mathcal{N}})^2}$ and $S(k)$ is still qualitatively interesting in the experimentally accessible range of small k values. The occurrence of the logarithmic term reflects the discontinuity embodied in the function $\mathcal{N}_\nu(x)$, whereas the definition of $S(k)$ involves only continuous functions.

APPENDIX 1-B

*Families of Radial Distribution Functions**

(a) Consider the functions

$$\begin{aligned} g(r) &= 1 - \operatorname{Re} \frac{e^{i\varphi}}{\cos\varphi} \exp(-s^2 e^{i\theta}/\cos\theta) \\ &= 1 - (\exp -s^2) \frac{\cos(\varphi - s^2 \tan\theta)}{\cos\varphi} \end{aligned} \tag{B.1}$$

* See Lee [21].

$$S(k) = 1 - a^3 \int (\exp i\mathbf{q}\cdot\mathbf{s})(\exp - s^2)\,\frac{\cos(\varphi - s^2 \tan\theta)}{\cos\varphi}\,d\mathbf{s}$$

$$= 1 - \left\{\exp\left[-\frac{1}{4}(\cos\theta)^2 q^2\right]\right\}\frac{\cos[\varphi - \frac{3}{2}\theta + \frac{1}{4}(\sin\theta\cos\theta)q^2]}{\cos(\varphi - \frac{3}{2}\theta)} \qquad \text{(B.2)}$$

with $s = \rho^{1/3} r/a$, $q = ak/\rho^{1/3}$, and the parameters φ, θ restricted to the rectangular range $-\pi/2 < \varphi < \pi/2$, $0 \le \theta < \pi/2$ (Fig. 1-1). The normalization condition

$$a^3 \pi^{3/2}\,\frac{(\cos\theta)^{3/2}\cos(\varphi - \frac{3}{2}\theta)}{\cos\varphi} = 1 \qquad \text{(B.3)}$$

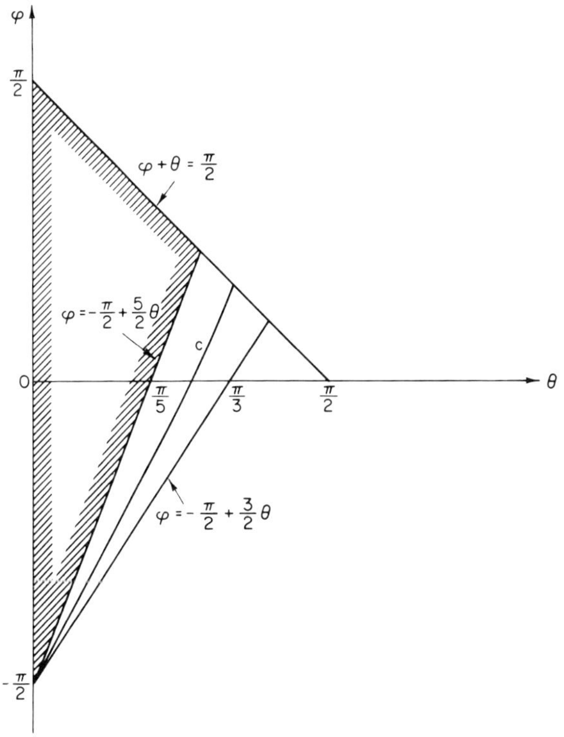

FIG. 1-1. Allowed region for Eq. (B.1).

has already been used in deriving Eq. (B.2). For small s ($s \ll 1$) the power series

$$g(r) = s^2 \frac{\cos(\varphi+\theta)}{\cos\varphi\cos\theta} - \frac{1}{2}s^4 \frac{\cos(\varphi+2\theta)}{(\cos\varphi)(\cos\theta)^2} + \cdots \tag{B.4}$$

and the necessary condition $g(r) \geq 0$ require the constraint

$$\cos(\varphi+\theta) \geq 0 \tag{B.5}$$

Consequently,

$$-\pi/2 < \varphi + \theta \leq \pi/2 \tag{B.6}$$

If the coefficient of s^2 in Eq. (B.4) vanishes ($\varphi + \theta = \frac{1}{2}\pi$), the coefficient of s^4 is positive.

A second constraint is imposed by the normalization. Since a is a positive-valued scale factor, Eq. (B.3) requires $\cos(\varphi - 3\theta) > 0$, or

$$-\pi/2 < \varphi - \tfrac{3}{2}\theta < \pi/2 \tag{B.7}$$

The condition $S(k) \geq 0$ determines a third constraint. For small q ($q \ll 1$)

$$S(k) = \frac{\cos\theta\cos(\varphi - \frac{5}{2}\theta)}{4\cos(\varphi - \frac{3}{2}\theta)} q^2 - \frac{(\cos\theta)^2\cos(\varphi - \frac{7}{2}\theta)}{32\cos(\varphi - \frac{3}{2}\theta)} q^4 + \cdots \tag{B.8}$$

yields

$$-\pi/2 < \varphi - \tfrac{5}{2}\theta \leq \pi/2 \tag{B.9}$$

The shaded border in Fig. 1-1 outlines the allowed region of θ, φ values.

The Coulomb inequality [Eq. (1.92)] now appears in the explicit form

$$\left(\frac{2}{\pi}\right)^{1/3} \frac{\cos(\varphi - \theta)}{(\cos\varphi)^{1/3}\cos(\varphi - \frac{3}{2}\theta)^{2/3}} \leq 1.243 \tag{B.10}$$

In Fig. 1-1 the region below the line C is excluded by Eq. (B.10).

In this example the Coulomb inequality adds nothing to the constraints imposed by $g(r) \geq 0$ and $S(k) \geq 0$.

Next we verify that the minimum values of $g(r)$ and $S(k)$ are all positive. The condition for an extreme value of $g(r)$ is $\cos(\varphi + \theta - s_n^2 \tan\theta) = 0$ with the solution

$$\varphi + \theta - s_n^2 \tan\theta = (-2n+1)\pi/2 \tag{B.11}$$

$n = 0, \pm 1, \ldots$. At the extrema

$$g(r_n) = 1 - (-1)^n \frac{\exp(-s_n^{\,2})}{\cos \varphi} \sin \theta \tag{B.12}$$

On the range $0 < \varphi \le \pi/2$ we have $\varphi + \theta \le \pi/2$ and $\sin \theta \le \sin[(\pi/2) - \varphi] = \cos \varphi$. On the lower range, $-\pi/2 < \varphi < 0$, $\theta \le \frac{1}{5}\pi - \frac{2}{5}|\varphi| \le \frac{1}{2}\pi - |\varphi|$. Here also $\sin \theta \le \cos \varphi$. Thus $g(r_n) \ge 0$ for the complete range of φ values.

Extreme values of $S(k)$ occur at q_n defined by

$$\varphi - \tfrac{5}{2}\theta + \tfrac{1}{4}(\sin \theta \cos \theta)\, q_n^{\,2} = \tfrac{1}{2}(2n + 1)\pi \tag{B.13}$$

$n = 0, \pm 1, \ldots$. At the extrema

$$S(k_n) = 1 + (-1)^n \left\{ \exp\left[-\left(\frac{\cos \theta}{2} \right)^2 q_n^{\,2} \right] \right\} \frac{\sin \theta}{\cos(\varphi - \frac{3}{2}\theta)} \tag{B.14}$$

On the upper range, $0 < \varphi \le \pi/2$, $\varphi - \frac{3}{2}\theta \le \frac{1}{2}\pi - \frac{5}{2}\theta$; $\cos(\varphi - \frac{3}{2}\theta) \ge \cos(\frac{1}{2}\pi - \frac{5}{2}\theta) = \sin \frac{5}{2}\theta$. But $\sin \frac{5}{2}\theta \ge \sin \theta$ (since $\theta \le \pi/5$) and, consequently, $\cos(\varphi - \frac{3}{2}\theta) \ge \sin \theta$. On the lower range, $-\pi/2 < \varphi < 0$, $\varphi - \frac{3}{2}\theta > \frac{1}{2}\pi + \theta$; since both terms are negative, the inequality implies $\frac{3}{2}\theta - \varphi < \frac{1}{2}\pi - \theta \le \pi/2$ between positive terms. Consequently, $\cos(\varphi - \frac{3}{2}\theta) \ge \cos(\frac{1}{2}\pi - \theta) = \sin \theta$. Thus $S(k_n) \ge 0$ for the complete range of φ values.

(b) The preceding example gives $S(k) \sim O(k^2)$ near the origin in k space. An example with linear behavior of $S(k)$ near the origin is

$$\begin{aligned} S(k) &= 1 - \operatorname{Re} \frac{e^{i\varphi}}{\cos \varphi} \exp\left[-\frac{e^{i\theta}}{\cos \theta} \frac{k}{k_0} \right] \\ &= 1 - [\exp(-k/k_0)] \frac{\cos[\varphi - (k/k_0) \tan \theta]}{\cos \varphi} \end{aligned} \tag{B.15}$$

Positive slope at the origin requires

$$-\pi/2 < \varphi + \theta < \pi/2 \tag{B.16}$$

The radial distribution function is

$$\begin{aligned} g(r) &= 1 - \frac{k_0^{\,3}}{\pi^2 \rho \cos \varphi \cos \theta} \operatorname{Re} \frac{e^{i(\varphi + \theta)}}{\{(k_0 r)^2 + [e^{2i\theta}/(\cos \theta)^2]\}^2} \\ &= 1 - \frac{k_0^{\,3}}{\pi^2 \rho \cos \varphi \cos \theta} \frac{\cos\left\{ \varphi + \theta - 2 \tan^{-1} \dfrac{2 \tan \theta}{(k_0 r)^2 + 1 - \tan^2 \theta} \right\}}{[(k_0 r)^4 + 2(k_0 r)^2 (1 - \tan^2 \theta) + 1/\cos \theta)^4]} \end{aligned} \tag{B.17}$$

Consider the function $g(r)$ in the context of a physical problem involving a two-particle interaction which is repulsive when the particles approach closely. Necessary conditions on a trial function then include

$$g(0) < 1 \tag{B.18}$$

$$(dg/dr^2)_{r=0} \geq 0 \tag{B.19}$$

Equation (B.18) requires

$$-\pi/2 < \varphi - 3\theta < \pi/2 \tag{B.20}$$

The stronger condition

$$-\pi/2 < \varphi - 5\theta < \pi/2 \tag{B.21}$$

is imposed by Eq. (B.19).

An upper limit on k_0 follows from the necessary condition $g(0) \geq 0$; thus

$$(4/3\pi)(k_0 r_s \cos\theta)^3 \cos(\varphi - 3\theta)/\cos\varphi \leq 1 \tag{B.22}$$

Finally, the Coulomb inequality of Eq. (1.92) imposes the condition

$$k_0 r_s (\cos\theta)\cos(\varphi - \theta)/\cos\varphi \leq 0.896\pi \tag{B.23}$$

To bring out the consequences of Eqs. (B.22) and (B.23), consider θ and φ on the line $\varphi = \frac{1}{2}\pi - m\theta$ for small values of $\theta[m > 1$ by Eq. (B.16)]. Eqs. (B.22) and (B.23) now reduce to

$$\tfrac{4}{3}\pi[1 + (3/m)](k_0 r_s)^3 \leq 1 \tag{B.24}$$

$$[1 + (1/m)]k_0 r_s \leq 0.896\pi \tag{B.25}$$

The smaller upper limit on $k_0 r_s$ is imposed by Eq. (B.24). Thus the Coulomb inequality is less effective in this example than more obvious physical conditions—in particular, $g(r) \geq 0$—in limiting the range of the variable parameters.

References

1. H. S. Green, "Handbuch der Physik," Vol. 10. Springer, Berlin, 1960.
2. T. L. Hill, "Statistical Mechanics," McGraw-Hill, New York, 1956.
3. N. S. Gingrich, *Rev. Mod. Phys.* **15**, 90 (1943).
4. M. Cohen and R. P. Feynman, *Phys. Rev.* **107**, 13 (1957).
5. J. K. Percus and G. J. Yevick, *Phys. Rev.* **110**, 1 (1958).
6. P. J. Price, *Phys. Rev.* **94**, 257 (1954).
7. R. P. Feynman and M. Cohen, *Phys. Rev.* **102**, 1189 (1956)—particularly Appendix B.
8. L. S. Ornstein and F. Zernicke, *Amsterdam Proc.* **17**, 793 (1914).
9. F. Zernicke and J. Prins, *Z. Physik* **41**, 184 (1927).
10. M. Yamada, *Prog. Theoret. Phys. (Kyoto)* **25**, 579 (1961).
11. A. J. Coleman, *Rev. Mod. Phys.* **35**, 668 (1963).
12. T. Ando, *Rev. Mod. Phys.* **35**, 690 (1963).
13. C. Garrod and J. K. Percus, *J. Math. Phys.* **5**, 1756 (1964).
14. J. E. Enderby, T. Gaskell, and N. H. March, *Proc. Phys. Soc. (London)* **85**, 217 (1965).
15. E. P. Wigner, *Trans. Faraday Soc.* **34**, 678 (1938).
16. E. P. Wigner and F. Seitz, *Phys. Rev.* **46**, 509 (1934).
17. K. Fuchs, *Proc. Roy. Soc. (London)* **A151**, 585 (1935).
18. E. Feenberg, *J. Math. Phys.* **6**, 658 (1965).
19. F. Y. Wu, H. T. Tan, and E. Feenberg, *J. Math. Phys.* **8**, 864 (1967).
20. J. W. Clark and T. P. Wang, *Ann. Phys. (N.Y.)* **40**, 127 (1966); D. A. Chakkālakal, unpublished doctoral dissertation, Washington University, 1968.
21. D. K. Lee, unpublished doctoral dissertation, Washington University, 1967.

CHAPTER 2

The Three Particle Distribution Function

2.1. INTRODUCTION

The discussion in the introductory section of Chapter 1 is continued with the remark that the sequential relation for $n = 1$ [Eq. (1.8)] can be written

$$\rho \int [g(r) - 1] \, d\mathbf{r} = -1 \tag{2.1}$$

Two cases may be distinguished, depending on the asymptotic behavior of $g(r) - 1$: the range of integration may be extended over all space if $g(r) - 1$ vanishes with sufficient rapidity for large r (faster than r^{-3} as $r \to \infty$); however, if $g(r) - 1$ is of order $1/N$ for large r ($r \gg \rho^{-1/3}$), the range of integration is limited to the fundamental cube Ω. In any event, when nothing is stated or implied about the asymptotic behavior of $g(r) - 1$ the range restricted to Ω is understood. It is worth stressing that Eq. (2.1) is a consequence of the periodic boundary condition, which in turn implies that $p^{(1)}(\mathbf{r})$ is independent of position.

For $n = 2$ the sequential relation

$$\rho^2 g(r_{12}) = [1/(N-2)] \int p^{(3)}(1, 2, 3) \, d\mathbf{r}_3 \tag{2.2}$$

is a linear, inhomogeneous integral equation for the symmetrical positive-valued function $p^{(3)}$. Some insight into the connection expressed by Eq. (2.2) can be gained by introducing a cluster type representation for the distribution functions. Let

$$g(r) = 1 + h(r), \qquad h(\infty) \sim O_v(1/N)$$

$$p^{(3)}(1, 2, 3) = \rho^3[1 + h(r_{12}) + h(r_{23}) + h(r_{31}) + h(r_{12})h(r_{23}) + h(r_{23})h(r_{31}) + h(r_{31})h(r_{12})] + \delta p(1, 2, 3) \tag{2.3}$$

The factor in brackets correctly represents the behavior of $p^{(3)}$ when all three points are well separated or when any two are close and far from the third. It also gives an approximate representation of the behavior when two points are moderately close to the third (say, $r_{12} \approx r_{13} \approx \frac{1}{2}r_{23} \approx \rho^{-1/3}$). The remainder term, $\delta p(1, 2, 3)$, is large only when all three points are close (within distances of order $\rho^{-1/3}$).

Equation (2.2) now appears in the reduced form

$$\int \delta p(1, 2, 3)\, d\mathbf{r}_3 = -\rho^3 \int h(r_{13})h(r_{23})\, d\mathbf{r}_3 \tag{2.4}$$

a linear, inhomogeneous integral equation for the unknown symmetrical function $\delta p(1, 2, 3)$. At this point it is useful to introduce the special assumption of strong repulsive forces acting between pairs of particles when they approach closely. This requires $g(0) = 0$ and $h(0) = -1$. Now, if two points coincide (say, 1 and 2), $p^{(3)}(1, 2, 3)$ vanishes, and Eq. (2.3) reduces to an explicit formula for $\delta p(1, 1, 3)$:

$$\delta p(\mathbf{r}_1, \mathbf{r}_1, \mathbf{r}_3) = -\rho^3 h(r_{13})^2 \tag{2.5}$$

2.2. APPROXIMATE FORMS

Our first concern is a particular solution of Eq. (2.4). The function

$$\delta p_c(1, 2, 3) = \rho^4 \int h(r_{14})h(r_{24})h(r_{34})\, d\mathbf{r}_4 \tag{2.6}$$

is indeed a solution in consequence of the normalization condition on h expressed by Eq. (2.1). However, this function fails to satisfy Eq. (2.5). The associated $p_c(1, 2, 3)$ generated by Eqs. (2.3) and (2.6) fails to vanish when two points coincide and is not necessarily positive-valued. Nevertheless, $p_c(1, 2, 3)$, the convolution form, has proved useful in several applications [1]–[3].

A general symmetrical form consistent with Eq. (2.5) is given by the simple product

$$p_K(1, 2, 3) = \rho^3 g(r_{12}) g(r_{23}) g(r_{31}) \tag{2.7}$$

In this case the remainder δp_K is equally simple:

$$\delta p_K = \rho^3 h(r_{12}) h(r_{23}) h(r_{31}) \tag{2.8}$$

The function $p_K(1, 2, 3)$ is the Kirkwood superposition form for the three-point distribution function. Now, $\delta p = \delta p_K$ satisfies Eq. (2.5), but fails in Eq. (2.4). The limited accuracy of the product form can be made explicit in an illuminating manner by substitution from Eq. (2.7) into the right-hand member of Eq. (2.2.) The result,

$$\frac{\rho^3}{N-2} \int g(r_{22}) g(r_{23}) g(r_{31})\, d\mathbf{r}_3 = \rho^2 g(r_{12}) \left[1 + \frac{\rho}{N-2} \int h(r_{13}) h(r_{32})\, d\mathbf{r}_3 \right] \tag{2.9}$$

exhibits an error term of relative magnitude $O(1/N)$. Physical effects are associated with the small region in coordinate space which contributes strongly to the integral $\rho \int h(r_{13}) h(r_{32})\, d\mathbf{r}_3$; this region is important, even though the volume is small compared to Ω.

These examples illustrate the manner in which Eqs. (2.4) and (2.5) can be used to test proposed approximate forms for $p^{(3)}$. Each test singles out a simple approximate form. Equation (2.5) is satisfied by the superposition form, which fails in Eq. (2.4). On the other hand, the convolution form satisfies Eq. (2.4), but fails to make $p^{(3)}$ vanish when two points coincide [Eq. (2.5)]. Because of the improper behavior when two points coincide, the convolution approximation (CA) cannot be used to compute expectation values of singular operators; however, it may be superior to the superposition form (KSA) under less extreme conditions, as in the theory of phonon–phonon and phonon–roton interaction [1] in liquid ^{4}He and for the evaluation of cluster integrals [2] in the theory of liquid ^{3}He.

The general solution of Eq. (2.4). is given by a linear combination of $\delta p_c(1, 2, 3)$ and a solution of the homogeneous equation

$$\int \delta p_h(1, 2, 3)\, d\mathbf{r}_3 = 0 \tag{2.10}$$

Equation (2.10) possesses a wide variety of solutions. In particular, the function

$$\delta p_h(1, 2, 3) = \Delta_1\, \Delta_2\, \Delta_3\, v(\mathbf{r}_{12}, \mathbf{r}_{23}, \mathbf{r}_{31}) \tag{2.11}$$

is obviously a solution for a wide class of functions $v(\mathbf{r}_{12}, r_{23}, \mathbf{r}_{31})$.

2.3. THE ABE FORM

The superposition and convolution forms are particularly simple in that they contain no free parameters. These approximations can be characterized in a general way as functionals in the "hole" function $h(r) = g(r) - 1$. We seek more accurate forms within the same characterization, extending it to include the condition that all free parameters in a trial form are expressed as functionals in h. A given functional form, no matter how complicated, then contains only one element of freedom, the function $h(r)$ itself; these forms may be called complete functionals in h. Any complete functional $p_{\mathrm{a}}(1, 2, 3)$ possesses a well-defined functional derivative $\delta p_{\mathrm{a}}(1, 2, 3)/\delta h(\mathbf{r})$.

Abe [4] has shown how to exhibit $p^{(3)}$ as an explicit complete functional in h for a particular class of $p^{(N)}(1, 2, \ldots, N)$ functions. Actually, Abe develops the formalism within the framework of the classical statistical mechanics of an imperfect gas, but the procedure and results are applicable immediately to the distribution functions defined by

$$p^{(N)}(1, 2, \ldots, N) = N! \left[\prod_{1 \le i < j \le N} \exp u(r_{ij}) \Big/ \int \prod_{1 \le i < j \le N} \exp u(r_{ij})\, d\mathbf{r}_{1, 2, \ldots, N} \right] \tag{2.12}$$

This includes the description of the ground state of a boson system by a Bijl–Dingle–Jastrow type of trial wave function.

The definitions of g and $p^{(3)}$ generated by the explicit statement of the sequential relations in terms of $p^{(N)}$ express g and $p^{(3)}$ as functionals in the two-point correlation factor e^u. Our problem is to eliminate u between these functionals and thus express $p^{(3)}$ as a functional in g. The analysis is based on the standard cluster expansion formalism as in the classical statistical mechanics of an imperfect gas. Abe's result is

$$p^{(3)}(1, 2, 3) = p_{\mathrm{K}}(1, 2, 3) e^{A(1, 2, 3)} \tag{2.13}$$

$$\begin{aligned} A(1, 2, 3) = {} & \rho \int h(r_{14}) h(r_{24}) h(r_{34})\, d\mathbf{r}_4 \\ & + \rho^2 \Big[\int h_{14} h_{24} h_{25} h_{35} h_{45}\, d\mathbf{r}_4\, d\mathbf{r}_5 \\ & + \int h_{24} h_{14} h_{15} h_{35} h_{45}\, d\mathbf{r}_4\, d\mathbf{r}_5 + \int h_{14} h_{34} h_{35} h_{25} h_{45}\, d\mathbf{r}_4\, d\mathbf{r}_5 \\ & + \int h_{14} h_{15} h_{24} h_{25} h_{34} h_{45}\, d\mathbf{r}_4\, d\mathbf{r}_5 \end{aligned}$$

$$+\int h_{14}h_{15}h_{34}h_{35}h_{24}h_{45}\,d\mathbf{r}_4\,d\mathbf{r}_5$$
$$+\int h_{34}h_{35}h_{24}h_{25}h_{14}h_{45}\,d\mathbf{r}_4\,d\mathbf{r}_5$$
$$\left.+\tfrac{1}{2}\int h_{14}h_{15}h_{24}h_{25}h_{34}h_{35}h_{45}\,d\mathbf{r}_4\,d\mathbf{r}_5\right] + O(\rho^3) \tag{2.14}$$

Abe gives only the first two terms in the formal series for A in powers of ρ; this is sufficient to ensure correct results for the fourth and fifth virial coefficients in the classical statistical mechanics of an imperfect gas. The general recipe for constructing the coefficient of ρ^n has been determined by F. Y. Wu [5]. Since g is a function of ρ, it is only in a formal sense that A can be considered as a power series in ρ. Nothing is known about the convergence properties of the formal series. However, some idea of the extent to which internal cancellation operates to reduce the magnitude of the leading terms in A can be gained by forming the integral of A with respect to the variables $\mathbf{r}_1, \mathbf{r}_2, \mathbf{r}_3$:

$$\rho^2 \int A(1, 2, 3)\,d\mathbf{r}_1\,d\mathbf{r}_2 = (\rho^2/\Omega) \int A(1, 2, 3)\,d\mathbf{r}_1\,d\mathbf{r}_2\,d\mathbf{r}_3$$
$$= (\rho/\Omega) \int h_{45}\Big[1 + 3\rho \int h_{14}h_{15}\,d\mathbf{r}_1$$
$$- 3\Big(\rho \int h_{14}h_{15}\,d\mathbf{r}_1\Big)^2$$
$$+ \tfrac{1}{2}\Big(\rho \int h_{14}h_{15}\,d\mathbf{r}_1\Big)^3 + \cdots\Big]\,d\mathbf{r}_4\,d\mathbf{r}_5 \tag{2.15}$$

A Gaussian approximation for h, $h(r) = -\exp(-\pi\rho^{2/3}r^2)$, may be used for the purpose of orientation to generate numerical estimates of the integrals occurring in Eq. (2.14). The result is

$$\rho^2 \int A(1, 2, 3)\,d\mathbf{r}_1\,d\mathbf{r}_2 = -1 - 0.45 + \cdots \tag{2.16}$$

the -1 from the first integral in Eq. (2.15) and the -0.45 from the remaining three integrals. The Gaussian form lacks the nearest-neighbor peak and the damped oscillatory behavior for large r characteristic of physical radial distribution functions. We surmise that a calculation with a physical radial distribution function would exhibit a more rapid convergence (as a formal series in ρ).

To see how the Abe form meets the test of Eq. (2.2), let us try

$$p_{A1}(1, 2, 3) = p_K\Big[1 + \rho \int h_{14}h_{24}h_{34}\,d\mathbf{r}_4\Big] \tag{2.17}$$

Equation (2.9) is replaced by

$$\frac{1}{N-2}\int p_{A1}\, d\mathbf{r}_3 = \rho^2 g(r_{12})\left[1 + \frac{2\rho^2}{N}\int h_{13}h_{14}h_{23}h_{24}\, d\mathbf{r}_3\, d\mathbf{r}_4 + \frac{\rho^2}{N}\int h_{13}h_{23}h_{14}h_{24}h_{34}\, d\mathbf{r}_3\, d\mathbf{r}_4 + \cdots\right] \quad (2.18)$$

Again, using the Gaussian h function, the coefficient of the $1/N$ error term, evaluated at $r_{12}=0$, decreases in proportion to the numbers 1, 0.38 along the sequence p_K, p_{A1}. If ρ^2 terms are included in the correction factor of Eq. (2.17), the ρ^2 error terms shown in Eq. (2.18) drop out, but are replaced by a large number of ρ^3 terms involving triple integrations over 5–10 h factors.

The following equation gives a diagrammatic representation of A, each line representing an h factor, a solid circle a factor ρ and integration over Ω, and open circles the points $\mathbf{r}_1$, $\mathbf{r}_2$, $\mathbf{r}_3$ in all distinct arrangements of the labels 1, 2, 3, on the open circles:

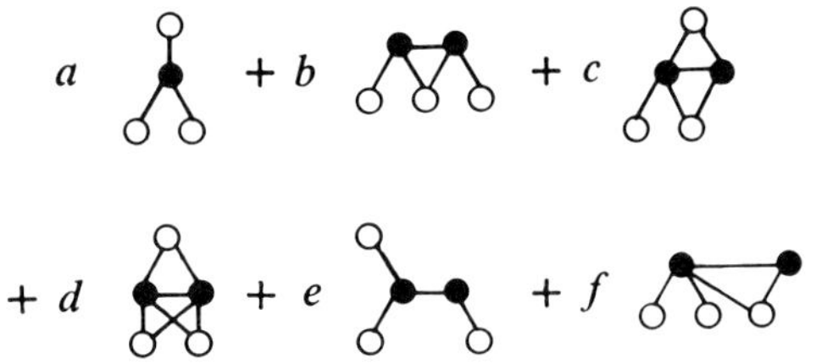

(2.19)

In Abe's formula $a=b=c=d=1$ and $e=f=0$. We may, however, take the coefficients as unknown quantities to be determined to eliminate the several error terms generated by a in Eq. (2.2) (see Ref. [6]). This procedure yields $a=b=c=1$. A unique error term in e is eliminated by setting $e=0$. In this context d and f remain indeterminate.

2.4. THE ABE FORM IN THE UNIFORM LIMIT

The Kirkwood and Abe forms were developed originally for use in the classical statistical mechanics of a liquid or imperfect gas of spherical molecules. In the applications the result $g(0)=0$ follows from the realistic hypothesis of strong repulsive interactions opposing the close approach of two molecules. The same result $[g(0)=0]$ is found in the quantum theory of the liquid and imperfect gas systems under the same realistic hypothesis. There are, however, interesting problems in which the interaction is not strongly singular at $r_{ij}=0$ and the radial distribution function does not vanish at the origin. The extreme condition in this direction, called the uniform limit [7], is defined by $|g(r)-1| \ll 1$ for all r. The uniform limit may occur at either high or low density, depending on the special properties of the two-particle interaction; consequently, the density ρ is not the best parameter for developing $p^{(3)}$ as a complete functional in g. A suitable parameter is provided by $\alpha = 1-g(0)$. We write

$$g(r) = 1 - \alpha G(s), \qquad s = (\alpha\rho)^{1/3} r, \qquad G(0) = 1 \tag{2.20}$$

Equation (2.1) becomes

$$\int G(s)\, d\mathbf{s} = 1 \tag{2.21}$$

The remark following Eq. (2.1) applies equally here, except that the volume Ω is converted into the dimensionless magnitude αN.

The derivation of $p^{(3)}$ as a complete functional in G now proceeds along the lines of Abe's discussion, but with α replacing ρ as the formal expansion parameter. We obtain the results [6]

$$\begin{aligned} A(1,2,3) = &-\alpha^2 \int G_{14} G_{24} G_{34}\, d\mathbf{s}_4 \\ &-\alpha^3 \Big[\int G_{14} G_{24} G_{25} G_{35} G_{45}\, d\mathbf{s}_4\, d\mathbf{s}_5 \\ &+ \int G_{14} G_{34} G_{35} G_{25} G_{45}\, d\mathbf{s}_4\, d\mathbf{s}_5 \\ &+ \int G_{24} G_{14} G_{15} G_{35} G_{45}\, d\mathbf{s}_4\, d\mathbf{s}_5 \\ &- \int G_{14} G_{25} G_{36} G_{45} G_{56} G_{64}\, d\mathbf{s}_4\, d\mathbf{s}\, d\mathbf{s}_6 \Big] + O(\alpha^4) \end{aligned} \tag{2.22}$$

$$\begin{aligned} p_{\mathrm{A}}(1,2,3) &= p_{\mathrm{K}}(1,2,3) e^{A(1,2,3)} \\ &= p_{\mathrm{K}}(1,2,3)[1 + A(1,2,3) + O(\alpha^4)] \end{aligned} \tag{2.23}$$

$$[1/(N-2)] \int p_{\mathrm{A}}(1,2,3)\, d\mathbf{r}_3 = \rho^2 g(r_{12})[1 + (1/N)O(\alpha^3)] \tag{2.24}$$

A diagrammatic representation of A with unknown coefficients is subject to conditions imposed on the coefficients by the sequential relation.

One finds an infinite class of diagrams associated with each power of α. In particular, the lowest power α^2 includes all diagrams of the type:

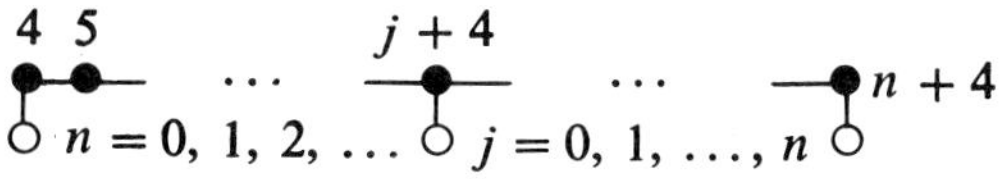

Here each line represents a G factor, open circles represent the points 1, 2, and 3, and closed circles an integration over the fundamental volume αN. At this general level the constraints imposed by the sequential relation are not strong enough to make the problem determinate.

The indeterminacy can be reduced by introducing two general rules to limit the range of diagrams in A. The first rule asserts that in each order of $\alpha(A = -\alpha^2 A_2 - \alpha^3 A_3 - \cdots)$ the sequential relation is to be satisfied with the simplest diagrams and the smallest possible number of diagrams (rule of minimal complexity). The second rule was stated by Meeron [8] in the context of his development of the hypernetted-chain formalism. Let $\mathscr{N}$ represent all solid circles in a diagram and $\mathscr{M}$ all open circles. In the immediate application $\mathscr{M} = 1, 2, 3$. Only such diagrams occur in A for which (1) every particle of the set $\mathscr{N}$ is connected to at least two particles of the set $\mathscr{M}$, either directly or by two or more independent paths, i.e., paths which involve mutually exclusive sets of intermediate particles; (2) all particles of the set $\mathscr{N}$ are also connected among themselves independently of the set $\mathscr{M}$; (3) particles of $\mathscr{M}$ are not directly connected among themselves; and (4) every particle of $\mathscr{M}$ is connected to at least one particle of $\mathscr{N}$.

As an illustration, consider the problem of determining A_2 and A_3. The vanishing of first- and second-order error terms in α in the sequential relation implies

$$\int A_2\, d\mathbf{s}_3 = \text{(diagram)} = \int G_{13}\, G_{23}\, d\mathbf{s}_3 \tag{2.25}$$

$$\int A_3\, d\mathbf{s}_3 = \int G_{31} + G_{32}\, A_2\, d\mathbf{s}_3 \tag{2.26}$$

Rule 1 limits the function A_2 to a single diagram,

$$A_2 = \int G_{14}\, G_{24}\, G_{34}\, d\mathbf{s}_4 = \text{(diagram)} \tag{2.27}$$

Equation (2.26) now becomes

$$\int A_3 \, d\mathbf{s}_3 = - \underset{1 \quad 2}{\text{(graph)}} = - \underset{1 \quad 2}{\text{(graph)}} - \underset{2 \quad 1}{\text{(graph)}} \qquad (2.28)$$

In accordance with rules 1 and 2, we seek a solution of the form

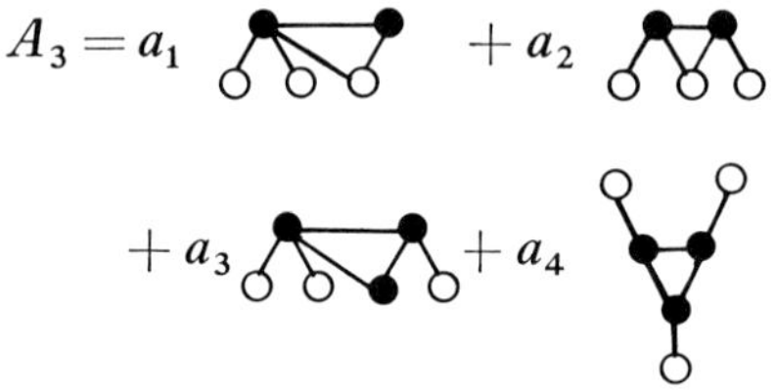

$$A_3 = a_1 \text{(graph)} + a_2 \text{(graph)}$$

$$+ a_3 \text{(graph)} + a_4 \text{(graph)} \qquad (2.29)$$

and obtain

$$a_2 = 1 - a_1, \qquad a_3 = -a_1, \qquad a_4 = -1 + 3a_1 \qquad (2.30)$$

Thus

$$A_3 = \left[\text{(graph)} - \text{(graph)} \right]$$

$$+ a_1 \left[\text{(graph)} - \text{(graph)} - \text{(graph)} + 3 \text{(graph)} \right] \qquad (2.31)$$

Equations (2.29) and (2.31) reveal the power of the sequential relation, but also exhibit its limitations, since the formula for A contains an arbitrary parameter [$a_1 = 0$ is required by Eq. (2.22)].

2.5. THE HYPERNETTED–CHAIN APPROXIMATION IN THE UNIFORM LIMIT

Equations (1.5) and (2.12) express the radial distribution function as a functional in u:

$$\rho^2 g(r_{12}) = N(N-1) \left\{ \int \prod_{i<j} \exp u(r_{ij}) \, d\mathbf{r}_{3,\,4,\,...,\,N} \right.$$

$$\times \left. \left[\int \prod_{i<j} \exp u(r_{ij}) \, d\mathbf{r}_{1,\,2,\,...,\,N} \right]^{-1} \right\} \qquad (2.32)$$

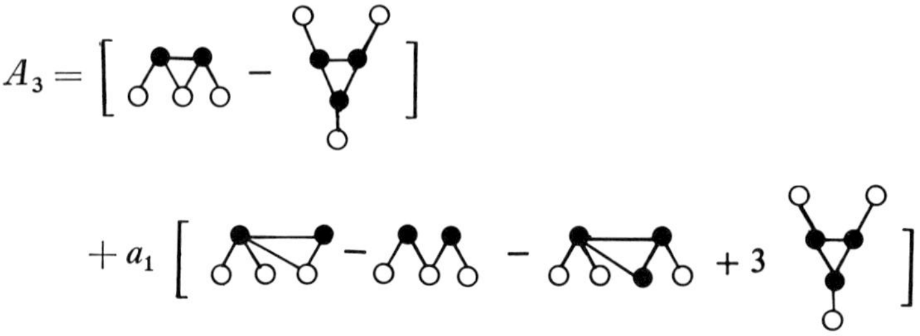

The inverse problem of exhibiting u as a functional in $g(r)$ can be solved in the uniform limit. The starting point is the equation generated by applying the gradient operator $\boldsymbol{\nabla}_1$ to both terms of Eq. (2.32)*:

$$\boldsymbol{\nabla}_1 u(r_{12}) = \boldsymbol{\nabla}_1 \ln g(r_{12}) - \frac{1}{\rho^2 g(r_{12})} \int p^{(3)}(1, 2, 3)\, \nabla_1 u(r_{13})\, d\mathbf{r}_3 \quad (2.33)$$

or

$$\boldsymbol{\nabla}_1[u(r_{12}) - \ln g(r_{12})] = -\int \frac{p^{(3)}(1, 2, 3) - \rho^2 g(r_{12}) g(r_{13})}{\rho^2 g(r_{12})}\, \nabla_1 u(r_{13})\, d\mathbf{r}_3 \quad (2.34)$$

The discussion of Eq. (2.34) in the uniform limit requires a suitable notation. We take over s and $G(s)$ defined by Eq. (2.20) and add

$$u(r) \equiv \mathscr{Y}(s) = \sum_1^\infty \alpha^n \mathscr{Y}_n(s), \qquad Z(q) = \sum_1^\infty \alpha^n Z_n(q)$$
$$\int (\exp i\mathbf{q}\cdot\mathbf{s}) \ln[1 - \alpha G(s)]\, d\mathbf{s} = -\sum_0^\infty (\alpha^n/n) F_n(q) \quad (2.35)$$

in which

$$Z_n(q) = \int (\exp i\mathbf{q}\cdot\mathbf{s}) \mathscr{Y}_n(s)\, d\mathbf{s}$$
$$F_n(q) = \int (\exp i\mathbf{q}\cdot\mathbf{s}) G^n(s)\, d\mathbf{s} \quad (2.36)$$
$$= \frac{1}{(2\pi)^3} \int F(\mathbf{q}' - \mathbf{q}) F_{n-1}(q')\, d\mathbf{q}'$$

Next, the Abe form for $p^{(3)}(1, 2, 3)$ [Eq. (2.22)] is introduced to reduce the right-hand member of Eq. (2.34) to a power series in α in which the coefficients of α^0, α, α^2, and α^3 are known functionals in $G(s)$:

$$p^{(3)}(1, 2, 3) = \rho^3 g_{12} g_{23} g_{31}[1 - \alpha^2 A_2 - \alpha^3 A_3 + O(\alpha^4)]$$
$$\frac{p^{(3)}(1, 2, 3) - \rho^3 g_{12} g_{13}}{\rho^3 g_{12}} = -\alpha\rho[G_{23} + \alpha(A_2\, G_{13}\, G_{23}) \quad (2.37)$$
$$+ \alpha^2\{A_3 - (G_{13} + G_{23})A_2\} + O(\alpha^3)]$$

* Equation (2.33) is one of the several sequences of equations associated with the names Bogoliubov, Born, Green, Kirkwood, and Yvon (BBGKY).

These definitions and relations when put into Eq. (2.34) reduce it to a sequence of equations for the unknown functions $\mathscr{Y}_n(s)$. The first three of the sequence are

$$\nabla_1\left[\mathscr{Y}_1(s_{12}) + G(s_{12}) - \int G(s_{23})\mathscr{Y}_1(s_{13})\, d\mathbf{s}_3\right] = 0$$

$$\nabla_1\left[\mathscr{Y}_2(s_{12}) + \tfrac{1}{2}G^2(s_{12}) - \int G(s_{23})\mathscr{Y}_2(s_{13})\, d\mathbf{s}_3\right]$$
$$= \int [A_2 - G(s_{13})G(s_{23})]\, \nabla_1\mathscr{Y}_1(s_{13})\, d\mathbf{s}_3 \tag{2.38}$$

$$\nabla_1\left[\mathscr{Y}_3(s_{12}) + \tfrac{1}{3}G^{(3)}(s_{12}) - \int G(s_{23})\mathscr{Y}_3(s_{13})\, d\mathbf{s}_3\right]$$
$$= \int [A_2 - G(s_{13})G(s_{23})]\, \nabla_1\mathscr{Y}_2(s_{13})\, d\mathbf{s}_3$$
$$+ \int \{A_3 - [G(s_{13}) + G(s_{23})]A_2\}\, \nabla_1\mathscr{Y}_1(s_{13})\, d\mathbf{s}_3$$

These equations can be solved in momentum space. Thus, for example,

$$\int (\exp i\mathbf{q}\cdot\mathbf{s}_{12})\, \nabla_1\left[\mathscr{Y}_1(s_{12}) + G(s_{12}) - \int G(s_{23})\mathscr{Y}_1(s_{13})\, d\mathbf{s}_3\right] d\mathbf{s}_1$$
$$= -i\mathbf{q}\{Z_1(q)[1 - F(q)] + F(q)\} = 0 \tag{2.39}$$

or

$$Z_1(q) = -F(q)/[1 - F(q)] \tag{2.40}$$

Equation (2.40) gives a particular solution of Eq. (2.39) excluding a possible delta-function singularity at the origin.

The remaining two equations in (2.38) generate the following explicit solutions in momentum space:

$$Z_2(q) = -\frac{1}{2}\frac{F_2(q)}{1 - F(q)}$$
$$- Z_1(q)\frac{1}{(2\pi)^3}\int \frac{\mathbf{q}\cdot\mathbf{q}'}{q^2} F(q')F(|\mathbf{q}' - \mathbf{q}|)\, d\mathbf{q}' \tag{2.41}$$

$$Z_3(q) = -\frac{1}{3}\frac{F_3(q)}{1-F(q)}$$
$$+ Z_1(q)\frac{1}{(2\pi)^3}\int \frac{\mathbf{q}\cdot\mathbf{q}'}{q^2} F(|\mathbf{q}'-\mathbf{q}|)[1-F(q')]Z_2(q')\, d\mathbf{q}'$$
$$- Z_1(q)\frac{1}{(2\pi)^6}\int \frac{\mathbf{q}\cdot\mathbf{q}'}{q^2} F(q'')F(|\mathbf{q}-\mathbf{q}''|)F(|\mathbf{q}''-\mathbf{q}'|)F(q')\, d\mathbf{q}'\, d\mathbf{q}''$$
$$+ \frac{1}{(2\pi)^6}\int \frac{\mathbf{q}\cdot\mathbf{q}'}{q^2} F(q'')F(|\mathbf{q}-\mathbf{q}''|)F(|\mathbf{q}''-\mathbf{q}'|)F(|\mathbf{q}'-\mathbf{q}|)$$
$$\times F(|\mathbf{q}'-\mathbf{q}|)F(q')\, d\mathbf{q}'\, d\mathbf{q}'' \tag{2.42}$$

These formulas can be simplified by introducnig the identity $2\mathbf{q}\cdot\mathbf{q}' = q^2 + q'^2 - (\mathbf{q}'-\mathbf{q})^2$ into the integral term of Eq. (2.41) and the last integral in the right-hand member of Eq. (2.42): where the integrands are symmetrical functions of $\mathbf{q}'$ and $\mathbf{q}'-\mathbf{q}$ the factor $\mathbf{q}\cdot\mathbf{q}'/q^2$ can be replaced by $\frac{1}{2}$. Thus the formula for $Z_2(q)$ reduces to

$$Z_2(q) = -\frac{1}{2}\frac{F_2(q)}{1-F(q)} + \frac{1}{2}\frac{F(q)F_2(q)}{1-F(q)}$$
$$= -\frac{1}{2}F_2(q) \tag{2.43}$$

These forms now yield

$$\frac{1}{(2\pi)^3}\int (\exp i\mathbf{q}\cdot\mathbf{s})Z_1(q)\, d\mathbf{q} = -\frac{1}{(2\pi)^3}\int (\exp i\mathbf{q}\cdot\mathbf{s})\left[F(q) + \frac{F^2(q)}{1-F(q)}\right] d\mathbf{q}$$
$$= -G(s) - \frac{1}{(2\pi)^3}\int (\exp i\mathbf{q}\cdot\mathbf{s})\frac{F^2(q)}{1-F(q)}\, d\mathbf{q}$$
$$\frac{1}{(2\pi)^3}\int (\exp i\mathbf{q}\cdot\mathbf{s})Z_2(q)\, d\mathbf{q} = -\frac{1}{2}G^2(s) \tag{2.44}$$

In $Z_3(q)$ the change of variable $\mathbf{q}''\to\mathbf{q}''+\mathbf{q}'$, $\mathbf{q}'\to\mathbf{q}'$, reveals the stated symmetry in the last integral mentioned above. The reduction of $Z_3 + \frac{1}{3}F_3$ to a final simple form is developed in Appendix 2-B based on unpublished research by D. K. Lee. The result is

$$Z_3(q) + \frac{1}{3}F_3(q) = \frac{1}{2(2\pi)^6}\int F(|\mathbf{q}-\mathbf{q}'|)F(q')F(|\mathbf{q}'-\mathbf{q}''|)$$
$$\times F(|\mathbf{q}''-\mathbf{q}|)F(q'')\, d\mathbf{q}'\, d\mathbf{q}'' \tag{2.45}$$

To express $u(r)$ in a familiar notation, we introduce the liquid structure function

$$S(k) = 1 - F(k) \tag{2.46}$$

with $k = (\alpha\rho)^{1/3}q$. Then

$$\begin{aligned}
u(r) &\equiv \mathcal{Y}(s) \\
&= -\alpha G(s) - \frac{1}{2}\alpha^2 G(s)^2 - \frac{1}{3}\alpha^3 G(s)^3 \\
&\quad - \frac{1}{(2\pi)^3\rho}\int (\exp i\mathbf{k}\cdot\mathbf{r})\frac{[S(k)-1]^2}{S(k)}\,d\mathbf{k} \\
&\quad + \alpha^3\frac{1}{(2\pi)^3}\int(\exp i\mathbf{q}\cdot\mathbf{s})\left[Z_3(q) + \frac{1}{3}F_3(q)\right]d\mathbf{q} + O(\alpha^4) \\
&= \ln g(r) - \frac{1}{(2\pi)^3\rho}\int(\exp i\mathbf{k}\cdot\mathbf{r})\frac{[S(k)-1]^2}{S(k)}\,d\mathbf{k} \\
&\quad + \alpha^3\frac{1}{(2\pi)^3}\int(\exp i\mathbf{q}\cdot\mathbf{s})\left[Z_3(q) + \frac{1}{3}F_3(q)\right]d\mathbf{q} + O(\alpha^4)
\end{aligned} \tag{2.47}$$

It is clear from Eqs. (2.32)–(2.34) that $\ln g(r)$ in Eq. (2.47) is exact, although the derivation generates only the first three terms in the representation of $\ln g(r)$ as a power series in α.

The formula

$$u(r)_{\mathrm{HNC}} = \ln g(r) - \frac{1}{(2\pi)^3\rho}\int(\exp i\mathbf{k}\cdot\mathbf{r})\frac{[S(k)-1)]^2}{S(k)}\,d\mathbf{k} \tag{2.48}$$

is known as the hypernetted-chain (HNC) connection [8], [9] between the correlation function $u(r)$ and the radial distribution function $g(r)$. Earlier derivations, in the context of the classical statistical mechanics of an imperfect gas at low densities, require the summation of infinite classes of cluster diagrams. These derivations place no restriction on α; in particular, $\alpha = 1$ [$g(0) = 0$] is not excluded. In applications the formula appears to be a useful approximation even at liquid densities [10, 11]. It is a remarkable coincidence that rather different conditions (uniform limit in one case, low density in the other) produce exactly the same leading terms in the formula for u as a functional in g.

2.6. A DYNAMICAL CONSISTENCY CONDITION

How can we recognize that a given $p^{(3)}$ is indeed generated by a solution of the Schrödinger equation? This question can be given a precise and practically useful formulation. Since the Schrödinger equation is involved in an essential manner, it is proper to speak of a dynamical consistency condition.

The starting point is the quadratic form

$$X^{(n)}(1, 2, \ldots, n) = N(N-1) \cdots (N-n+1) \int \psi_0(H-E_0)\psi_0 \, d\mathbf{r}_{n+1, \ldots, N} \tag{2.49}$$

which vanishes if $H\psi_0 = E_0 \psi_0$. To convert Eq. (2.49) into a useful relation, the right-hand member must be expressed as a functional in the distribution functions. If these distribution functions are correctly generated from ψ_0, then $X^{(n)}$ vanishes; otherwise, it will, in general, differ from zero.

The occurrence of the quantity $\psi \, \Delta\psi$ in the integral formula for $X^{(n)}$ appears to require the introduction of the general density matrix $(1', 2', \ldots n'|\rho|1, 2, \ldots, n)$ rather than the purely diagonal form $p^{(n)}(1, 2, \ldots n)$. However, the density matrices can be avoided by introducing the identity

$$\Delta\psi^2 + \psi^2 \, \Delta \, (\ln \psi^2) = 4\psi \, \Delta\psi \tag{2.50}$$

and writing

$$\psi_0(H-E_0)\psi_0 = -\frac{\hbar^2}{8m}\left(\sum_1^N \Delta_l\right)\psi_0^2 - E_0 \, \psi_0^2 + \left[\sum_{i<j} v(r_{ij}) - \frac{\hbar^2}{8m}\left(\sum_1^N \Delta_l\right) \ln \psi_0^2\right] \psi_0^2 \tag{2.51}$$

Next E_0 must be eliminated because it is a large quantity of order N and is never known with absolute accuracy. To conceal the presence of E_0, let

$$V^*(1, 2, \ldots, N) = \sum_{i<j} v(r_{ij}) - \frac{\hbar^2}{8m} \sum_l \Delta_l(\ln \psi_0^2) \tag{2.52}$$

and introduce the generalized normalization integral

$$I_0(\beta) = \int \psi_0^2 \exp(\beta V^*) \, d\mathbf{r}_{1, 2, \ldots, N} \tag{2.53}$$

The distribution functions and their Fourier transforms are generalized to functions of β: $p^{(n)}(1, 2, \ldots, n; \beta)$, $h(r; \beta) = g(r; \beta) - 1$, $S(k; \beta)$, etc., by the substitution of $[1/I_0(\beta)](\exp \beta V^*)\psi_0{}^2$ for $\psi_0{}^2$ in the defining equations.

The first useful consequence of Eq. (2.53) is

$$E_0 = \left[\frac{d}{d\beta} I_0(\beta)\right]_{\beta=0} \tag{2.54}$$

Equation (2.51) assumes the form

$$\psi_0(H - E_0)\psi_0 = \left[\frac{d}{d\beta} \frac{1}{I_0(\beta)} (\exp \beta V^*)\psi_0{}^2\right]_{\beta=0} - \frac{\hbar^2}{8m} \sum \Delta_l \psi_0{}^2 \tag{2.55}$$

and Eq. (2.49) reduces to

$$X^{(n)}(1, 2, \ldots, n) = \left[\frac{d}{d\beta} p^{(n)}(1, 2, \ldots, n; \beta)\right]_{\beta=0} - \frac{\hbar^2}{8m} \sum_1^n \Delta_l p^{(n)}(1, 2, \ldots, n; 0) \tag{2.56}$$

At $n = 2$ the condition $X^{(2)}(1, 2) = 0$ implies

$$\left[\frac{d}{d\beta} g(r; \beta)\right]_{\beta=0} = \frac{\hbar^2}{4m} \Delta g(r) \tag{2.57}$$

Equation (2.57) may be interpreted as the definition of the left-hand member. This definition is the key to the evaluation of $X_a(1, 2, 3)$, the subscript "a" denoting use of an approximate form $p_a(1, 2, 3)$ in evaluating $X(1, 2, 3)$. The evaluation is possible only if $p_a(1, 2, 3; \beta)$ is expressed as a complete functional in $h(r; \beta)$. The functions p_K, p_c, and p_A are examples of the required type. If $p_a(1, 2, 3; \beta)$ is a complete functional in h, the derivative of p_a with respect to β at $\beta = 0$ can be evaluated with the aid of Eq. (2.57). Thus the actual direct evaluation of integrals involving V^* is never necessary.

The dynamical consistency condition can be formulated in momentum space. This amounts to introducing Fourier transforms of suitable X functions. However, a direct approach through Eq. (2.55) is more convenient. Introduce a symmetrical function F as a multiplying factor in Eq. (2.55) and integrate over all coordinates to obtain

$$Y(F) = \left[\frac{d}{d\beta}\frac{1}{I_0(\beta)}\int F(\exp \beta V^*)\psi_0{}^2 \, d\mathbf{r}_{1,2,\ldots,N}\right]_{\beta=0} - \frac{\hbar^2}{8m}\int \psi_0{}^2 \sum_1^N \Delta_l F \, d\mathbf{r}_{1,2,\ldots,N} \tag{2.58}$$

Consider in succession the functions

$$\begin{aligned} F_1 &= 1 \\ F_2 &= (1/N)\sum_{m,n} \exp i\mathbf{k}\cdot\mathbf{r}_{mn} \\ F_3 &= \sum_{l\neq m\neq n\neq l} \exp i(\mathbf{k}_1\cdot\mathbf{r}_l + \mathbf{k}_2\cdot\mathbf{r}_m + \mathbf{k}_3\cdot\mathbf{r}_n) \end{aligned} \tag{2.59}$$

with $k \neq 0$, $\mathbf{k}_1, \mathbf{k}_2, \mathbf{k}_3 \neq 0$, and $\mathbf{k}_1 + \mathbf{k}_2 + \mathbf{k}_3 = 0$. The third function is interesting only if $\mathbf{k}_1 + \mathbf{k}_2 + \mathbf{k}_3 = 0$; otherwise, $X(F_3)$ vanishes in consequence of trivial orthogonality relations (we introduce the periodic boundary conditions to determine a discrete set of wave vectors). Clearly $Y(F_1) = 0$. The second function yields

$$Y(F_2) = \left[\frac{d}{d\beta} S(k;\beta)\right]_{\beta=0} + \frac{\hbar^2 k^2}{4m}[S(k) - 1] \tag{2.60}$$

or, setting $Y(F_2) = 0$,

$$\left[\frac{d}{d\beta} S(k;\beta)\right]_{\beta=0} = -\frac{\hbar^2 k^2}{4m}[S(k) - 1] \tag{2.61}$$

Equation (2.61) is the equivalent in momentum space of Eq. (2.57).

The third function F_3 generates

$$\begin{aligned} Y(F_3) = {} & \left\{\frac{d}{d\beta}\int [\exp i(\mathbf{k}_1\cdot\mathbf{r}_1 + \mathbf{k}_2\cdot\mathbf{r}_2 + \mathbf{k}_3\cdot\mathbf{r}_3)] \right. \\ & \left. \times\, p^{(3)}(1,2,3;\beta)\, d\mathbf{r}_{1,2,3}\right\}_{\beta=0} \\ & + \frac{\hbar^2}{8m}(k_1{}^2 + k_2{}^2 + k_3{}^2)\int [\exp i(\mathbf{k}_1\cdot\mathbf{r}_1 + \mathbf{k}_2\cdot\mathbf{r}_2 + \mathbf{k}_3\cdot\mathbf{r}_3)] \\ & \times\, p^{(3)}(1,2,3;\beta)\, d\mathbf{r}_{1,2,3} \end{aligned} \tag{2.62}$$

The integral occurring in Eq. (2.62) is a natural extension of the notion of a liquid structure function to three variables. Let

$$S^{(3)}(\mathbf{k}_1, \mathbf{k}_2, \mathbf{k}_3; \beta) = (1/N) \int [\exp i(\mathbf{k}_1 \cdot \mathbf{r}_1 + \mathbf{k}_2 \cdot \mathbf{r}_2 + \mathbf{k}_3 \cdot \mathbf{r}_3)] \times p^{(3)}(1, 2, 3; \beta)\, d\mathbf{r}_{1,2,3} \tag{2.63}$$

subject to the constraint $\mathbf{k}_1 + \mathbf{k}_2 + \mathbf{k}_3 = 0$. Properties of complete symmetry and rotational invariance for $S^{(3)}$ follow directly from the same properties of $p^{(3)}$. Also, for $k \neq 0$,

$$S^{(3)}(\mathbf{k}, -\mathbf{k}, 0; \beta) = (N-2)[S(\mathbf{k}; \beta) - 1] \tag{2.64}$$

In terms of $S^{(3)}$,

$$\frac{1}{N} Y(F_3) = \left[\frac{d}{d\beta} S^{(3)}(\mathbf{k}_1, \mathbf{k}_2, \mathbf{k}_3; \beta)\right]_{\beta=0} + \frac{\hbar^2}{8m} ({k_1}^2 + {k_2}^2 + {k_3}^2) S^{(3)}(\mathbf{k}_1, \mathbf{k}_2, \mathbf{k}_3; 0) \tag{2.65}$$

Equations (2.64) and (2.65) now require

$$Y(F_3) = 0 \qquad \text{if} \quad k_1 \quad \text{or} \quad k_2 \quad \text{or} \quad k_3 = 0 \tag{2.66}$$

Equations (2.66) remains valid for an approximate form $p_{\mathrm{a}}^{(3)}$ provided only that $p_{\mathrm{a}}^{(3)}$ satisfies the sequential relation. In that event $Y_{\mathrm{a}}(F_3) = 0$ if k_1 or k_2 or $k_3 = 0$. Of the approximate forms discussed earlier, p_{K} leads to a failure of Eq. (2.66), the equation is satisfied exactly by p_{c}, and very nearly by p_{A}.

The dynamical consistency condition in momentum space is $Y(F_3) = 0$; or, for an approximate form $p_{\mathrm{a}}^{(3)}$,

$$|Y_{\mathrm{a}}(F_3)| \ll |Y_c(F_3)|_{\text{average}} \tag{2.67}$$

The corresponding condition in coordinate space is

$$|X_{\mathrm{a}}^{(3)}| \ll |X_{\mathrm{K}}^{(3)}|_{\text{average}} \tag{2.68}$$

In each case the particular choice of approximate form for a comparison standard is dictated by a criterion of simplicity. The averages are taken over a range of variables large enough to mask the illusory smallness produced by possible nodal surfaces.

To evaluate $Y_c(F_3)$ and $Y_K(F_3)$ when $k_1 k_2 k_3 \neq 0$, we need the functions

$$\begin{aligned} S_c^{(3)}(k_1, k_2, k_3; \beta) = {} & [S(k_1; \beta) - 1][S(k_2; \beta) - 1] \\ & + [S(k_2; \beta) - 1][S(k_3; \beta) - 1] \\ & + [S(k_3; \beta) - 1][S(k_1; \beta) - 1] \\ & + [S(k_1; \beta) - 1][S(k_2; \beta) - 1][S(k_3; \beta) - 1] \end{aligned} \tag{2.69}$$

$$\begin{aligned} S_k^{(3)}(\mathbf{k}_1, \mathbf{k}_2, \mathbf{k}_3; \beta) = {} & [S(k_1; \beta) - 1][S(k_2; \beta) - 1] \\ & + [S(k_2; \beta) - 1][S(k_3; \beta) - 1] \\ & + [S(k_3; \beta) - 1][S(k_1; \beta) - 1] \\ & + \frac{1}{(2\pi)^3 \rho} \int [S(k; \beta) - 1][S(\mathbf{k} + \mathbf{k}_1; \beta) - 1] \\ & \times [S(\mathbf{k} - \mathbf{k}_2; \beta) - 1] \, d\mathbf{k} \end{aligned} \tag{2.70}$$

Observe that $S^{(3)}$ experiences an order-of-magnitude discontinuity at the surface $k_1 k_2 |\mathbf{k}_1 + \mathbf{k}_2| = 0$. Equations (2.69)–(2.70) and the two preceding formulas lead to

$$\begin{aligned} \frac{8m}{N\hbar^2} Y_c^{(3)}(F_3) = {} & (k_3^2 - k_1^2 - k_2^2)[S(k_1) - 1][S(k_2) - 1] \\ & + (k_1^2 - k_2^2 - k_3^2)[S(k_2) - 1][S(k_3) - 1] \\ & + (k_2^2 - k_3^2 - k_1^2)[S(k_3) - 1][S(k_1) - 1] \\ & + (k_1^2 + k_2^2 + k_3^2)[S(k_1) - 1][S(k_2) - 1][S(k_3) - 1] \end{aligned} \tag{2.71}$$

$$\begin{aligned} \frac{8m}{N\hbar^2} Y_k^{(3)}(F_3) = {} & (k_3^2 - k_1^2 - k_2^2)[S(k_1) - 1][S(k_2) - 1] \\ & + (k_1^2 - k_2^2 - k_3^2)[S(k_2) - 1][S(k_3) - 1] \\ & + [k_2^2 - k_3^2 - k_1^2][S(k_3) - 1][S(k_1) - 1] \\ & + \frac{1}{(2\pi)^3 \rho} \int [k^2 + (\mathbf{k} - \mathbf{k}_1)^2 + (\mathbf{k} + \mathbf{k}_2)^2] \\ & \times [S(k) - 1][S(\mathbf{k} - \mathbf{k}_1) - 1][S(\mathbf{k} + \mathbf{k}_2) - 1] \, d\mathbf{k} \end{aligned} \tag{2.72}$$

A brief discussion of these functions appears in reference [1]. Numerical calculations using the experimental $S(k)$ of liquid ^{4}He establish that $|Y_c| \ll |Y_K|$ on the range k_1 or k_2 or $k_3 < 0.6$ Å^{-1}. Outside of this range the two functions are generally similar in magnitude.

In coordinate space the superposition approximation reduces $X^{(3)}$ to

$$\begin{aligned}\frac{4m}{\rho^3\hbar^2} X_K(1, 2, 3) = &-g_{23} \frac{dg_{12}}{dr_{12}} \frac{dg_{13}}{dr_{13}} \cos(12, 13)\\ &-g_{31} \frac{dg_{23}}{dr_{23}} \frac{dg_{21}}{dr_{21}} \cos(23, 21)\\ &-g_{12} \frac{dg_{31}}{dr_{31}} \frac{dg_{32}}{dr_{32}} \cos(31, 32)\end{aligned} \tag{2.73}$$

Contour plots of X_K [based on $g(r)$ computed from the measured $S(k)$ of liquid ^{4}He] are given in references 6 and 12. These single out certain straight-line configurations and equilateral-triangle configurations for which p_K is apparently most seriously inadequate. For equilateral configurations the major discrepancy is associated with $r = r_{12} = r_{23} = r_{31}$ on the first rising slope of $g(r)$. Beyond that, secondary peaks of X_K alternate with the peaks and valleys of $g(r)$. A straight-line configuration gives two of the cosine factors the value 1 and the remaining cosine factor the value -1. To illustrate the behavior of X_K in this case, choose $r = r_{12} = r_{23}$ and $2r = r_{13}$, placing r on the first rising slope of $g(r)$ and $2r$ on the falling slope of the nearest-neighbor peak. Then all three terms making up the right-hand member of Eq. (2.73) are large and have the same sign.

Equations (2.56) and (2.57) can be interpreted as the infinitesimal form of the statement that two sets of generalized distribution functions are equivalent. One set is defined by the transformation

$$\hat{p}^{(n)}(1, 2, \ldots, n|g) = \prod_1^n \{\exp[(\hbar^2\beta/8m)\,\Delta_l]\} p^{(n)}(1, 2, \ldots, n|g) \tag{2.74}$$

Here the notation $p^{(n)}(1, 2, \ldots, n|g)$ emphasizes the restriction to complete functionals in g. The "caret" functions satisfy the sequential relation, since

$$\int \hat{p}^{(n)}(1, 2, \ldots, n|g)\, d\mathbf{r}_n = \left[\prod_1^{n-1} \exp\left(\frac{\hbar^2\beta}{8m}\Delta_l\right)\right]\left\{\exp\left[\frac{\hbar^2\beta}{8m}\left(\sum_1^{n-1}\mathbf{\nabla}_l\right)^2\right]\right\}$$

$$\times \int p^{(n)}(1, 2, \ldots, n|g)\, d\mathbf{r}_n$$

$$= (N-n+1)\left\{\exp\left[\frac{\hbar^2\beta}{8m}\left(\sum_1^{n-1}\mathbf{\nabla}_l\right)^2\right]\right\}$$

$$\times \hat{p}^{(n-1)}(1, 2, \ldots, n-1|g)$$

$$= (N-n+1)\hat{p}^{(n-1)}(1, 2, \ldots, n-1|g) \qquad (2.75)$$

the right-hand statements following from the general requirements that $p^{(n)}$ be continuous with continuous derivatives of all order and invariant under a uniform displacement. The same properties must then hold also for $p^{(n-1)}(1, 2, \ldots, n-1|g)$.

The sequential relations are also satisfied by $p^{(n)}(1, 2, \ldots, n|\hat{g})$, with $\hat{g}$ defined by Eq. (2.74) for $n = 2$. The difference function

$$Z(1, 2, \ldots, n|\beta) \equiv p^{(n)}(1, 2, \ldots, n|\hat{g}) - \hat{p}^{(n)}(1, 2, \ldots, n|g) \qquad (2.76)$$

provides a measure of the amount by which the nth order consistency condition fails. The derivative of $Z(1, 2, \ldots, n|\beta)$ with respect to β at $\beta = 0$ is in fact identical to $X(1, 2, \ldots, n)$:

$$Z'(1, 2, \ldots, n|0) = X(1, 2, \ldots, n) \qquad (2.77)$$

under the assumptions (1) $X(1, 2) = 0$ [Eq. (2.57)] and (2) $p^{(n)}(1, 2, \ldots, n|g)$ is a complete functional in g.

The point I wish to make here is that Eqs. (2.74)–(2.77) tell us nothing about the magnitude of $Z(1, 2, \ldots, n|\beta)$ and $Z'(1, 2, \ldots, n|0)$ for $n > 2$ if we do not invoke the dynamical condition on $X(1, 2, \ldots, n)$. In particular $Z'(1, 2, 3|0)$ can be arbitrarily large, since the only restriction imposed by Eqs. (2.74)–(2.77) is that $Z'(1, 2, 3|0)$ is a solution of the homogeneous integral equation of Eq. (2.10). It is therefore clear that the stronger statement of Eq. (2.68) involves the dynamical connections implicit in the derivation of Eq. (2.68). If Eq. (2.68) fails, either (1) $g(r)$ cannot be generated by a good approximation to the ground-state eigenfunction, or (2) $p^{(3)}(1, 2, 3|g)$ is not a close approximation to $p^{(3)}(1, 2, 3)$ generated by the same wave-function which produces $g(r)$, or both (1) and (2). The convolution form $p_c(1, 2, 3)$ provides an illuminating illustration of point (2), especially relevant because $p_c(1, 2, 3)$ satisfies the sequential relation for $n = 3$.

APPENDIX 2-A

A Convolution Form for $p^{(4)}$ and Asymmetrical Forms for $p^{(3)}$ and $p^{(4)}$*

The three- and four-particle functions represented by the diagramatic equations

$(1/\rho^3)p_c(1, 2, 3) =$ 1+ 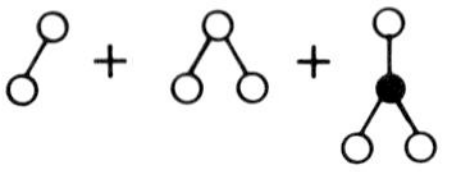 (A.1)

and [3]

$(1/\rho^4)p_c(1, 2, 3, 4) =$ 1+ 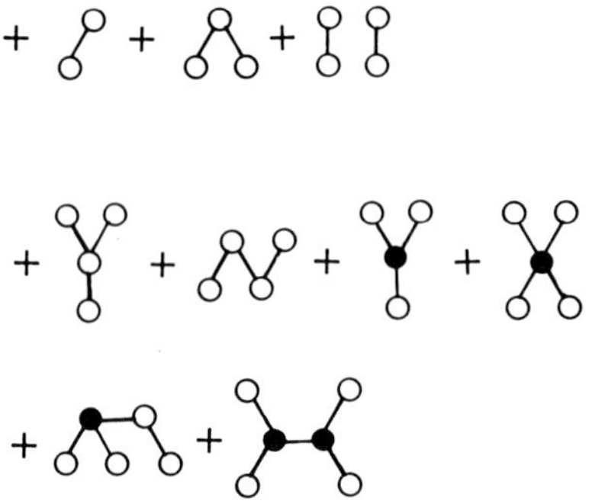 (A.2)

satisfy the sequential relations

$$p_c(1, 2, 3) = [1/(N-3)] \int p_c(1, 2, 3, 4)\, d\mathbf{r}_4$$

$$p^{(2)}(1, 2) = \rho^2 g(r_{12}) = [1/(N-2)] \int p_c(1, 2, 3)\, d\mathbf{r}_3$$

Each diagram represents a sum of all distinct products of h factors [ranging over 1, 2, and 3 in Eq. (A1) and over 1, 2, 3, and 4 in Eq. (A.2)], with solid circles denoting the operations $\rho \int \cdots d\mathbf{r}_5$ and $\rho^2 \int \cdots d\mathbf{r}_5\, d\mathbf{r}_6$. Diagrams without solid circles can be interpreted as elements of an exact formula; diagrams with solid circles represent an approximate form of the remainder.

* Appendix 2-A exhibits a four-point distribution function $p_c(1, 2, 3, 4)$ which generates $p_c(1, 2, 3)$ in the sequential relation connecting $p^{(4)}$ and $p^{(3)}$. The four-point function is useful in estimating interaction matrix elements in a condensed boson system for the elementary process in which the initial and final states each contain two elementary excitations (scattering of two elementary excitations). See Lee [3].

Both $p_c(1, 2, 3)$ and $p_c(1, 2, 3, 4)$ are symmetrical functions of the point coordinates, but are not necessarily positive-valued everywhere. These functions also fail to vanish when any two points coincide. Alternative distribution functions embodying different selections of good and bad qualities can be generated using Eqs. (A.1) and (A.2) as guides. In particular, useful formulas are obtained by dropping the symmetry condition and requiring that the approximate distribution functions contain $g(r_{12})$ as a factor and satisfy the sequential relations when integrated over points 3 or 4. These conditions are met by introducing the functions $p_c(12|3)$ and $p_c(12|34)$ defined by Eqs. (A.1) and (A.2) with the supplementary statement that the function $h(r_{12})$ does not occur as a link in the diagrammatic representation. Thus  in Eq. (A.1) now represents $h(r_{13})$ and $h(r_{23})$;  in the same equation represents $h(r_{13})h(r_{23})$. The new approximations for $p^{(3)}$ and $p^{(4)}$ are

$$p_a^{(3)}(12|3) = g(r_{12})p_c(12|3), \quad p_a^{(4)}(12|34) = g(r_{12})p_c(12|34) \tag{A.3}$$

These functions are useful in estimating diagonal matrix elements of

$$\begin{aligned}\sum_{i\neq j} v(\mathbf{r}_{ij}) \sum_{m\neq n} w(\mathbf{r}_{mn}) \to\ & 2N(N-1)v(\mathbf{r}_{12})w(\mathbf{r}_{12}) \\ & + 4N(N-1)(N-2)v(\mathbf{r}_{12})w(\mathbf{r}_{13}) \\ & + N(N-1)(N-2)(N-3)v(\mathbf{r}_{12})w(\mathbf{r}_{34})\end{aligned} \tag{A.4}$$

where $v(\mathbf{r})$ is a singular short-range function and $w(\mathbf{r})$ is a bounded, slowly varying function. The singular $v(\mathbf{r}_{12})$ is associated with $\rho^2 g(r_{12})$, and $w(\mathbf{r}_{13})$ and $w(\mathbf{r}_{34})$ with $p_a^{(3)}(12|3)$ and $p_a^{(4)}(12|34)$, respectively.

The choice $w(\mathbf{r}) = \exp(i\mathbf{k}\cdot\mathbf{r})$ generates the matrix element

$$(1/2N)\langle 0||\rho_{\mathbf{k}}|^2\left\{\sum_{i\neq j} v(\mathbf{r}_{ij}) - \langle 0|\sum_{i\neq j} v(\mathbf{r}_{ij})|0\rangle\right\}|0\rangle = \rho\int M(\mathbf{r}|\mathbf{k})v(\mathbf{r})\,d\mathbf{r} \tag{A.5}$$

in which

$$\begin{aligned}M(\mathbf{r}|\mathbf{k}) \approx\ & S^2(k)g(r) \\ & \times\left\{\frac{\sin kr}{kr} + \frac{1}{(2\pi)^3\rho}\int [S^2(k') - 1][S(|\mathbf{k}+\mathbf{k}'|) - 1]\,\frac{\sin k'r}{k'r}\,d\mathbf{k}'\right\}\end{aligned} \tag{A.6}$$

Equations (A.5)–(A.6) should give reasonable order-of-magnitude estimates, but are not likely to attain semiquantitative accuracy. A more accurate evaluation is developed in Chapter 5, Section 10.

APPENDIX 2-B

Reduction of Eq. (2.42) for $Z_3 + \frac{1}{3}F_3$*

Two identities serve to eliminate several terms in the last right-hand member of Eq. (2.42). First

$$\tfrac{1}{2}\int (\mathbf{q}\cdot\mathbf{q}')F(q')F(|\mathbf{q}'-\mathbf{q}|)F_2(q')\,d\mathbf{q}'$$
$$=[1/2(2\pi)^3]\int (\mathbf{q}\cdot\mathbf{q}')F(q')F(|\mathbf{q}'-\mathbf{q}|)F(|\mathbf{q}''-\mathbf{q}'|)F(q'')\,d\mathbf{q}'\,d\mathbf{q}'' \quad \text{(B.1)}$$

The identity $\mathbf{q}'=(\mathbf{q}'-\mathbf{q}'')+\mathbf{q}''$and the observation that $F(|\mathbf{q}''-\mathbf{q}'|)F(\mathbf{q}'')$ is invariant under the replacement of $\mathbf{q}''$ by $\mathbf{q}'-\mathbf{q}''$ permit writing

$$\tfrac{1}{2}\int (\mathbf{q}\cdot\mathbf{q}')F(q')F(|\mathbf{q}'-\mathbf{q}|)F_2(q')\,d\mathbf{q}'$$
$$=[1/(2\pi)^3]\int (\mathbf{q}\cdot\mathbf{q}'')F(q')F(|q'-\mathbf{q}|)F(|\mathbf{q}''-\mathbf{q}'|)F(q'')\,d\mathbf{q}'\,d\mathbf{q}''$$
$$=[1/(2\pi)^3]\int \mathbf{q}\cdot\mathbf{q}'F(q')F(|\mathbf{q}''-\mathbf{q}|)F(|q''-q'|)F(q'')\,d\mathbf{q}'\,d\mathbf{q}'' \quad \text{(B.2)}$$

the last line resulting from interchanging $\mathbf{q}'$ and $\mathbf{q}''$.

The second identity is developed from

$$\tfrac{1}{2}\int (\mathbf{q}\cdot\mathbf{q}')F(|q'-q|)F_2(q')\,d\mathbf{q}'$$
$$=[1/2(2\pi)^3]\int (\mathbf{q}\cdot\mathbf{q}')F(|q'-q|)F(|\mathbf{q}''-\mathbf{q}'|)F(q'')\,d\mathbf{q}'\,d\mathbf{q}'' \quad \text{(B.3)}$$

The argument used to convert Eq. (B.1) into (Eq. (B.2) now yields

$$\tfrac{1}{2}\int (\mathbf{q}\cdot\mathbf{q}')F(|\mathbf{q}'-\mathbf{q}|)F_2(q')\,d\mathbf{q}'$$
$$=\frac{1}{(2\pi)^3}\int (q\cdot q'')F(|q'-q|)F(|q''-q'|)F(q'')\,d\mathbf{q}'\,d\mathbf{q}'' \quad \text{(B.4)}$$

Next observe that

$$\begin{aligned}\mathbf{q}\cdot\mathbf{q}'' &= \tfrac{1}{3}\mathbf{q}\cdot\mathbf{q}''+\tfrac{2}{3}\mathbf{q}\cdot\mathbf{q}''\\ &\to \tfrac{1}{3}\mathbf{q}\cdot(\mathbf{q}-\mathbf{q}')+\tfrac{1}{3}\mathbf{q}\cdot\mathbf{q}'\\ &= \tfrac{1}{3}q^2\end{aligned} \quad \text{(B.5)}$$

* See Lee [13].

the arrow denoting the substitution $\mathbf{q}'' \to \mathbf{q} - \mathbf{q}'$, $\mathbf{q}' \to \mathbf{q} - \mathbf{q}''$ in one addend and the reversal of the argument leading from Eq. (B.3) to Eq. (B.4) in the other. Equations (B.4) and (B.5) produce the second identity

$$\tfrac{1}{2}\int (\mathbf{q}\cdot\mathbf{q}')F(|\mathbf{q}'-\mathbf{q}|)F_2(q')\,d\mathbf{q}' = \tfrac{1}{3}q^2\int F(\mathbf{q}-\mathbf{q}'|)F_2(q')\,d\mathbf{q}'$$
$$= \tfrac{1}{3}(2\pi)^3 q^2 F_3(q) \qquad \text{(B.6)}$$

Substitution from Eqs. (B.2) and (B.6) into Eq. (2.42) leaves

$$Z_3(q) + \frac{1}{3}F_3(q) = \frac{1}{2}\frac{1}{(2\pi)^6}\int F(q')F(|\mathbf{q}'-\mathbf{q}|)F(|\mathbf{q}''-\mathbf{q}'|)$$
$$\cdot F(|\mathbf{q}''-\mathbf{q}|)F(q'')\,d\mathbf{q}'\,d\mathbf{q}''$$
$$= \frac{1}{2}\int G(s)\left|\int (\exp i\mathbf{t}\cdot\mathbf{q})G(t)G(|\mathbf{t}+\mathbf{s}|)\,d\mathbf{t}\right|^2 d\mathbf{s} \qquad \text{(B.7)}$$

References

1. H. W. Jackson and E. Feenberg, *Rev. Mod. Phys.* **34**, 686 (1962).
2. E. Feenberg and C. W. Woo, *Phys. Rev.* **137**, A391 (1956).
3. D. K. Lee, unpublished doctoral dissertation, Washington University, 1967.
4. R. Abe, *Progr. Theoret. Phys.* (*Kyoto*) **21**, 421 (1959).
5. F. Y. Wu, private communication.
6. D. K. Lee, H. W. Jackson, and E. Feenberg, *Ann. Phys.* (*N.Y.*) **44**, 84 (1967).
7. D. K. Lee and E. Feenberg, *Phys. Rev.* **137**, A731 (1965).
8. E. Meeron, *Phys. Fluids* **1**, 139 (1958).
9. T. Morita, *Progr. Theoret. Phys.* (*Kyoto*) **20**, 920 (1958).
10. A. A. Khan, *Phys. Rev.* 134, A367 (1964); *Ibid.* **136**, A1260 (1964).
11. A. A. Khan and A. A. Broyles, *J. Chem. Phys.* **43** (1965).
12. H. W. Jackson, unpublished doctoral dissertation, Washington University, 1962.
13. D. K. Lee, private communication and preprint.

CHAPTER 3

The Classical Sound Field and the Correspondence Principle

3.1. INTRODUCTION

The physical system under study is a uniform fluid of N particles occupying a cubical box of volume Ω. We are concerned primarily with the theoretical description and analysis of the ground state and the low excited states. The essential concepts here are the one-particle density matrix, the two- and three-particle distribution functions, and the liquid structure function. Statistical and dynamical correlations among the particles are involved in the characterization of these functions and, through them, in the properties of the low states. Both short-range and long-range correlations occur in an adequate theoretical formulation; the former are essential for a semiquantitative theory of the ground state, the latter for the correct behavior of all low states. Correlated basis functions (CBF) are introduced in later chapters for the purpose of generating the essential short-range correlations required by the presence of singular two-particle potentials in the Hamiltonian operator. The same functions may also serve to generate long-range correlations.

Some information on the magnitude and structure of the long-range correlations can be derived, with the help of the correspondence principle, from the classical theory of small density fluctuations at constant temperature. This theory will now be developed subject to the restriction that the system can be treated as a continuous medium (the wavelengths involved in the fluctuations are large compared to the mean particle spacing). The restriction to density fluctuation at constant temperature may appear artificial from the point of view of real sound propagation in most real fluids, but it permits a direct connection with the number fluctuation analysis leading up to the Ornstein–Zernicke relation [Eq. (1.73)] and also corresponds to the physical conditions under which first sound is propagated in liquid ^{4}He below the λ-transition temperature.

3.2. THEORY OF DENSITY FLUCTUATIONS*

The classical theory of small density fluctuations in the fluid involves the equation of motion,

$$m\rho_0 \frac{\partial}{\partial t} \mathbf{v}(\mathbf{r}, t) = -\nabla[p(\mathbf{r}, t) - p_0] \tag{3.1}$$

the conservation of matter in the statement

$$\frac{\partial}{\partial t}[\rho(\mathbf{r}, t) - \rho_0] + \rho_0 \boldsymbol{\nabla} \cdot \mathbf{v}(\mathbf{r}, t) = 0 \tag{3.2}$$

and the equation of state for small deviations from uniformity,

$$p(\mathbf{r}, t) - p_0 = (1/K_{\mathrm{T}}\rho_0)[\rho(\mathbf{r}, t) - \rho_0] \tag{3.3}$$

Here $\mathbf{v}(\mathbf{r}, t)$ is the velocity of the fluid at the point $\mathbf{r}$, $m\rho(\mathbf{r}, t)$ is the mass density compounded from the mass per particle m and the number density ρ, $p(\mathbf{r}, t)$ is the pressure, and K_{T} is the compressibility coefficient at constant temperature.

Equations (3.1)–(3.3) require

$$\left(\Delta - \frac{1}{c^2}\frac{\partial^2}{\partial t^2}\right) F(\mathbf{r}, t) = 0 \tag{3.4}$$

in which $c = (m\rho_0 K_{\mathrm{T}})^{-1/2}$ is the isothermal sound velocity and $F(\mathbf{r}, t)$ is any of the quantities v_x, v_y, v_z, ρ, p. An exponential function

$$\exp i(\omega_k t - \mathbf{k} \cdot \mathbf{r})$$

is a possible solution if frequency and wave vector are related through the equation

$$\omega_k = kc \tag{3.5}$$

The theory is limited to the wavelength range $\lambda \gg \rho^{-1/3}$ or $k \ll 2\pi\rho^{1/3}$.

* See Cohen and Feynman [1].

A quantized version of the theory can be developed from a Hamiltonian formalism equivalent to Eqs. (3.1)–(3.3). Density fluctuations in the fluid generate a potential energy

$$\text{P.E.} = (1/2K_T \rho_0^2) \int [\rho(\mathbf{r}, t) - \rho_0]^2 \, d\mathbf{r} \tag{3.6}$$

and a kinetic energy

$$\text{K.E.} = \tfrac{1}{2} m\rho_0 \int v^2(\mathbf{r}, t) \, d\mathbf{r} \tag{3.7}$$

These quantities may be expressed in terms of normal coordinates $q_k(t)$ and $\mathbf{v}_k(t)$ defined by

$$\begin{aligned} \rho(\mathbf{r}, t) - \rho_0 &= (1/\Omega) \sum_{\mathbf{k}}{}' q_{\mathbf{k}} \exp(-i\mathbf{k} \cdot \mathbf{r}) \\ \mathbf{v}(\mathbf{r}, t) &= (1/\Omega) \sum_{\mathbf{k}}{}' \mathbf{v}_{\mathbf{k}} \exp(-i\mathbf{k} \cdot \mathbf{r}) \end{aligned} \tag{3.8}$$

The allowed wave vectors $\mathbf{k}$ are chosen, most conveniently, to satisfy the periodic boundary condition defined in Chapter 1, Section 1.1. Equation (3.8) determines the Fourier coefficients

$$\begin{aligned} q_{\mathbf{k}} &= \int [\rho(\mathbf{r}, t) - \rho_0] \exp(i\mathbf{k} \cdot \mathbf{r}) \, d\mathbf{r} \\ \mathbf{v}_{\mathbf{k}} &= \int \mathbf{v}(\mathbf{r}, t) \exp(i\mathbf{k} \cdot \mathbf{r}) \, d\mathbf{r} \end{aligned} \tag{3.9}$$

In terms of the normal coordinates the formulas for P.E. and K.E. reduce to

$$\text{P.E.} = (1/2K_T \rho_0 N) \sum_{\mathbf{k}}{}' q_{\mathbf{k}}^* q_{\mathbf{k}}, \qquad \text{K.E.} = (m\rho_0/2\Omega) \sum_{\mathbf{k}}{}' \mathbf{v}_{\mathbf{k}}^* \cdot \mathbf{v}_{\mathbf{k}} \tag{3.10}$$

Conservation of matter requires

$$\dot{q}_{\mathbf{k}} = i\rho_0 \mathbf{k} \cdot \mathbf{v}_{\mathbf{k}}, \qquad |\dot{q}_{\mathbf{k}}| = \rho_0 k |\mathbf{v}_{\mathbf{k}}| \tag{3.11}$$

The second equation of (3.11) follows from recognition of the fact that only longitudinal waves are propagated by density fluctuations. Thus

$$\text{K.E.} = (m/2N) \sum_{\mathbf{k}}{}' (1/k^2) \dot{q}_{\mathbf{k}}^* \dot{q}_{\mathbf{k}} \tag{3.12}$$

At this point the theory becomes perfectly transparent if real amplitudes $Q_{\mathbf{k}}$ are introduced through the definition

$$Q_{\mathbf{k}} = 2^{-1/2}(q_{\mathbf{k}} + q_{-\mathbf{k}}) \tag{3.13}$$

for $k_x > 0$; $k_x = 0$, $k_y > 0$; and $k_x = k_y = 0$, $k_z > 0$; and the definition

$$Q_{\mathbf{k}} = i2^{-1/2}(q_{\mathbf{k}} - q_{-\mathbf{k}}) \tag{3.14}$$

for $k_x < 0$; $k_x = 0$, $k_y < 0$; and $k_x = k_y = 0$, $k_z < 0$. Using $|q_{\mathbf{k}}|^2 + |q_{\mathbf{k}}|^2 = Q_{\mathbf{k}}^2 + Q_{-\mathbf{k}}^2$, the energy formulas become

$$\begin{aligned} \text{P.E.} &= \frac{1}{2K_T \rho_0 N} \sum_{\mathbf{k}}{}' Q_{\mathbf{k}}^2 \\ \text{K.E.} &= \frac{m}{2N} \sum_{\mathbf{k}}{}' \frac{1}{k^2} \dot{Q}_{\mathbf{k}}^2 \\ &= \frac{N}{2m} \sum_{\mathbf{k}}{}' k^2 P_{\mathbf{k}}^2 \end{aligned} \tag{3.15}$$

the last line introducing the momentum $P_{\mathbf{k}} = (m/NkL)\dot{Q}_{\mathbf{k}}$ conjugate to $Q_{\mathbf{k}}$. The Hamiltonian function

$$H = \frac{mc^2}{2N} \sum_{\mathbf{k}}{}' Q_{\mathbf{k}}^2 + \frac{N}{2mc^2} \sum_{\mathbf{k}}{}' (ck)^2 P_{\mathbf{k}}^2 \tag{3.16}$$

now generates the equations of motion

$$\begin{aligned} \dot{Q}_{\mathbf{k}} &= \partial H/\partial P_{\mathbf{k}} = (N/m)k^2 P_{\mathbf{k}} \\ \dot{P}_{\mathbf{k}} &= -\partial H/\partial Q_{\mathbf{k}} = -(mc^2/N)Q_{\mathbf{k}} \end{aligned} \tag{3.17}$$

and, consequently, both $Q_{\mathbf{k}}$ and $P_{\mathbf{k}}$ are harmonic functions of the time with the frequency $\omega_k = ck$.

A more general classical theory of density fluctuations is outlined briefly in Appendix 3-A. The improvement over the preceding formulation consists in using a general functional in $\rho(\mathbf{r})$ for the potential energy [2]. The change from function to functional permits the occurrence of dispersion in the theory based on the quadratic approximation for the potential energy.

3.3. QUANTUM THEORY OF THE CONTINUOUS MEDIUM

The quantized version of the theory associates the energy eigenvalues

$$\begin{aligned} e(\mathbf{k}, n_{\mathbf{k}}) &= (n_{\mathbf{k}} + \tfrac{1}{2})\hbar\omega_{\mathbf{k}}, \qquad n_{\mathbf{k}} = 0, 1, 2, \ldots \\ &= (mc^2/N)\langle n_{\mathbf{k}} | Q_{\mathbf{k}}^2 | n_{\mathbf{k}} \rangle \end{aligned} \tag{3.18}$$

with the **k**th degree of freedom. Here $|n_{\mathbf{k}}\rangle$ denotes a normalized eigenstate of the **k** oscillator. The second line of Eq. (3.18) expresses the fact that kinetic and potential energy terms in the harmonic oscillator Hamiltonian make equal contributions to the energy eigenvalue (when it is given as an expectation value). Since $n_{\mathbf{k}}$ can take on all integral values, the elementary excitations of the sound field are bosons with the mean occupation numbers.

$$\bar{n}_{\mathbf{k}} = 1/(e^{\beta\hbar ck} - 1) \tag{3.19}$$

in the state of thermal equilibrium. The statistical average value of $(1/N)\langle n_{\mathbf{k}}|Q_{\mathbf{k}}^2|n_{\mathbf{k}}\rangle$ is then

$$\begin{aligned} \overline{(1/N)\langle n_{\mathbf{k}}|Q_{\mathbf{k}}^2|n_{\mathbf{k}}\rangle} &= (\hbar k/mc)(\bar{n}_{\mathbf{k}} + \tfrac{1}{2}) \\ &= (\hbar k/2mc) \coth \tfrac{1}{2}\beta\hbar kc \\ &\to \hbar k/2mc, \qquad T \to 0 \\ &\to 1/\beta mc^2, \qquad \tfrac{1}{2}\beta\hbar kc \ll 1 \end{aligned} \tag{3.20}$$

We will see presently that the left-hand member of Eq. (3.20) is essentially the liquid structure function $S(k, T)$ of the many-particle system in the long-wavelength limit.

A second significant aspect of the quantized continium theory is the state function describing the zero-point fluctuations [3],

$$\langle \cdots Q_{\mathbf{k}} \cdots | \cdots n_{\mathbf{k}} = 0 \cdots \rangle = \text{const} \prod_{\mathbf{k}}{}' \exp\left(-\frac{mc}{2N\hbar k} Q_{\mathbf{k}}^2\right) \tag{3.21}$$

The prime on the product symbol stands for omission of $k = 0$ and the presence of a cutoff factor limiting the k's included in the product to the range in which the continium theory is valid (essentially $k < k_c \ll 2\pi\rho^{1/3}$). An analytically simple formulation of the cutoff condition is provided by including an exponential factor $\exp(-k/k_c)$ in the coefficient of $Q_{\mathbf{k}}^2$ and writing

$$\langle \cdots Q_{\mathbf{k}} \cdots | \cdots n_{\mathbf{k}} = 0 \cdots \rangle = \text{const} \prod_{\mathbf{k}}{}' \exp\left[-\frac{mc \exp(-k/k_c)}{2N\hbar k} Q_{\mathbf{k}}^2\right] \tag{3.22}$$

To see the connection between Eqs. (3.20) and (3.22) and the quantum theory of the particle system, we introduce the discrete character of the fluid through the substitutions

$$\begin{aligned} \rho(\mathbf{r}, t) &\to e^{-(i/\hbar)Ht}\rho(\mathbf{r})e^{(i/\hbar)Ht} = \sum_{1}^{N} e^{-(i/\hbar)Ht}\,\delta(\mathbf{r}-\mathbf{r}_l)e^{(i/\hbar)Ht} \\ q_{\mathbf{k}} &\to e^{-(i/\hbar)Ht}\rho_{\mathbf{k}}\,e^{(i/\hbar)Ht} = e^{-(i/\hbar)Ht}\int \rho(\mathbf{r})(\exp i\mathbf{k}\cdot\mathbf{r})\,d\mathbf{r}\,e^{(i\hbar)Ht} \\ &= \sum_{1}^{N} e^{-(i/\hbar)Ht}(\exp i\mathbf{k}\cdot\mathbf{r}_l)\,e^{(i/\hbar)Ht} \end{aligned} \tag{3.23}$$

and observe that the statistical average of $(1/N)|\rho_{\mathbf{k}}|^2$ is the liquid structure function $S_N(k; T)$ as defined by Eq. (1.61). The identification of the statistical average values of $(1/N)|q_{\mathbf{k}}|^2$ and $(1/N)|\rho_{\mathbf{k}}|^2$ yields

$$S_N(k; T) \to \hbar k/2mc, \qquad T=0, \quad k \ll 2\pi\rho^{1/3} \tag{3.24a}$$

$$\to 1/\beta mc^2, \qquad k \to 0 \tag{3.24b}$$

Equation (3.24a), first derived by Cohen and Feynman, represents valuable information on long-range correlations in the ground-state wave function; the second line is the well-known Ornstein–Zernicke relation.

The identification of $S_N(k)$ with the statistical average of $(1/N)q_{\mathbf{k}}{}^*q_{\mathbf{k}}$ relies on the correspondence principle in the sense that long-wavelength phenomena must find effectively equivalent descriptions in the quantum theory of interacting particles and the quantized formulation of classical continium theory.

The particle interpretation in Eq. (3.22) is simply that the symmetrical coordinate function

$$\psi_{\mathrm{LRC}} = \prod_{\mathbf{k}}{}' \exp\left[-\frac{mc\exp(-k/k_c)}{2N\hbar k}\,|\rho_{\mathbf{k}}|^2\right] \tag{3.25}$$

occurs as a factor in the ground-state wave function of the many-particle system. The long-range correlations (LRC) implicit in ψ_{LRC} show up in the behavior of $S_N(k; 0)$ near the origin as exhibited in the Feynman relation [Eq. (3.24a)].

It is a noteworthy fact that recognition of Eq. (3.24a) as a consequence of the correspondence principle long preceded full awareness of the presence of ψ_{LRC} in the ground-state wave function. The latter point was first made explicitly by Chester and Reatto [3]; however, Enderby, Gaskell, and March [4] gave a more indirect, but closely related statement somewhat earlier.

The function ψ_{LRC} is actually a product of two-particle functions. Suppose $u_{\mathrm{LRC}}(r)$ is a function possessing a Fourier transform:

$$u_{\mathrm{LRC}}(r) = -(1/N) \sum_{\mathbf{k}} C_{\mathbf{k}} \exp i\mathbf{k} \cdot \mathbf{r} \tag{3.26}$$

and

$$\begin{aligned} \sum_{i<j} u_{\mathrm{LRC}}(r_{ij}) &= -(1/2N) \sum_{\mathbf{k}} C_{\mathbf{k}} \sum_{i \neq j} \exp i\mathbf{k} \cdot \mathbf{r}_{ij} \\ &= -(1/2N) \sum_{\mathbf{k}} C_{\mathbf{k}}(|\rho_{\mathbf{k}}|^2 - N) \end{aligned} \tag{3.27}$$

Choose $C_k = (2mc/\hbar k) \exp(-k/k_c)$; then

$$\begin{aligned} u_{\mathrm{LRC}}(r) &= -\frac{2mc}{(2\pi)^3 \rho\hbar} \int \exp(i\mathbf{k} \cdot \mathbf{r}) \frac{1}{k} \exp\left(-\frac{k}{k_c}\right) d\mathbf{k} \\ &= -\frac{mc}{\pi^2 \rho\hbar} \frac{1}{r^2 + k_c^{-2}} \end{aligned} \tag{3.28}$$

and

$$\psi_{\mathrm{LRC}} = \mathrm{const} \prod_{i<j} \exp\left[-\frac{mc}{2\pi^2 \rho\hbar} \frac{1}{r_{ij}^2 + k_c^{-2}}\right] \tag{3.29}$$

3.4. CONSEQUENCES OF THE LONG-RANGE CORRELATIONS IN THE PARTICLE FORMULATION*

Let $\bar{\psi}_0$ represent an approximate normalized trial function for the ground state including all essential short-range correlations and approximating fairly well to the exact solution when all the particles are more or less uniformly spaced. Under these conditions the liquid structure function

$$\begin{aligned} S_0(k) &= N^{-1} \int \bar{\psi}_0{}^2 |\rho_{\mathbf{k}}|^2 \, d\mathbf{r}_{1,2,\ldots,N} \\ &= \langle N^{-1} |\rho_{\mathbf{k}}|^2 \rangle_0 \end{aligned} \tag{3.30}$$

* See Chester and Reatto [3].

should approximate fairly well to the exact ground-state structure function $S(k)$ except in the long-wavelength region ($k \lesssim k_c$). Correct behavior in the long-wavelength region should obtain when $\psi_1 = \bar{\psi}_0 \psi_{LRC}$ is used as a trial function. The corresponding liquid structure function is

$$S(k) = \frac{1}{N} \frac{\int \bar{\psi}_0{}^2 \psi_{LRC}^2 |\rho_{\mathbf{k}}|^2 \, d\mathbf{r}_{1,2,\ldots,N}}{\int \bar{\psi}_0{}^2 \psi_{LRC}^2 \, d\mathbf{r}_{1,2,\ldots,N}}$$

$$= \langle N^{-1} |\rho_{\mathbf{k}}|^2 \rangle_{0,\,LRC} \tag{3.31}$$

Our objective is to establish a connection expressing $S(k)$ in terms of $S_0(k)$ and $C(k)$ and so prove that $S(k)$ behaves properly [as required by Eq. (3.24a)] in the long-wavelength limit.

We begin the argument with a more modest undertaking, by considering a trial function containing only one exponential factor in $|\rho_{\mathbf{k}}|^2$. Let

$$I_0(k, x) = \int \bar{\psi}_0{}^2 \exp\left[-\frac{xC_k}{N} |\rho_{\mathbf{k}}|^2 \right] d\mathbf{r}_{1,2,\ldots,N} \tag{3.32}$$

$$S_0(k, x) = \frac{1}{I_0(k, x)} \int \bar{\psi}_0{}^2 \exp\left[-\frac{xC_k}{N} |\rho_{\mathbf{k}}|^2 \right] \frac{1}{N} |\rho_{\mathbf{k}}|^2 \, d\mathbf{r}_{1,2,\ldots,N}$$

$$= -\frac{1}{C_k} \frac{d}{dx} \ln I_0(k, x)$$

$$= \langle N^{-1} |\rho_{\mathbf{k}}|^2 \rangle_{0,\,\mathbf{k}} \tag{3.33}$$

Differentiation of $S_0(k, x)$ with respect to x yields

$$\frac{d}{dx} S_0(k, x) = C_k S_0(k, x)^2 - C_k \langle N^{-2} |\rho_{\mathbf{k}}|^4 \rangle_{0,\,\mathbf{k}} \tag{3.34}$$

Appendix 3-B contains the proof [5] that the expectation value of $N^{-2}|\rho_{\mathbf{k}}|^2$ is double the square of the expectation value of $N^{-1}|\rho_{\mathbf{k}}|^2$. Entering Eq. (3.34) with this result, the differential equation is reduced to

$$\frac{d}{dx} \frac{1}{S_0(k, x)} = C_k \tag{3.35}$$

The integral of Eq. (3.35) between the limits 0 and x is

$$S_0(k, x) = S_0(k, 0)/[1 + xC_k S_0(k, 0)]$$

$$= S_0(k)/[1 + xC_k S_0(k)] \tag{3.36}$$

Equation (3.33) yields

$$I_0(k, x) = 1/[1 + xC_k S_0(k)] \tag{3.37}$$

Equations (3.32) and (3.37) imply a general explicit formula for the expectation value of $(N^{-1}|\rho_{\mathbf{k}}|^2)^p$. To derive the formula, suppose x so small that $xC_k S_0(k) < 1$; then Eq. (3.32) generates one power series in x, Eq. (3.37) another. The identity of the two series requires

$$\langle (N^{-1}|\rho_{\mathbf{k}}|^2)^p \rangle_0 = p!\, S_0(k)^p \tag{3.38}$$

Equation (3.38) is a known result [5] but the present derivation is strikingly simple compared with the original.

The physical implications of Eq. (3.36) are associated with the behavior of C_k and $S_0(k)$ in the long-wavelength region. The first is a known function [line preceding Eq. (3.28)], but the second can be computed only when the two-particle distribution function generated by $\bar{\psi}_0$ is known. However, it is highly plausible that $S_0(k)$ approaches a constant (positive) value as $k \to 0$. This statement is supported by interpreting $-\ln \bar{\psi}_0{}^2$ as an N-particle potential energy in the classical partition function of a hypothetical N-particle system (arbitrarily setting $\beta = 1$). By the Ornstein–Zernicke relation for the hypothetical system, the associated liquid structure function [in this case $S_0(k)$] does not vanish at the origin [6]. Suppose now that k is taken so small that $C_k S_0(k) \gg 1$; then Eq. (3.36) reduces to

$$S_0(k, 1) \approx 1/C_k \approx \hbar k/2mc \tag{3.39}$$

in agreement with the Feynman relation [Eq. (3.24a)].

The poorly known quantities k_c and $S_0(0+)$ do not appear in Eq. (3.39). However, they are not entirely independent. The condition that phonons propagate as stable entities may be applied to the Bijl–Feynman formula (as derived in Chapter 4) in the long wavelength limit with the result

$$\left[\frac{d}{dk}\frac{k}{S(k)}\right]_{k=0} \simeq \frac{1}{S_0(0+)} - \frac{2mc}{\hbar k_c} \leq 0 \tag{3.40}$$

Choosing $k_c = 0.1$ Å^{-1}, the necessary condition becomes $S_0(0+) \geq 0.033$.

The connection between $S(k)$ defined by Eq. (3.31) and $S_0(k, 1)$ must now be determined. Consider the functions

$$I_1(k, x) = \int \bar{\psi}_0{}^2 \prod_{l \neq \pm \mathbf{k}}' \exp\left[-\frac{C_l}{2N}|\rho_l|^2\right] \exp\left[-x\frac{C_k}{N}|\rho_\mathbf{k}|^2\right] d\mathbf{r}_{1,2,\ldots,N} \tag{3.41}$$

$$\begin{aligned} S_1(k, x) &= \frac{1}{NI_1(k, x)} \int \bar{\psi}_0{}^2 \prod_{l \neq \pm \mathbf{k}}' \exp\left[-\frac{C_l}{2N}|\rho_l|^2\right] \\ &\quad \times \exp\left[-x\frac{C_k}{N}|\rho_\mathbf{k}|^2\right] |\rho_\mathbf{k}|^2 \, d\mathbf{r}_{1,2,\ldots,N} \\ &= -\frac{1}{C_k}\frac{d}{dx} \ln I_1(k, x) \\ &= \langle N^{-1}|\rho_\mathbf{k}|^2\rangle_{\mathrm{LRC};\, x,\, \mathbf{k}} \end{aligned} \tag{3.42}$$

The analysis leading from Eq. (3.34) to Eq. (3.39) and the intermediate equations can be repeated with no complications to yield the results

$$S_1(k, x) = S_1(k, 0)/[1 + xC_k S_1(k, 0)] \tag{3.43}$$

$$I_1(k, x) = 1/[1 + xC_k S_1(k, 0)] \tag{3.44}$$

$$\langle (N^{-1}|\rho_\mathbf{k}|^2)^p \rangle_{\mathrm{LRC};\, 0,\, k} = p!\, S_1(k, 0)^p \tag{3.45}$$

Notice that now $S_1(\mathbf{k}, 0)$ is not identical with $S_0(k, 0)$. The presence of the LRC factor makes a difference even though the exponential function of $|\rho_\mathbf{k}|^2$ is absent when $x = 0$. How much or how little difference can be estimated by studying the functions

$$I(x) = \int \bar{\psi}_0{}^2 \psi_{\mathrm{LRC}}^{2x} \, d\mathbf{r}_{1,2,\ldots,N} \tag{3.46}$$

$$\begin{aligned} S(k, x) &= \frac{1}{NI(x)} \int \bar{\psi}_0{}^2 \psi_{\mathrm{LRC}}^{2x} |\rho_\mathbf{k}|^2 \, d\mathbf{r}_{1,2,\ldots,N} \\ &= -\frac{1}{x}\frac{d}{dC_\mathbf{k}} \ln I(x) \\ &= \langle N^{-1}|\rho_\mathbf{k}|^2\rangle_{\mathrm{LRC};\, x} \end{aligned} \tag{3.47}$$

The analog of Eq. (3.34) is now

$$\frac{d}{dx} S(k, x) = -C_k S(k, x)^2 + \sum_{l \neq \pm \mathbf{k}} C_l [\langle N^{-1} |\rho_l|^2 \rangle_{\text{LRC}; x} \langle N^{-1} |\rho_\mathbf{k}|^2 \rangle_{\text{LRC}; x} - \langle N^{-2} |\rho_l|^2 |\rho_\mathbf{k}|^2 \rangle_{\text{LRC}; x}] \tag{3.48}$$

We draw again on Appendix 3-B for the result that the coefficient of C_l in Eq. (3.48) is of order $1/N$. The sum over $l \neq \pm \mathbf{k}$ in Eq. (3.48) is then negligible. This is a consequence of the fact that the total number of allowed wave vectors in the volume $(4\pi/3)k_c^3$ is small compared to N. To get a semiquantitative estimate, let k_N denote the radius of a sphere in k space containing N allowed wave vectors:

$$\tfrac{4}{3}\pi k_N{}^3 \Omega/(2\pi)^3 = N \tag{3.49}$$

The corresponding number in the sphere of radius k_c is

$$\tfrac{4}{3} k_c{}^3 \Omega/(2\pi)^3 = N(k_c/k_N)^3 \tag{3.50}$$

Now, $k_N \approx 1$ Å^{-1} in liquid ^{4}He, and a reasonable upper limit on k_c is 0.1 Å^{-1}. Consequently, the k_c sphere contains fewer than $10^{-3}\,N$ allowed k vectors, and the sum in Eq. (3.48) is smaller than the leading term by a factor of 10^{-3}. We drop the sum and obtain (with an error considerably smaller than 1%)

$$\begin{aligned} S(k, x) &\approx S(k, 0)/[1 + xC_k S(k, 0)] \\ &= S_0(k)/[1 + xC_k S_0(k)] \end{aligned} \tag{3.51}$$

Also,

$$I(x) \approx \prod_{\mathbf{k},\, k_x > 0} \frac{1}{1 + xC_k S_0(k)} \tag{3.52}$$

with a correspondingly small error. Equation (3.52) exhibits the separability of the exponential factors in the integrand of the integral defining $I(x)$. Each exponential factor contributes to the integral as if the others were absent.

APPENDIX 3-A

Nonlocal Potential Energy in the Theory of Density Fluctuations in the Classical Fluid

The basic assumption is that the potential energy of the fluid is a general functional in $\rho(\mathbf{r})$. Equation (3.36) is replaced by

$$\delta U = \text{P.E.} = \int \left[\frac{\delta U}{\delta\rho(\mathbf{r})}\right]_0 \delta\rho(\mathbf{r})\, d\mathbf{r} + \frac{1}{2}\int \left[\frac{\delta^2 U}{\delta\rho(\mathbf{r})\,\delta\rho(\mathbf{r}')}\right]_0 \delta\rho(\mathbf{r})\,\delta\rho(\mathbf{r}')\, d\mathbf{r}\, d\mathbf{r}' + \cdots \tag{A.1}$$

the subscript 0 denoting evaluation of the derivatives for the uniform density $\rho = \rho_0$. Invariance of the derivatives under arbitrary displacements and rotations implies $[\delta U/\delta\rho(\mathbf{r})]_0$ independent of $\mathbf{r}$ and $[\delta^2 U/\delta\rho(\mathbf{r})\,\delta\rho(\mathbf{r}')]_0$ a function of $|\mathbf{r} - \mathbf{r}'|$ only. I write

$$\left[\frac{\delta^2 U}{\delta\rho(\mathbf{r})\,\delta\rho(\mathbf{r}')}\right]_0 = \frac{1}{K_T \rho_0^2}\,\varphi(|\mathbf{r}' - \mathbf{r}|) \tag{A.2}$$

and impose the normalization condition $\int\varphi\, d\mathbf{r} = 1$ to maintain the connection with Eq. (3.36) in the limit of slowly varying density fluctuations. Equation (A.1) reduces to [2]

$$\text{P.E.} = \frac{1}{2K_T \rho_0^2}\int \varphi(|\mathbf{r}' - \mathbf{r}|)\,\delta\rho(\mathbf{r}')\,\delta\rho(\mathbf{r})\, \mathbf{dr}\, \mathbf{dr}' \tag{A.3}$$

The Fourier coefficients

$$\varphi_k = \int \varphi(r) \exp i\mathbf{k}\cdot\mathbf{r}\, d\mathbf{r}$$

then appear in the modified potential-energy formula

$$\text{P.E.} = \frac{1}{2K_T \rho_0 N}\sum_{\mathbf{k}}{}' \varphi_k Q_{\mathbf{k}}^2 \tag{A.4}$$

The modified Hamiltonian and equations of motion are

$$H = \frac{mc^2}{2N}\sum_{\mathbf{k}}{}' \varphi_k Q_{\mathbf{k}}^2 + \frac{N}{2m}\sum_{\mathbf{k}} k^2 P_{\mathbf{k}}^2 \tag{A.5}$$

and

$$\dot{Q}_{\mathbf{k}} = \frac{N}{m} k^2 P_{\mathbf{k}}, \qquad \dot{P}_{\mathbf{k}} = -\frac{mc^2}{N} \varphi_k Q_{\mathbf{k}} \tag{A.6}$$

Consequently,

$$\ddot{Q}_{\mathbf{k}} + (ck)^2 \varphi_k Q_{\mathbf{k}} = 0$$

$$\omega_k^{\,2} = (ck)^2 \varphi_k \tag{A.7}$$

In addition,

$$\frac{1}{N} \langle 0 | Q_{\mathbf{k}}^{\,2} | 0 \rangle = \frac{\hbar \omega_k}{2mc^2 \varphi_k} \tag{A.8}$$

using the notation $|0\rangle$ for the ground-state eigenfunction of the $\mathbf{k}$ harmonic oscillator. Let $S_{\text{cp}}(k)$ denote the left-hand member of Eq. (A.8). The correspondence principle requires

$$\lim_{k \to 0} S_{\text{cp}}(k)/S(k) = 1 \tag{A.9}$$

A more detailed specification of $S_{\text{cp}}(k)$ implies a specific theory or model for the determination of the function $\varphi(r)$. In any case, ω_k and φ_k can be expressed in terms of $S_{\text{cp}}(k)$:

$$\varphi_k = \left[\frac{\hbar k}{2mcS_{\text{cp}}(k)} \right]^2, \qquad \hbar \omega_k = \frac{\hbar^2 k^2}{2mS_{\text{cp}}(k)} \tag{A.10}$$

The necessities of the correspondence principle are exhausted by the limit statement of Eq. (A.9); consequently, the possible relevance of identifying $S_{\text{cp}}(k)$ with $S(k)$ must be judged on the basis of convenience.

APPENDIX 3-B

Variance and Independence in the $|\rho_{\mathbf{k}}|^2$ Space

A normalized symmetrical trial function ψ^2 is used to compute expectation values of $(1/N)|\rho_{\mathbf{k}}|^2$, $(1/N^2)|\rho_{\mathbf{k}}|^4$, and $(1/N^2)|\rho_{\mathbf{k}}|^2|\rho_{\boldsymbol{l}}|^2$. The first is the liquid structure function $S(k)$; the other two must be evaluated. The calculations are simplified by using the identities

$$N^{-2}\langle |\rho_{\mathbf{k}}|^4 \rangle = -1 + 2S(k) + N^{-2}\langle (|\rho_{\mathbf{k}}|^2 - N)^2 \rangle$$

$$\text{(B.1)}$$

$$N^{-2}\langle |\rho_{\mathbf{k}}|^2 |\rho_{\boldsymbol{l}}|^2 \rangle = -1 + S(k) + S(l) + N^{-2}\langle (|\rho_{\mathbf{k}}|^2 - N)(|\rho_{\boldsymbol{l}}|^2 - N) \rangle$$

and the equivalent factor in the integrand:

$$(|\rho_{\mathbf{k}}|^2 - N)(|\rho_{\boldsymbol{l}}|^2 - N) \rightarrow N(N-1)(\exp i\mathbf{k}\cdot\mathbf{r}_{12}) \times [(\exp i\mathbf{l}\cdot\mathbf{r}_{12}) + (\exp -i\mathbf{l}\cdot\mathbf{r}_{12}) + 2(N-2)(\exp i\mathbf{l}\cdot\mathbf{r}_{13}) + 2(N-2)(\exp -i\mathbf{l}\cdot\mathbf{r}_{13}) + (N-2)(N-3)(\exp i\mathbf{l}\cdot\mathbf{r}_{34}] \quad \text{(B.2)}$$

These yield

$$\langle N^{-2}(|\rho_{\mathbf{k}}|^2 - N)(|\rho_{\boldsymbol{l}}|^2 - N)\rangle = \delta_{\mathbf{k},\pm\boldsymbol{l}}\{1 + 2[S(k)-1]\} + (1 + \delta_{\mathbf{k},\pm\boldsymbol{l}})[S(k)-1][S(l)-1] + O(1/N) = [S(k)-1][S(l)-1] + \delta_{\mathbf{k},\pm\boldsymbol{l}}\, S(k)^2 + O(1/N) \quad \text{(B.3)}$$

and, finally,

$$\langle N^{-2}|\rho_{\mathbf{k}}|^2|\rho_{\boldsymbol{l}}|^2\rangle = (1 + \delta_{\mathbf{k},\pm\boldsymbol{l}})S(k)S(l) + O(1/N) \quad \text{(B.4)}$$

Also, for $\mathbf{k} \neq \pm\boldsymbol{l}$,

$$\langle N^{-2}|\rho_{\mathbf{k}}|^2|\rho_{\boldsymbol{l}}|^2\rangle = \langle N^{-1}|\rho_{\mathbf{k}}|^2\rangle\langle N^{-1}|\rho_{\boldsymbol{l}}|^2\rangle + O(1/N) \quad \text{(B.5)}$$

signifying that the quantities $|\rho_{\mathbf{k}}|^2$ and $|\rho_{\boldsymbol{l}}|^2$ function as nearly independent variables with nearly independent statistical distributions.

The remainder term of order $1/N$ in Eq. (B.3) comes in part from the integral

$$(2/N^2)\int p^{(3)}(1, 2, 3) \exp i(\mathbf{k}\cdot\mathbf{r}_{12} + \mathbf{l}\cdot\mathbf{r}_{13})\, d\mathbf{r}_{1,2,3} \sim O(1/N) \quad \text{(B.6)}$$

estimated with the help of the cluster-type representation of $p^{(3)}(1, 2, 3)$ given by Eq. (2.3).

The expansion

$$p^{(4)}(1, 2, 3, 4) = \rho^4[1 + h(r_{12}) + \cdots + h(r_{34}) + h(r_{21})h(r_{23}) + \cdots + h(r_{23})h(r_{34}) + h(r_{12})h(r_{34}) + h(r_{13})h(r_{24}) + h(r_{14})h(r_{23})] + \delta p^{(4)}(1, 2, 3, 4) \quad \text{(B.7)}$$

is used in evaluating the contribution from the factor $\exp i(k\cdot\mathbf{r}_{12} + \boldsymbol{l}\cdot\mathbf{r}_{34})$.

Here the leading term is generated by the component $\rho^4[h(r_{12})h(r_{34}) + h(r_{13})hr_{24})]$. Notice that for $\mathbf{k} = \boldsymbol{l}$ the identity $\mathbf{r}_{12} + \mathbf{r}_{34} = \mathbf{r}_{14} + \mathbf{r}_{32}$ means that the two addends $\rho^4 h_{12} h_{34}$ and $\rho^4 h_{13} h_{24}$ occurring in the expansion of $p^{(4)}$ make equal contributions to the matrix element. Other components in $p^{(4)}$ make contributions reduced by a factor $1/N$. This is true in particular of the remainder $\delta p^{(4)}$, which is large only when at least three points are fairly close together (within distances of order $\rho^{-1/3}$). Consequently, the results in Eqs. (B.4) and (B.5) are exact except for terms of order $1/N$, as stated.

References

1. M. Cohen and R. P. Feynman, *Phys. Rev.* **107**, 13 (1957).
2. L. P. Pitaevskii, *Soviet Phys.—JETP* **4**, 439 (1957).
3. G. V. Chester and L. Reatto, *Phys. Letters*, **22**, 276 (1966).
4. J. E. Enderby, T. Gaskell, and N. H. March, *Proc. Phys. Soc.* (*London*) **85**, 217 (1965).
5. H. W. Jackson and E. Feenberg, *Ann. Phys.* (*N.Y.*) **15**, 266 (1961); also see Chapter 5 of the present book.
6. D. Levesque, D. Schiff, T. Khiet, and L. Verlet, preprint.

CHAPTER 4

Elementary Excitations in a Boson System—Landau Spectrum*

4.1. THE BIJL–FEYNMAN DISPERSION FORMULA

The elementary excitations in a many-particle boson system are characterized by a momentum $\hbar\mathbf{k}$ and an energy $\varepsilon(k)$. We are interested in the smallest energy associated with the given momentum, excluding always states of uniform mass flow. Let $|0\rangle$ denote the normalized ground-state wave function in the N-particle configuration space and $|\mathbf{k}, \varepsilon(k)\rangle$ the normalized excited state with excitation energy $\varepsilon(k)$ and total linear momentum $\mathbf{P}' = \hbar\mathbf{k}$. The $\mathbf{k}$-function space

$$\prod_{i=1}^{p} \rho_{\mathbf{k}_i}|0\rangle, \qquad \sum_{1}^{p} \mathbf{k}_i = \mathbf{k}, \qquad p = 1, 2, \ldots \tag{4.1}$$

provides the raw material for constructing $|\mathbf{k}, \varepsilon(k)\rangle$ by variational and perturbation techniques. States of uniform mass flow (with $\mathbf{P}' = \hbar\mathbf{k}$ and kinetic energy $\hbar^2k^2/2Nm$) may be disregarded, since they are very nearly orthogonal to all functions in $\mathbf{k}$-function space suitable for describing an elementary excitation.

In the $\mathbf{k}$-function space $\rho_{\mathbf{k}}|0\rangle$ is singled out by its simplicity and by the close analogy with the classical theory of the sound field, where the continuum limit of $\rho_{\mathbf{k}}$ serves as a normal coordinate [Eq. (3.23)]. The expectation

* See Landau [1].

value of H with respect to $\rho_{\mathbf{k}}|0\rangle$ yields an upper limit on $\varepsilon(k)$;

$$\varepsilon_0(k) = \frac{\hbar^2 N}{2m} \frac{\langle 0|\nabla_1\rho_{\mathbf{k}} \cdot \nabla_1\rho_{-\mathbf{k}}|0\rangle}{\langle 0|\,|\rho_{\mathbf{k}}|^2\,|0\rangle}$$

$$= \frac{\hbar^2 k^2}{2mS(k)} \geq \varepsilon(k) \tag{4.2}$$

This is the Bijl–Feynman (BF) formula for the energy of an elementary excitation [2], [3]. Curve B–F in Fig. 4-1, computed from the measured $S(k)$ of liquid ^{4}He, exhibits qualitative features similar to the empirical Landau dispersion curve as determined from the inelastic scattering of slow neutrons in liquid ^{4}He. The "roton" minimum occurs correctly near $k = 2$ Å^{-1}, but gives an energy gap about double that observed.

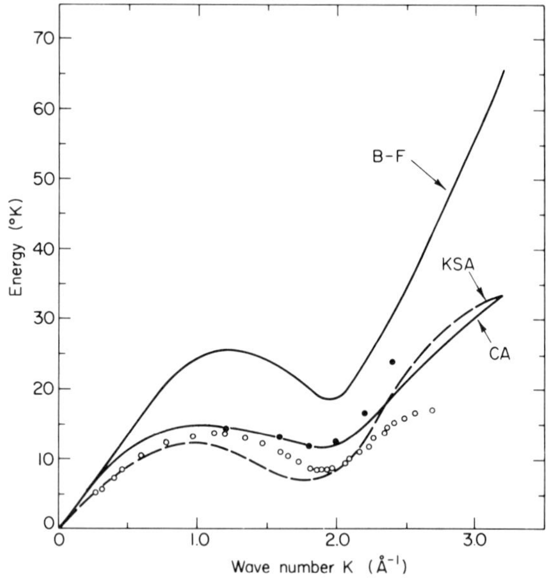

FIG. 4-1. The energy of elementary excitations. B–F labels the Bijl–Feynman curve calculated from Eq. (4.2). The curve KSA is based on the Kirkwood superposition approximation and CA is based on the convolution approximation; both are calculated using Eq. (4.46). The open circles mark points found experimentally by Henshaw and Woods, *Phys. Rev.* **121**, 1266 (1961), from inelastic neutron scattering. The solid circles mark the points calculated by Feynman and Cohen using Eqs. (4.35)–(4.36).

For long wavelengths the elementary excitations are identified with the phonons of the sound field; consequently,

$$\hbar^2 k^2/2mS(k) \geq \hbar ck, \qquad k \ll 2\pi\rho^{1/3} \tag{4.3}$$

or

$$S(k) \leq \hbar k/2mc, \qquad k \ll 2\pi\rho^{1/3} \tag{4.4}$$

Here c is the velocity of first sound at $T=0$ (where $K_T = K_S$). Equation (4.4) reproduces the relation Eq. (1.39) derived from sum rules. Equality in Eq. (4.4) is implied by the theory of the quantized classical sound field.

4.2. CONSEQUENCES OF SUM RULES

A change in notation proves helpful in extracting physical information from the sum rules [Eqs. (1.35)–(1.37)]. Let

$$x = \omega/\hbar kc, \qquad R(k, x) = 2mc^2 S(k, \hbar ckx) \tag{4.5}$$

The rules become [4]

$$(2mc/\hbar k)S(k) = \int_0^\infty R(k, x)\, dx \tag{4.6}$$

$$1 = \int_0^\infty R(k, x)x\, dx \tag{4.7}$$

$$1 = \lim_{k\to 0} \int_0^\infty R(k, x)(1/x)\, dx \tag{4.8}$$

One consequence is immediately clear,

$$\lim_{k\to 0} 2\left[1 - \frac{2mc}{\hbar k} S(k)\right] = \lim_{k\to 0} \int_0^\infty R(k, x)x\left(1 - \frac{1}{x}\right)^2 dx$$
$$\geq 0 \tag{4.9}$$

a restatement of Eqs. (1.38) and (4.4).

The equality between the extreme members of Eq. (4.9) is possible only if $R(k, x)$ possesses a strong peak at $x=1$ for small values of k with the limiting behavior $R(0+, x) = \lambda\, \delta(x-1)$. The sum rules all require $\lambda = 1$. Notice that the concentrated peak at $x=1$ for small k is also required by the phonon dispersion relation [$\varepsilon(k) = \hbar ck$] generated by the quantized theory of the classical sound field. In the same context the associated relation $S(k) = \hbar k/2mc$ brings the BF formula into agreement with the phonon dispersion relation.

The connections described in the preceding paragraph may be summarized in the *working hypothesis* that $\rho_{\mathbf{k}}|0\rangle$ approaches an exact eigenstate as $k \to 0$. If now

$$|\mathbf{k}\rangle \equiv \rho_{\mathbf{k}}|0\rangle/[NS(k)]^{1/2} \tag{4.10}$$

the infinite sums over intermediate states in Eqs. (1.16), (1.17), and (1.26) reduce to single terms ($n = \mathbf{k}$), all others vanishing because of the orthogonality property of eigenfunctions belonging to different eigenvalues. Equations (1.16), (1.17), and (1.26) then express directly the properties inferred from $R(0+, x) = \delta(x - 1)$.

It seems probable that the Bose–Einstein statistics and strong repulsive forces (acting to prevent two or more atoms from occupying the same volume) are together sufficient conditions for the stated working hypothesis [4]. Existing proofs appear to involve more special conditions. Sum rules for ω^2 and ω^3 are useful in this context. The relations are derived in Appendix 4-A.

The noninteracting fermion system (failing both presumptive sufficient conditions) supplies a counterexample for which $\rho_{\mathbf{k}}|0\rangle$ does not approach an exact eigenfunction as $k \to 0$. The exact analysis is very simple, using $S(k)$ as given by Eq. (1.58):

$$\lim_{k\to 0} S(k)/k = 3/4k_F \tag{4.11}$$

$$\begin{aligned} e(\rho) &\equiv E_0/\Omega = \tfrac{3}{5}\rho\hbar^2 k_F{}^2/2m \\ &= (6\pi^2)^{2/3}\rho^{2/3}3\hbar^2/10m \end{aligned} \tag{4.12}$$

$$\begin{aligned} mc^2 &= 1/\rho K = \rho\, d^2e/d\rho^2 \\ &= \hbar^2 k_F{}^2/3m \end{aligned} \tag{4.13}$$

Consequently,

$$\lim_{k\to 0} [\hbar^2 k/2mS(k)] = (2/\sqrt{3})\hbar c > \hbar c \tag{4.14}$$

The phonon energy ($\hbar ck$) should be compared with the excitation energy required to lift a particle from the $\mathbf{k}_1$ orbital just inside the Fermi surface to the neighboring $\mathbf{k}_2$ orbital just outside. Let

$$\mathbf{k} = \mathbf{k}_1 - \mathbf{k}_2, \qquad k \ll 2k_F$$

$$\mathbf{k}' = \mathbf{k}_1 + \mathbf{k}_2, \qquad k' \approx 2k_F$$

Then

$$\begin{aligned}\delta\varepsilon(k) &= (\hbar^2/2m)(k_2{}^2 - k_1{}^2) \\ &\approx (\hbar^2 k_{\mathrm{F}}/m)k \cos(\mathbf{k}', \mathbf{k}) \\ &= \sqrt{3}\hbar ck \cos(\mathbf{k}', \mathbf{k}) \end{aligned} \tag{4.15}$$

exhibiting a range of elementary excitations with momentum $\hbar\mathbf{k}$ and energies between 0 and $\hbar ck\sqrt{3}$.

4.3. IMPROVED THEORY OF THE ELEMENTARY EXCITATIONS

The discrepancy between the Bijl–Feynman formula (as shown in Fig. 4.1) and the observed dispersion relation, particularly the factor of two in the energy gap at the roton minimum, points to an essential physical effect or requirement neglected in the elementary theory. Feynman directed attention to the requirement that the elementary excitations should transport momentum and energy without an actual macroscopic transport of mass. With periodic boundary conditions a flow across the boundaries of the fundamental cube is permissible, but surely is not required to describe an elementary excitation. To investigate the flow of matter, consider the conservation equation for probability density,

$$\frac{\partial}{\partial t}\rho(1, 2, \ldots, N; t) + \sum_{l=1}^{N} \nabla_l \cdot \mathbf{j}_l(1, 2, \ldots, N; t) = 0 \tag{4.16}$$

with

$$\begin{aligned}\rho(1, 2, \ldots, N; t) &= \psi^*\psi \\ \mathbf{j}_l(1, 2, \ldots, N; t) &= (\hbar/2im)(\psi^*\nabla_l\psi - \psi\nabla_l\psi^*)\end{aligned} \tag{4.17}$$

We write $\psi = F|0\rangle = F\psi_0$ and obtain

$$\begin{aligned}\rho(1, 2, \ldots, N; t) &= |F|^2\psi_0{}^2 \\ \mathbf{j}_l(1, 2, \ldots, N; t) &= (\hbar/2im)\psi_0{}^2(F^*\nabla_l F - F^*\nabla_l F)\end{aligned} \tag{4.18}$$

A single-particle formulation of the conservation condition is generated by integrating all quantities in Eq. (4.18) over the coordinates of $N-1$

particles. With

$$\begin{aligned} \rho_F(\mathbf{r}_1, t) &= \int |F|^2 \psi_0^2 \, d\mathbf{r}_{2,\ldots,N} \\ \mathbf{j}_F(\mathbf{r}_1, t) &= (\hbar/2im) \int \psi_0^2 (F^* \nabla_1 F - F \nabla_1 F^*) \, d\mathbf{r}_{2,\ldots,N} \end{aligned} \tag{4.19}$$

Equation (4.16) reduces to

$$\frac{\partial}{\partial t} \rho_F(\mathbf{r}, t) + \nabla \cdot \mathbf{j}_F(\mathbf{r}, t) = 0 \tag{4.20}$$

Surface integrals occurring in the derivation of Eq. (4.20) vanish because of the periodic boundary condition imposed on ψ_0 and F.

The physical content of the BF trial function becomes more evident if the plane wave elements $\exp(i\mathbf{k} \cdot \mathbf{r})$ are replaced by wave packets $\mathscr{X}(\mathbf{r}) \exp(i\mathbf{k} \cdot \mathbf{r})$. Here $\mathscr{X}(\mathbf{r})$ is a slowly varying function with a maximum at the point $\mathbf{R}$. We require $|\mathscr{X}(\mathbf{r})|^2 \ll \rho$ and also

$$\int |\mathscr{X}(\mathbf{r})|^2 \, d\mathbf{r} = 1, \qquad \left| \int |\mathscr{X}(\mathbf{r})|^2 \exp i\mathbf{k} \cdot \mathbf{r} \, d\mathbf{r} \right| \ll 1 \tag{4.21}$$

The special function

$$\mathscr{X}(\mathbf{r}) = (\rho^{2/3}\alpha/\pi)^{3/4} \exp[-\tfrac{1}{2}\alpha\rho^{2/3}(\mathbf{r} - \mathbf{R})^2] \tag{4.22}$$

is suitable if α is chosen properly. In fact, since

$$\int |\mathscr{X}(\mathbf{r})|^2 \exp i\mathbf{k} \cdot \mathbf{r} \, d\mathbf{r} = \exp(-k^2/4\alpha\rho^{2/3}) \exp i\mathbf{k} \cdot \mathbf{R} \tag{4.23}$$

a sufficient condition on α is

$$\left(\frac{\pi}{N^{1/3}}\right)^2 \ll \alpha \ll \begin{cases} (k/2\rho^{1/3})^2 \\ 1 \end{cases} \tag{4.24}$$

The two-sided inequality is needed to exclude the possibility that the wave packet occupies a substantial fraction of the total volume. Equation (4.24) requires $k \gg 2\pi/L$, but this is not a significant constraint on the range of k values. The restrictions on $\mathscr{X}(\mathbf{r})$ are designed to produce simple forms for the excitation energy and $\mathbf{j}_F$. We compute

$$\begin{aligned} \int \psi_0^2 |F|^2 \, d\mathbf{r}_{1,2,\ldots,N} &= N \int \psi_0^2 |\mathscr{X}(\mathbf{r}_1)|^2 \, d\mathbf{r}_{1,2,\ldots,N} \\ &\quad + N(N-1) \int \psi_0^2 \mathscr{X}^*(\mathbf{r}_2) \mathscr{X}(\mathbf{r}_1) \exp i\mathbf{k} \cdot \mathbf{r}_{12} \, d\mathbf{r}_{1,2,\ldots,N} \\ &\approx \rho\left[1 + \rho \int [g(r_{12}) - 1] |\mathscr{X}(\mathbf{r}_1)|^2 \exp i\mathbf{k} \cdot \mathbf{r}_{12} \, d\mathbf{r}_1 \, d\mathbf{r}_2\right] \\ &= \rho S(k) \end{aligned} \tag{4.25}$$

using the fact that $\rho[1-g(r)]$ is essentially a delta-function on the scale of slowly varying functions such as $\mathscr{X}(\mathbf{r})$. Next

$$\mathbf{j}_{\mathrm{F}}(\mathbf{r}_1)=\frac{1}{\rho S(k)}\int \psi_0{}^2\,\frac{\hbar}{2im}\,(F^*\boldsymbol{\nabla}_1 F-F\boldsymbol{\nabla}_1 F^*)\,d\mathbf{r}_{2,\ldots,N}$$

$$=\frac{\hbar\mathbf{k}}{mNS(k)}\,\{|\mathscr{X}(\mathbf{r}_1)|^2+[S(k)-1]\,|\mathscr{X}(\mathbf{r}_1)|^2\}$$

$$=\frac{\hbar\mathbf{k}}{mN}\,|\mathscr{X}(\mathbf{r}_1)|^2 \tag{4.26}$$

$$\varepsilon_{\mathrm{exc}}=\frac{\hbar^2 N}{2m\rho S(k)}\int \psi_0{}^2\,|\boldsymbol{\nabla}_1 F|^2\,d\mathbf{r}_{1,2,\ldots,N}$$

$$\approx\frac{\hbar^2 k^2}{2mS(k)} \tag{4.27}$$

Since $\boldsymbol{\nabla}\cdot j_{\mathrm{F}}(\mathbf{r})\neq 0$, $\mathbf{j}_{\mathrm{F}}$ cannot be the current density of a stationary state. The form of the current implies a region of variable density traversing the fundamental cube with velocity $\hbar k/m$.

A classical type of stationary flow is described by the trial function

$$\psi=\psi_0\exp\left[i\sum_i \varphi(\mathbf{r}_i)+(i/\hbar)(E_0+\varepsilon_{\mathrm{exc}})t\right] \tag{4.28}$$

In this case $\rho_{\mathrm{F}}=\rho/N$ and $\mathbf{j}_{\mathrm{F}}(\mathbf{r})=\rho_{\mathrm{F}}(\hbar/m)\,\boldsymbol{\nabla}\varphi(\mathbf{r})$. The conservation condition [Eq. (4.20)] defines the irrotational motion of an incompressible fluid ($\Delta\varphi=0$). In addition

$$\varepsilon_{\mathrm{exc}}=(N\hbar^2/2m)\int \psi_0{}^2\,|\boldsymbol{\nabla}_1\varphi(\mathbf{r}_1)|^2\,d\mathbf{r}_{1,2,\ldots,N}$$

$$=(\hbar^2\rho/2m)\int |\nabla\varphi|^2\,d\mathbf{r} \tag{4.29}$$

expressing the excitation energy as the kinetic energy of the moving fluid. Clearly, $(\hbar/m)\,\boldsymbol{\nabla}\varphi$ must be interpreted as the velocity of mass flow. Observe that the condition $\Delta\varphi=0$ makes $\varepsilon_{\mathrm{exc}}$ stationary with respect to arbitrary small variations in φ which vanish on the boundary.

So far we have considered two forms of F, first a sum of single-particle functions, and second a product of single-particle functions. These may be be combined to give a third type of trial function:

$$\psi=\psi_0\prod_1^N\,[\exp i\varphi(\mathbf{r}_l)]\sum_1^N \mathscr{X}(\mathbf{r}_m)\exp i\mathbf{k}\cdot\mathbf{r}_m \tag{4.30}$$

combining periodic density fluctuations with hydrodynamic mass motion. The combination offers the possibility of generating a stationary current system with no mass flow across the boundary, the central region of density fluctuation serving as a source and sink for the extended irrotational flow. We compute

$$\mathbf{j}_F(\mathbf{r}) = \frac{\hbar \mathbf{k}}{mN} |\mathscr{X}(\mathbf{r})|^2 + \frac{\hbar \rho}{mN} \nabla \varphi(\mathbf{r})$$

$$\varepsilon_{\mathrm{exc}} \approx \frac{\hbar^2 k^2}{2mS(k)} + \frac{\hbar^2}{m} \int |\mathscr{X}(\mathbf{r})|^2 \mathbf{k} \cdot \nabla \varphi(\mathbf{r})\, d\mathbf{r} + \frac{\hbar^2 \rho}{2m} \int |\nabla \varphi|^2\, d\mathbf{r} \tag{4.31}$$

The velocity potential can be chosen so that $\varepsilon_{\mathrm{exc}}$ is stationary with respect to small variations $\delta\varphi$ which vanish on the boundary. This consideration yields $\nabla \cdot \mathbf{j}_F = 0$ and the explicit solution

$$\varphi(\mathbf{r}) = \mathbf{k} \cdot \nabla \frac{1}{4\pi\rho} \int \frac{|\mathscr{X}(\mathbf{r}')|^2}{|\mathbf{r} - \mathbf{r}'|}\, d\mathbf{r}'$$
$$\to \frac{1}{4\pi\rho} \mathbf{k} \cdot \nabla \int \frac{1}{|\mathbf{r} - \mathbf{R}|}, \qquad |\mathbf{r} - \mathbf{R}| \to \infty \tag{4.32}$$

Thus the wave packet generates a dipole source-sink flow of strength $\mathbf{k}/4\pi\rho$. Higher multipole flows are also present.

The energy correction associated with the dipole flow is small, of order $\alpha^{3/2}$. However, the significant point here is that the excitation energy is reduced by the association of a back flow with the density fluctuations. In detail,

$$\varepsilon_{\mathrm{exc}} = \frac{\hbar^2 k^2}{2mS(k)} - \frac{\hbar^2 \rho}{m} \int \varphi \left(\Delta\varphi + \frac{1}{\rho} \mathbf{k} \cdot \nabla |\mathscr{X}(\mathbf{r})|^2 \right) d\mathbf{r} + \frac{\hbar^2 \rho}{2m} \int \varphi\, \Delta\varphi\, d\mathbf{r}$$
$$= \frac{\hbar^2 k^2}{2mS(k)} - \frac{\hbar^2 \rho}{2m} \int |\nabla \varphi|^2\, d\mathbf{r} \tag{4.33}$$

The failure to achieve a quantitative lowering of the energy can be blamed on the absence of particle correlations in the excitation factor F. Correlations and more intimate association of the two types of flow can be produced by centering the back flow functions on the particle positions:

$$F = \sum_l (\exp(i\mathbf{k} \cdot \mathbf{r}_l) \exp\left[i \sum_m{}' \varphi(\mathbf{r}_{lm}) \right] \tag{4.34}$$

or the related, but more practical,

$$F = \sum_l (\exp i\mathbf{k} \cdot \mathbf{r}_l)\left[1 + iA \sum_m{}' \varphi(\mathbf{r}_{lm})\right] \tag{4.35}$$

The wave-packet factor $\mathscr{X}(\mathbf{r})$ is not needed in the analysis based on Eq. (4.35). Feynman and Cohen [5], using Eq. (4.35) and

$$\varphi(\mathbf{r}) = (1/4\pi\rho)\mathbf{k} \cdot \boldsymbol{\nabla}(1/r) \tag{4.36}$$

find a substantial improvement in the computed energy, as shown in Fig. 4.1. Minimum excitation energy for $k = 2$ Å^{-1} occurs for $A = 0.93$, close to the "hydrodynamic" value $A = 1$ given by Eq. (4.32).

An illuminating alternative interpretation of the back flow is brought out by using a Fourier representation of $\varphi(\mathbf{r})$ in Eq. (4.35). With

$$\varphi(\mathbf{r}) = \sum_{\mathbf{h}} (\exp -i\mathbf{h} \cdot \mathbf{r})\varphi_{\mathbf{h}}, \qquad \varphi_{\mathbf{h}} = (1/\Omega)\int \varphi(\mathbf{r}) \exp i\mathbf{h} \cdot \mathbf{r}\, d\mathbf{r} \tag{4.37}$$

we obtain

$$F = \rho_{\mathbf{k}} + iA \sum_{\boldsymbol{l}} \varphi_{\boldsymbol{l}}[\rho_{\mathbf{k}-\boldsymbol{l}}\rho_{\boldsymbol{l}} - \rho_{\mathbf{k}}] \tag{4.38}$$

The descriptive name "free phonon" factor for $\rho_{\mathbf{k}}$ supplies a physical language for discussing the structure of the amplitude factor F. Equation (4.38) reveals that virtual processes of free phonon dissociation and recombination ($\mathbf{k} \to \mathbf{k} - \boldsymbol{l}, \boldsymbol{l}$; $\mathbf{k} - \boldsymbol{l}, \boldsymbol{l} \to \mathbf{k}$) are involved in the description of the stationary state representing a single real phonon.

4.4. PHONON–PHONON INTERACTION*†

The possibility of virtual processes in which a free phonon dissociates into two phonons can be used to generate an improved description of an elementary excitation as a linear combination of one- and two-free-phonon states. These objects are represented by the function space

$$|\mathbf{k}\rangle = \rho_{\mathbf{k}}\psi_0/[NS(k)]^{1/2}$$
$$|\mathbf{k} - \boldsymbol{l}, \boldsymbol{l}\rangle = \rho_{\mathbf{k}-\boldsymbol{l}}\rho_{\boldsymbol{l}}\psi_0/[N^2S(|\mathbf{k} - \boldsymbol{l}|)S(l)]^{1/2} \tag{4.39}$$

* See Kuper [6].

† See Jackson and Feenberg [7].

forming a normalized and nearly orthogonal set of free-phonon states characterized by the total linear momentum $\mathbf{P}' = \hbar\mathbf{k}$. A nearly optimum linear combination is produced by the first-order state function of the Brillouin–Wigner perturbation procedure:

$$\psi = |\mathbf{k}\rangle + \frac{1}{2} \sum_{\boldsymbol{l} \neq 0, \mathbf{k}} \frac{\langle \mathbf{k} - \boldsymbol{l}, \boldsymbol{l} | \delta H | \mathbf{k} \rangle | \mathbf{k} - \boldsymbol{l}, \boldsymbol{l} \rangle}{\varepsilon(k) - \varepsilon_0(l) - \varepsilon_0(|\mathbf{k} - \boldsymbol{l}|)} \tag{4.40}$$

Here $\varepsilon(k)$ is the energy of the elementary excitation (the real phonon) and

$$\delta H = H - E_0 - \varepsilon_0(k) \tag{4.41}$$

The constant term in the interaction operator δH is fixed by the condition

$$\langle \mathbf{k} | \delta H | \mathbf{k} \rangle = 0 \tag{4.42}$$

This in turn permits neglecting the slight failure of orthogonality in the basis functions $(\langle \mathbf{k} - \mathbf{l}, \boldsymbol{l} | 1 | \mathbf{k} \rangle \sim O(1/N^{1/2}))$ in computing the second-order Brillouin–Wigner energy. The factor $\frac{1}{2}$ in Eq. (4.40) is required because the identical states $\langle \mathbf{k} - \boldsymbol{l}, \boldsymbol{l}|$ and $\langle \boldsymbol{l}, \mathbf{k} - \boldsymbol{l}|$ both occur in the summation over $\boldsymbol{l}$.

The expectation value of $H - E_0$ with respect to ψ now yields an implicit equation for the excitation energy:

$$\varepsilon(k) = \varepsilon_0(k) + \frac{1}{2} \sum_{\boldsymbol{l} \neq 0, \mathbf{k}} \frac{|\langle \mathbf{k} - \boldsymbol{l}, \boldsymbol{l} | \delta H | \mathbf{k} \rangle|^2}{\varepsilon(k) - \varepsilon_0(\mathbf{k} - \boldsymbol{l}) - \varepsilon_0(\boldsymbol{l})} \tag{4.43}$$

Third-order terms in δH are neglected in Eq. (4.43); a partial justification for the neglect is supplied by computing the weight $P(k)$ of the two-phonon components in ψ and showing that $P(k) \ll 1$. An elementary calculation yields

$$\frac{P}{1-P} = \frac{1}{2} \sum_{\boldsymbol{l} \neq 0, \mathbf{k}} \frac{|\langle \mathbf{k} - \boldsymbol{l}, \boldsymbol{l} | \delta H | \mathbf{k} \rangle|^2}{[\varepsilon(k) - \varepsilon_0(|\mathbf{k} - \boldsymbol{l}|) - \varepsilon_0(\boldsymbol{l})]^2} \tag{4.44}$$

again neglecting third-order terms in δH. In computing with ψ, it is helpful to replace $|\mathbf{k} - \boldsymbol{l}, \boldsymbol{l}\rangle$ by a slightly modified function $|\mathbf{k} - \boldsymbol{l}, \boldsymbol{l}\rangle'$, orthogonal to $|\mathbf{k}\rangle$ and normalized. The modification disappears from the final formulas for $\varepsilon(k)$ and $P(k)$.

Next let

$$(\hbar^2/2m) Y(k) = \varepsilon_0(k) - \varepsilon(k) \tag{4.45}$$

and replace the sums over $\boldsymbol{l}$ by integrals. The energy formula reduces to an implicit integral equation for $Y(k)$:

$$Y(k) = \frac{1}{8\pi^2 \rho k} \int_0^\infty h\, dh \int_{|k-h|}^{k+h} l\, dl \frac{N|\langle \boldsymbol{l}, \mathbf{h}|\, \delta H\, |\mathbf{k}\rangle|^2}{Y(k) + [h^2/S(h)] + [(l^2/S(l)] - [k^2/S(k)]} \tag{4.46}$$

subject to the constraint $\mathbf{h} = \mathbf{k} - \boldsymbol{l}$ in evaluating the matrix element.

The second-order Schrödinger energy can be extracted from Eq. (4.46) by setting $Y(k) = 0$ in the right-hand member. The resulting formula for $Y(k)$ exhibits nonphysical singular behavior generated by the vanishing of the energy denominator over part of the range of integration (where the "virtual" dissociation and recombination process is no longer completely virtual). In the Brillouin–Wigner formulation the energy denominator cannot vanish.

Explicit formulas for the matrix elements of the identity and of δH are developed in Appendix 4-A. Observe that approximations in $p^{(3)}$ and $p^{(4)}$ do not enter into the evaluation of the normalization coefficient $N^2 S(|\mathbf{k} - \boldsymbol{l}|)S(l)$ associated with the two-phonon states. However, the evaluation of $\langle \mathbf{k} - \boldsymbol{l}, \boldsymbol{l}|1|\mathbf{k}\rangle$ and $\langle \mathbf{k} - \boldsymbol{l}, \boldsymbol{l}|\, \delta H\, |\mathbf{k}\rangle$ requires explicit assumptions on $p^{(3)}(1, 2, 3)$. Results are given for the superposition and convolution forms. Both forms give $\varepsilon(k)$ proportional to k in the long-wavelength limit; however, $\varepsilon_c(k)$ has the same slope as $\varepsilon_0(k)$ at the origin, while $\varepsilon_K(k)$ has the smaller slope. The usual assumption $\hbar c = (d\varepsilon_0/dk)_{k=0}$ implies that the modified slope of $\varepsilon_K(k)$ at the origin is a nonphysical consequence of the superposition approximation [because p_K fails to satisfy the sequential relation—Eq. (2.2)—exactly].

Numerical results derived from the measured liquid structure function of liquid ^{4}He are shown in Fig. 4-1. A reasonable conclusion from the results shown in Fig. 4-1 is that the back flow and phonon–phonon descriptions are essentially equivalent.

D. K. Lee [8] has treated the important special case $k \ll 2\pi\rho^{1/3}$ more accurately by a complete evaluation of the expectation value of δH with respect to the ψ function of Eq. (4.40). Overlap integrals

$$\langle \mathbf{k} - \mathbf{h}, \mathbf{h}|1|\mathbf{k} - \boldsymbol{l}, \boldsymbol{l}\rangle$$

and interaction matrix elements $\langle \mathbf{k} - \mathbf{h}, \mathbf{h}|\delta H|\mathbf{k} - \boldsymbol{l}, \boldsymbol{l}\rangle$ are evaluated with the help of the convolution form $p_c(1, 2, 3, 4)$ of Appendix 2-A. However, these explicit formulas are not needed in the prescribed limiting situation, where Lee shows that the uncertainties in $p^{(3)}$ and $p^{(4)}$ do not enter into the evaluation of the leading correction terms. Results are

$$\varepsilon_2(k) = -0.542(\hbar k/mc)^2\varepsilon_0(k), \qquad \varepsilon_3(k) = -0.154(\hbar k/mc)^2\varepsilon_0(k) \quad (4.47)$$

for the second- and third-order energy corrections, respectively, of the Brillouin–Wigner perturbation method. The total excitation energy is

$$\begin{aligned}\varepsilon(k) &= \varepsilon_0(k) + \varepsilon_2(k) + \varepsilon_3(k)\\ &= [1 - 0.696(\hbar k/mc)^2]\varepsilon_0(k) \qquad (4.48)\end{aligned}$$

The improved variational formula of Goldhammer and Feenberg [9], [10] gives the still lower excitation energy

$$\begin{aligned}\varepsilon(k) &= \varepsilon_0(k) + \{\varepsilon_2(k)^2/[\varepsilon_2(k) - \varepsilon_3(k)]\}\\ &\approx \varepsilon_0(k)[1 - 0.757(\hbar k/mc)^2], \qquad k \ll 2\pi\rho^{1/3} \qquad (4.49)\end{aligned}$$

Lee's calculation and result suggest the question of how $\varepsilon_0(k)/\hbar ck = \hbar k/2mcS(k)$ depends on k in the long-wavelength range. No answer is yet available in the context of the microscopic theory.

A study of dispersion by Eckstein and Varga [11] using the quantized version of the classical theory of density fluctuations yields the formula

$$\varepsilon(k) = \varepsilon_0(k)[1 - \gamma(\hbar k/mc)^2] \qquad (4.50)$$

in which

$$\gamma = 0.175\left[\left(\frac{\rho}{c}\frac{\partial c}{\partial \rho}\right)^2 - \frac{3}{5}\right] \qquad (4.51)$$

and $\varepsilon_0(k)$ is taken to be $\hbar kc$. The identification of $\varepsilon_0(k)$ with the Bijl–Feynman formula is, however, permissible and sensible in the classical theory of density flucutations (although not necessary—cf. Appendix 3-A). I make this identification and equate the two formulas for $\varepsilon(k)$ [retaining only the second-order correction in Eq. (4.48)] to obtain a numerical evaluation of the physical quantity $(\rho/c)\, \partial c/\partial\rho$:

$$\begin{aligned}\frac{\rho}{c}\frac{\partial c}{\partial \rho} &= \left[\frac{3}{5} + \frac{542}{175}\right]^{1/2}\\ &\approx 1.92, \qquad \rho = 0.0218\ \text{Å}^{-3} \qquad (4.52)\end{aligned}$$

not far from the direct experimental estimate of 2.6 at $T = 1.25$°K (quoted in reference 11). The unknown dispersive term implicit in $\varepsilon_0(k)$ stands in the way of a meaningful comparison with the observed dispersion and attentuation properties of high-frequency sound.

The equivalence assumed in Eq. (4.52) amounts to a consistency test. In one procedure the interaction matrix element associated with the three-phonon vertex is given by $\langle \boldsymbol{l}, \mathbf{k} - \boldsymbol{l} | \delta H | \mathbf{k} \rangle_c$ of Appendix 4-B. In the other procedure it is generated by third-order perturbation terms in the classical energy density [12] subject to a renormalization correction as described in Reference [11]. The two forms differ in details of the dependence on the three wave vectors and also in the fact that $(\rho/c)\, \partial c/\partial \rho$ occurs explicitly in one form and not in the other. They differ also in the contexts in which they occur (orthogonal free-phonon basis functions in the semiclassical treatment, nonorthogonal basis functions in the N-particle coordinate function space).

APPENDIX 4-A

Sum Rules for ω^2 and ω^3

Our problem is to express the left-hand members of the defining relations

$$N^{-1}\langle 0|\rho_{-\mathbf{k}}[H,[H,\rho_{\mathbf{k}}]]|0\rangle = N^{-1}\sum_n (E_n - E_0)^2 |\langle 0|\rho_{\mathbf{k}}|n\rangle|^2$$
$$= \int_0^\infty \omega^2 S(k,\omega)\, d\omega = \frac{(\hbar kc)^3}{2mc^2}\int_0^\infty x^2 R(k,x)\, dx \tag{A.1}$$

$$-N^{-1}\langle 0|\,[H,\rho_{-\mathbf{k}}][H,[H,\rho_{\mathbf{k}}]]\,|0\rangle = N^{-1}\sum_n (E_n - E_0)^3 |\langle 0|\,\rho_{\mathbf{k}}\,|n\rangle|^2$$
$$= \int_0^\infty \omega^3 S(k,\omega)\, d\omega$$
$$= \frac{(\hbar kc)^4}{2mc^2}\int_0^\infty x^3 R(k,x)\, dx \tag{A.2}$$

in forms suitable for numerical evaluation. Equation (A.1) is equivalent to

$$\langle \mathbf{k}|[H - E_0 - \varepsilon_0(k)]^2|\mathbf{k}\rangle = \frac{1}{S(k)}\int_0^\infty [\omega - \varepsilon_0(k)]^2 S(k,\omega)\, d\omega$$
$$= \varepsilon_0(k)\hbar ck \int_0^\infty \left(x - \frac{\hbar k}{2mcS(k)}\right)^2 R(k,x)\, dx \tag{A.3}$$

defining the variance of $H - E_0 - \varepsilon_0(k)$ with respect to the normalized trial function $|\mathbf{k}\rangle$.

The exact relation

$$[H - E_0 - \varepsilon_0(k)]\rho_{\mathbf{k}}\psi_0 = \left[\frac{\hbar^2 k^2}{2m} - \varepsilon_0(k)\right]\rho_{\mathbf{k}}\psi_0 - \frac{\hbar^2}{m}\sum_j (\exp i\mathbf{k}\cdot\mathbf{r}_j) i\mathbf{k}\cdot\nabla_j\psi_0 \tag{A.4}$$

has the consequence

$$\frac{1}{N}\langle 0|\rho_{-\mathbf{k}}[H - E_0 - \varepsilon_0(k)]^2\rho_{\mathbf{k}}|0\rangle = -\left(\frac{\hbar^2 k^2}{2m}\right)^2\left\{[S(k)]^{1/2} - \frac{1}{[S(k)]^{1/2}}\right\}^2 + \left(\frac{\hbar^2}{m}\right)^2\int \mathbf{k}\cdot\nabla_1\psi_0[\mathbf{k}\cdot\nabla_1\psi_0 + (N-1) \times (\exp i\mathbf{k}\cdot\mathbf{r}_{12})\mathbf{k}\cdot\nabla_2\psi_0]\, d\mathbf{r}_{1,2,\ldots,N} \tag{A.5}$$

Conservation of momentum in the ground state expressed by the equation

$$\sum_1^N \nabla_j\psi_0 = 0 \tag{A.6}$$

can be used to generate the integral relation

$$\int \mathbf{k}\cdot\nabla_1\psi_0[\mathbf{k}\cdot\nabla_1\psi_0 + (N-1)\mathbf{k}\cdot\nabla_2\psi_0]\, d\mathbf{r}_{1,2,\ldots,N} = 0 \tag{A.7}$$

Equations (A.5) and (A.7) combine to give [4], [13]

$$\frac{1}{N}\langle 0|\rho_{-\mathbf{k}}[H - E_0 - \varepsilon_0(k)]^2\rho_{\mathbf{k}}|0\rangle = -\left(\frac{\hbar^2 k^2}{2m}\right)^2\left\{[S(k)]^{1/2} - \frac{1}{[S(k)]^{1/2}}\right\}^2 + \left(\frac{\hbar^2}{m}\right)^2 (N-1)\int (\cos\mathbf{k}\cdot\mathbf{r}_{12} - 1) \times (\mathbf{k}\cdot\nabla_1\psi_0)(\mathbf{k}\cdot\nabla_2\psi_0)\, d\mathbf{r}_{1,2,\ldots,N} \tag{A.8}$$

The left-hand member of Eq. (A.8) has the form $\langle 0|A^\dagger A|0\rangle$; furthermore, A does not vanish identically. Consequently, the left-hand member of Eq. (A.8) is a positive number and Eq. (A.8) can be interpreted as an inequality satisfied by the integral appearing in the right-hand member. We refer to the integral as the kinetic structure function and write

$$D(k) \equiv (N-1)k^{-2} \int (\cos \mathbf{k} \cdot \mathbf{r}_{12} - 1)(\mathbf{k} \cdot \nabla_1 \psi_0)(\mathbf{k} \cdot \nabla_2 \psi_0)\, d\mathbf{r}_{1,2,\ldots,N} \tag{A.9}$$

It is clear that $D(k)$ does not depend on the orientation of $\mathbf{k}$; it is also independent of N in the limit $N \to \infty$ while ρ is held constant.

The behavior of $D(k)$ as $k \to \infty$ can be derived from the definition by dropping the term in cos $(\mathbf{k} \cdot \mathbf{r}_{12})$. Equations (A.7) and (A.9) produce the limiting form

$$\begin{aligned} D(k) &\approx k^{-2} \int (\mathbf{k} \cdot \nabla_1 \psi_0)^2\, d\mathbf{r}_{1,2,\ldots,N} \\ &= (2m/3\hbar^2)N^{-1}\langle 0|\text{K.E.}|0\rangle, \qquad k \gg 2\pi\rho^{1/3} \end{aligned} \tag{A.10}$$

with the consequence that

$$\frac{1}{N}\langle 0|\rho_{\mathbf{k}}[H - E_0 - \varepsilon_0(k)]^2 \rho_{\mathbf{k}}|0\rangle \approx \frac{4}{3}\frac{\hbar^2 k^2}{2m}\frac{1}{N}\langle 0|\text{K.E.}|0\rangle, \qquad k \gg 2\pi\rho^{1/3} \tag{A.11}$$

Equation (A.8) requires

$$D(k) > \tfrac{1}{4}k^2\{[S(k)]^{1/2} - [S(k)]^{-1/2}\}^2 \tag{A.12}$$

The Feynman limiting formula $[S(k) \to \hbar k/2mc,\ k \ll 2\pi\rho^{1/3}]$ in Eq. (1.12) reduces it to

$$D(k) > mck/2\hbar, \qquad k \ll 2\pi\rho^{1/3} \tag{A.13}$$

The factor $1 - \cos(\mathbf{k} \cdot \mathbf{r}_{12})$ in the integrand of Eq. (A.9) suggests a quadratic dependence of $D(k)$ on k in the limit $k \to 0$. However, such behavior is ruled out by Eq. (A.13). Clearly, the power-series expansion of $\cos(\mathbf{k} \cdot \mathbf{r}_{12})$ cannot be used on a term-by-term basis to evaluate $D(k)$. What is required is a proper asymptotic behavior of the integrand for large values of r_{12}. For an explicit statement of the essential relations it is convenient to introduce the definition

$$C[r_{12}, \cos(\mathbf{k}, \mathbf{r}_{12})] \equiv -[N(N-1)/k^2] \int (\mathbf{k} \cdot \nabla_1 \psi_0)(\mathbf{k} \cdot \nabla_2 \psi_0)\, d\mathbf{r}_{3,4,\ldots,N} \tag{A.14}$$

If now, allowing a minimum margin of safety,

$$C[r, \cos(\mathbf{k}, \mathbf{r})] \to \{a[\cos(\mathbf{k}, \mathbf{r})]/r^4\} + O(1/r^{5+\nu}) \tag{A.15}$$

for $r \gg \rho^{-1/3}$ and $\nu > 0$, the behavior of $D(k)$ for small values of k ($k \ll 2\pi\rho^{1/3}$) is given correctly by

$$D(k) \to \frac{2\pi k}{\rho} \int_0^\infty \frac{dx}{x^2} \int_{-1}^1 (1 - \cos x\mu) a(\mu)\, d\mu$$

$$+ \frac{\pi k^2}{\rho} \int_0^\infty \int_{-1}^1 \mu^2 r^4 \left[C(r, \mu) - \frac{a(\mu)}{r^4} \right] d\mu\, dr \tag{A.16}$$

Equation (A.12) is satisfied if

$$\frac{2\pi}{\rho} \int_0^\infty \frac{dx}{x^2} \int_{-1}^1 (1 - \cos \mu x) a(\mu)\, d\mu > \frac{mc}{2\hbar} \tag{A.17}$$

Equality is also a possiblity in Eq. (A.17) if the coefficients of k^2 in the left- and right-hand terms of Eq. (A.12) maintain the inequality.

Equations (A.12)–(A.17) provide a severe test for any trial function introduced to serve as an approximation to ψ_0. In particular, the application of these conditions to kinetic structure functions generated by the BDJ product form [Eq. (2.12)] leads to strong conclusions on the asymptotic behavior of the correlation function $u(r)$. The evaluation starts from the relation

$$(\mathbf{k} \cdot \nabla_1 \psi)(\mathbf{k} \cdot \nabla_2 \psi) = \tfrac{1}{4} \left[\sum_j \mathbf{k} \cdot \nabla_1 u(r_{1j}) \right] \mathbf{k} \cdot \nabla_2 \psi^2$$

$$\to \tfrac{1}{4} [\mathbf{k} \cdot \nabla_1 u(r_{12}) + (N-2) \mathbf{k} \cdot \nabla_1 u(r_{13})] \mathbf{k} \cdot \nabla_2 \psi^2 \tag{A.18}$$

the arrow indicating equivalence in the integrand of the integral defining $D(k)$. In terms of the two- and three-particle distribution functions

$$D(k) \approx \frac{N-1}{4k^2} \int (\cos \mathbf{k} \cdot \mathbf{r}_{12} - 1)$$

$$\times [\mathbf{k} \cdot \nabla_1 u(r_{12}) + (N-2) \mathbf{k} \cdot \nabla_1 u(r_{13})] \mathbf{k} \cdot \nabla_2 \psi^2\, d\mathbf{r}_{1,2,\ldots,N}$$

$$= \frac{1}{4Nk^2} \int (\cos \mathbf{k} \cdot \mathbf{r}_{12} - 1) [\mathbf{k} \cdot \nabla_1 u(r_{12})] \mathbf{k} \cdot \nabla_2 p^{(2)}(1, 2)\, d\mathbf{r}_1\, d\mathbf{r}_2$$

$$+ \frac{1}{4Nk^2} \int (\cos \mathbf{k} \cdot \mathbf{r}_{12} - 1) [\mathbf{k} \cdot \nabla_1 u(r_{13})] \mathbf{k} \cdot \nabla_2 p^{(3)}(1, 2, 3)\, d\mathbf{r}_{1,2,3} \tag{A.19}$$

The three-particle distribution function can be eliminated by introducing the exact BBGKY relation

$$g(r_{12})\nabla_1 u(r_{12}) = \nabla_1 g(r_{12}) - (1/\rho^2)\int p^{(3)}(1, 2, 3)\nabla_1 u(r_{13})\, d\mathbf{r}_3 \quad \text{(A.20)}$$

with the result

$$\begin{aligned} D(k) &\approx \frac{\rho}{4k^2}\int (1 - \cos \mathbf{k}\cdot\mathbf{r})[(\mathbf{k}\cdot\nabla)^2 g(r) - g(r)(\mathbf{k}\cdot\nabla)^2 u(r)]\, d\mathbf{r} \\ &= \frac{1}{4}k^2[S(k) - 1] - \frac{\rho}{4k^2}\int (1 - \cos \mathbf{k}\cdot\mathbf{r}) g(r)(\mathbf{k}\cdot\nabla)^2 u(r)\, d\mathbf{r} \\ &= \frac{1}{4}k^2[S(k) - 1] - \frac{\pi\rho}{k}\int_0^\infty \left(1 - \frac{\sin x}{x}\right) x g\left(\frac{x}{k}\right)\frac{d}{dx}u\left(\frac{x}{k}\right) dx \\ &\quad - \frac{\pi\rho}{k}\int_0^\infty \left(\frac{1}{3} + \frac{d^2}{dx^2}\frac{\sin x}{x}\right) g\left(\frac{x}{k}\right)\left(x^2\frac{d^2}{dx^2} - x\frac{d}{dx}\right) u\left(\frac{x}{k}\right) dx \end{aligned} \quad \text{(A.21)}$$

Sufficient conditions on u to meet the demands of Eq. (A.13) *with a minimum margin of safety* are easily stated. Suppose

$$u(r) \to -(b/r^2) + O(1/r^4) \quad \text{(A.22)}$$

for $r \gg \rho^{-1/3}$. Each of the integrals occuring in Eq. (A.21) can be resolved into two summands, one depending entirely on the asymptotic behavior of $u(k)$, the other on the near behavior, which we do not specify. The resulting form for $D(k)$ in the limit of small k ($k \ll 2\pi\rho^{1/3}$) is

$$\begin{aligned} D(k) &\approx -2\pi\rho b k\left[\int_0^\infty \left(1 - \frac{\sin x}{x}\right)\frac{1}{x^2}\, dx \right. \\ &\qquad \left. - 4\int_0^\infty \left(\frac{1}{3} + \frac{d^2}{dx^2}\frac{\sin x}{x}\right)\frac{1}{x^2}\, dx\right] \\ &= \frac{1}{2}\pi^2\rho b k + O(k^2) \end{aligned} \quad \text{(A.23)}$$

Equation (A.13) now requires

$$b \geq mc/\pi^2\hbar\rho \quad \text{(A.24)}$$

The lower limit here is just the value determined by Enderly, Gaskell, and March [14] employing the Percus–Yevick and hypernetted-chain approximations for the connection between $g(r)$ and $u(r)$. It is also required if the BDJ type trial function is to include correctly the zero-point fluctuations of the quantized version of the classical sound field.

Equality in Eq. (A.24) implies a particularly small value of the variance of $H - E_0 - \varepsilon_0(k)$ and a particularly close approach of $\rho_{\mathbf{k}}\psi_0$ to the exact eigenfunction for small values of k, and thus closes the circle of reasoning which starts from the working hypothesis that the long-wavelength excitations are identical with the long-wavelength phonons of the quantized sound field.

The connection of these possibilities with Eq. (A.8) in the limit of small k ($k \ll 2\pi\rho^{1/3}$) can be summarized in the statement

$$N^{-1}\langle 0|\rho_k[H - E_0 - \varepsilon_0(k)]^2\rho_{\mathbf{k}}|0\rangle \sim O(k^4), \qquad b = mc/\pi^2\hbar\rho \qquad (A.25)$$

The equivalent statement

$$\begin{aligned}\Delta(k) = [\varepsilon_0(k)]^{-2}\,\langle\mathbf{k}|[H - E_0 - \varepsilon_0(k)]^2|\mathbf{k}\rangle \\ \sim O(k), \qquad b = mc/\pi^2\hbar\rho\end{aligned} \qquad (A.26)$$

is useful in developing a dispersion formula for the dynamic structure function $S(k, \omega)$[4].

The preceding discussion falls short of full rigor because the DBJ trial function ψ is certainly not the exact eigenfunction as assumed in the analysis through Eq. (A.17). However, the exact eigenfunction can be expressed as a product

$$\psi_0 = \varphi_0 \exp\left[\tfrac{1}{2}\sum_{i<j}\delta u(r_{ij})\right] \qquad (A.27)$$

in which $\delta u(r)$ is generated by the zero-point vibrations of the quantized version of the classical sound field. Then

$$\mathbf{k}\cdot\nabla_1\psi = (\mathbf{k}\cdot\nabla_1\psi_0)\exp\left[\tfrac{1}{2}\sum_{i<j}\delta u(r_{ij})\right] + \tfrac{1}{2}\left[\sum_j \mathbf{k}\cdot\nabla_1\,\delta u(r_{1j})\right]\psi_0 \qquad (A.28)$$

The analysis and conclusions represented by Eqs. (A.18)–(A.26) are still valid if (1) δu is identified with u in Eq. (A.22) with $b = mc/\pi^2\hbar\rho$, and (2) the summands in $C[r_{12}, \cos(\mathbf{r}_{12}, \mathbf{k})]$ generated by $\mathbf{k}\cdot\nabla_1\varphi_0$ and $\mathbf{k}\cdot\nabla_2\varphi_0$ contribute nothing to the leading term in the asymptotic formula of Eq. (A.15). Statements (1) and (2) are highly plausible sufficient conditions for the variance of $H - E_0 - \varepsilon_0(k)$ to be small in the sense defined by Eq. (A.25).

To evaluate the diagonal matrix element in Eq. (A.2), we introduce the formulas

$$[H, \rho_{\mathbf{k}}] = \frac{\hbar^2 k^2}{2m} \rho_{\mathbf{k}} - \frac{\hbar^2}{m} \sum_j (\exp i\mathbf{k} \cdot \mathbf{r}_j) i\mathbf{k} \cdot \nabla_j \tag{A.29}$$

$$[H, [H, \rho_{-\mathbf{k}}]] \to N(\exp -i\mathbf{k} \cdot \mathbf{r}_1)\left(\frac{\hbar^2 k^2}{2m} + \frac{\hbar^2}{m} i\mathbf{k} \cdot \nabla_1\right)^2$$

$$- N(N-1) \frac{\hbar^2}{m} (\exp -i\mathbf{k} \cdot \mathbf{r}_1) i\mathbf{k} \cdot \nabla_1 v(r_{12}) \tag{A.30}$$

and compute

$$\frac{1}{N} \langle 0|[H, \rho_{\mathbf{k}}][H, [H, \rho_{-\mathbf{k}}]]|0\rangle$$

$$= - \int \psi_0 \left(\frac{\hbar^2 k^2}{2m} + \frac{\hbar^2}{m} i\mathbf{k} \cdot \nabla_1\right)^3 \psi_0 \, d\mathbf{r}_{1,2,\ldots,N}$$

$$+ (N-1) \int \psi_0 (\exp -i\mathbf{k} \cdot \mathbf{r}_{12}) \left(\frac{\hbar^2 k^2}{2m} - \frac{\hbar^2}{m} i\mathbf{k} \cdot \nabla_1\right)$$

$$\times \left(\frac{\hbar^2 k^2}{2m} + \frac{\hbar^2}{m} i\mathbf{k} \cdot \nabla_1\right)^2 \psi_0 \, d\mathbf{r}_{1,2,\ldots,N}$$

$$- (N-1)\left(\frac{\hbar^2}{m}\right)^2 \int \psi_0 \Big[(\mathbf{k} \cdot \nabla_1)^2 v(r_{12}) + \mathbf{k} \cdot \nabla_1 v(r_{12}) \mathbf{k} \cdot \nabla_1$$

$$- \frac{1}{2} k^2 i\mathbf{k} \cdot \nabla_1 v(r_{12})\Big] \psi_0 \, d\mathbf{r}_{1,2,\ldots,N}$$

$$- (N-1) \left(\frac{\hbar^2}{m}\right)^2 \int \psi_0 (\exp -i\mathbf{k} \cdot \mathbf{r}_{12}) \Big[-(\mathbf{k} \cdot \nabla_1)^2 v(r_{12})$$

$$+ \mathbf{k} \cdot \nabla_1 v(r_{12}) \mathbf{k} \cdot \nabla_2 + \frac{1}{2} k^2 i\mathbf{k} \cdot \nabla_1 v(r_{12})\Big] \psi_0 \, d\mathbf{r}_{1,2,\ldots,N}$$

$$- (N-1)(N-2)\left(\frac{\hbar^2}{m}\right)^2 \int \psi_0 (\exp -i\mathbf{k} \cdot \mathbf{r}_{13})$$

$$\times \left[\frac{1}{2} k^2 i\mathbf{k} \cdot \nabla_1 v(r_{12}) + \mathbf{k} \cdot \nabla_1 v(r_{12}) \mathbf{k} \cdot \nabla_3\right] \psi_0 \, d\mathbf{r}_{1,2,\ldots,N} \tag{A.31}$$

We reduce these integrals in order:

$$\int \psi_0 \left(\frac{\hbar^2 k^2}{2m} + \frac{\hbar^2}{m} i\mathbf{k} \cdot \boldsymbol{\nabla}_1 \right)^3 \psi_0 \, d\mathbf{r}_{1,2,\ldots,N} = \left(\frac{\hbar^2 k^2}{2m} \right)^2 \left[\frac{\hbar^2 k^2}{2m} + 4 \frac{\langle 0|\text{K.E.}|0\rangle}{N} \right] \tag{A.32}$$

The second integral vanishes in consequence of the operator formula

$$(\exp - i\mathbf{k} \cdot \mathbf{r})(k^2 + 2i\mathbf{k} \cdot \boldsymbol{\nabla}) = -(k^2 - 2i\mathbf{k} \cdot \boldsymbol{\nabla})(\exp - i\mathbf{k} \cdot \mathbf{r}) \tag{A.33}$$

and the reversal in sign generated by an integration by parts;

$$\begin{aligned}(N-1)(\hbar^2/m)^2 &\int \psi_0 [(\mathbf{k} \cdot \boldsymbol{\nabla}_1)^2 v(r_{12}) + \mathbf{k} \cdot \boldsymbol{\nabla}_1 v(r_{12}) \mathbf{k} \cdot \boldsymbol{\nabla}_1 - \tfrac{1}{2} k^2 i\mathbf{k} \cdot \boldsymbol{\nabla}_1 v(r_{12})] \\ &\times \psi_0 \, d\mathbf{r}_{1,2,\ldots,N} \\ &= \tfrac{1}{2}(\hbar^2/m)^2 \rho \int g(r)(\mathbf{k} \cdot \boldsymbol{\nabla})^2 v(r) \, d\mathbf{r}\end{aligned} \tag{A.34}$$

$$\begin{aligned}(N-1)(\hbar^2/m)^2 &\int \psi_0 (\exp - i\mathbf{k} \cdot \mathbf{r}_{12})[-(\mathbf{k} \cdot \boldsymbol{\nabla}_1)^2 v(r_{12}) + \mathbf{k} \cdot \boldsymbol{\nabla}_1 v(r_{12}) k \cdot \boldsymbol{\nabla}_2 \\ &+ \tfrac{1}{2} k^2 i\mathbf{k} \cdot \boldsymbol{\nabla}_1 v(r_{12})] \psi_0 \, d\mathbf{r}_{1,2,\ldots,N} \\ &= -\tfrac{1}{2}(\hbar^2/m)^2 \rho \int g(r)(\exp - i\mathbf{k} \cdot \mathbf{r})(\mathbf{k} \cdot \boldsymbol{\nabla})^2 v(r) \, d\mathbf{r}\end{aligned} \tag{A.35}$$

$$\begin{aligned}(N-1)(N-2)(\hbar^2/m)^2 &\int \psi_0 (\exp - i\mathbf{k} \cdot \mathbf{r}_{13})[\tfrac{1}{2} k^2 ik \cdot \boldsymbol{\nabla}_1 v(r_{12}) \\ &+ \mathbf{k} \cdot \boldsymbol{\nabla}_1 v(r_{12}) \mathbf{k} \cdot \boldsymbol{\nabla}_3] \psi_0 \, d\mathbf{r}_{1,2,\ldots,N} \\ &= 0\end{aligned} \tag{A.36}$$

The final reduced formula is [15], [16]

$$\begin{aligned}-\frac{1}{N} \langle 0|[H, \rho_{\mathbf{k}}][H, [H, \rho_{-\mathbf{k}}]]|0\rangle &= \frac{\hbar^2 k^2}{2m} \left[\left(\frac{\hbar^2 k^2}{2m} \right)^2 + 4 \frac{\hbar^2 k^2}{2m} \frac{\langle 0|\text{K.E.}|0\rangle}{N} \right. \\ &\left. + \frac{\hbar^2 \rho}{m} \int (1 - \cos \mathbf{k} \cdot \mathbf{r}) g(r) \frac{1}{k^2} (\mathbf{k} \cdot \boldsymbol{\nabla})^2 v(r) \, d\mathbf{r} \right] \\ &= \frac{\hbar^2 k^2}{2m} \left[\left(\frac{\hbar^2 k^2}{2m} \right)^2 + 4 \frac{\hbar^2 k^2}{2m} \frac{\langle 0|\text{K.E.}|0\rangle}{N} \right. \\ &+ \frac{\hbar^2 \rho}{m} \int \left(1 - \frac{\sin kr}{kr} \right) g(r) \frac{1}{r} \frac{dv}{dr} \, d\mathbf{r}\end{aligned}$$

$$-\frac{\hbar^2\rho}{m}\int\left(\frac{1}{3}+\frac{d^2}{dx^2}\frac{\sin x}{x}\right)_{x=kr}$$
$$\times\left[\frac{1}{r}\frac{dv}{dr}-\frac{d^2v}{dr^2}\right]g(r)\,d\mathbf{r}\Bigg] \tag{A.37}$$

The sum rules for ω^2 and ω^3 can now be stated in forms suitable for numerical evaluation:

$$2mc^2\int_0^\infty\left[x-\frac{\hbar k}{2mcS(k)}\right]^2 R(k,x)\,dx$$
$$=-\hbar kc\left\{[S(k)]^{1/2}-\frac{1}{[S(k)]^{1/2}}\right\}^2+4\frac{\hbar c}{k}D(k) \tag{A.38}$$

$$2mc^2\int_0^\infty x^3R(k,x)\,dx=\frac{\hbar^2k^2}{2m}+\frac{4}{N}\langle 0|\text{K.E.}|0\rangle$$
$$+\frac{2\rho}{k^2}\int(1-\cos\mathbf{k}\cdot\mathbf{r})g(r)\frac{1}{k^2}(\mathbf{k}\cdot\boldsymbol{\nabla})^2v(r)\,d\mathbf{r} \tag{A.39}$$

These formulas can be used to compute an upper limit on the excitation energy $\varepsilon(k)$ [17]. The linear combination trial form

$$\psi_{\mathbf{k}}=a|\mathbf{k}\rangle+b|b\rangle$$
$$|b\rangle=\frac{[H-E_0-\varepsilon_0(k)]|\mathbf{k}\rangle}{\{\langle\mathbf{k}|[H-E_0-\varepsilon_0(k)]^2|\mathbf{k}\rangle\}^{1/2}} \tag{A.40}$$

generates the energy formula

$$\varepsilon(k)=\varepsilon_0(k)\left[1+\frac{\langle\mathbf{k}|[H-E_0-\varepsilon_0(k)]^3|\mathbf{k}\rangle}{2\varepsilon_0(k)^3\,\Delta(k)}\right.$$
$$\left.-\frac{1}{2}\left\{\frac{\langle\mathbf{k}|[H-E_0-\varepsilon_0(k)]^3|\mathbf{k}\rangle^2}{\varepsilon_0(k)^6\,\Delta(k)^2}+4\,\Delta(k)\right\}^{1/2}\right] \tag{A.41}$$

still an upper limit on the true minimum excitation energy for momentum $\hbar\mathbf{k}$.

The statistical weight of the b component is

$$\frac{b^2}{a^2+b^2}=\frac{[\varepsilon(k)-\varepsilon_0(k)]^2}{[\varepsilon(k)-\varepsilon_0(k)]^2+\langle\mathbf{k}|[H-E_0-\varepsilon_0(k)]^2|\mathbf{k}\rangle} \tag{A.42}$$

The mean excitation energy of the b component is given directly by the formula

$$\langle b|H - E_0|b\rangle = \varepsilon_0(k) + \frac{\langle \mathbf{k}|[H - E_0 - \varepsilon_0(k)]^3|\mathbf{k}\rangle}{\langle \mathbf{k}|[H - E_0 - \varepsilon_0(k)]^2|\mathbf{k}\rangle} \tag{A.43}$$

Numerical results for $\varepsilon(k)$, $\Delta(k)$, $b^2/(a^2 + b^2)$, and $\langle b|H - E_0|b\rangle$ computed by D. Hall [17] are plotted in Fig. 4-2. Liquid structure functions determined by Massey and Woo (MW) and by Schiff and Verlet (SV) are used

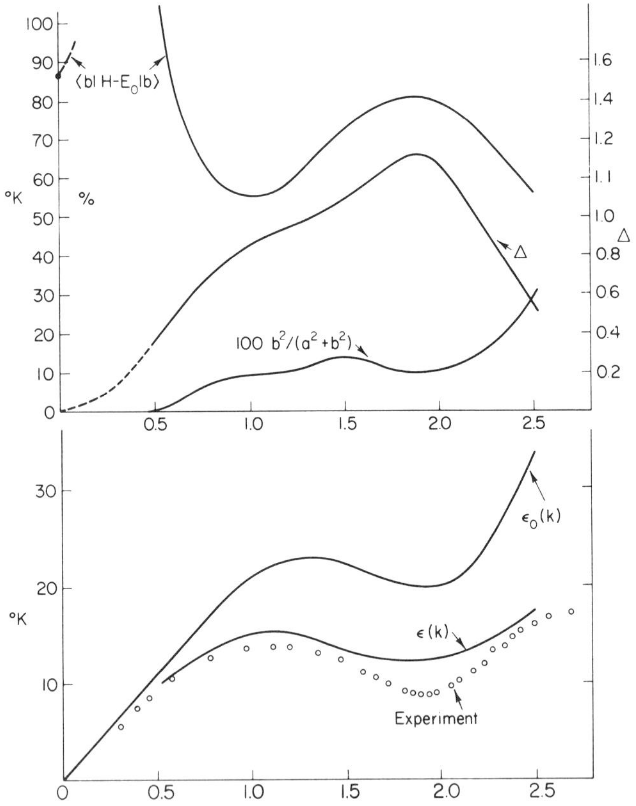

FIG. 4-2. Theory of elementary excitations using first, second, and third moments of $H - E_0 - \varepsilon_0(k)$. Experiment: D. G. Henshaw and A. D. B. Woods, Phys. Rev. **121**, 1266 (1961). $\varepsilon_0(k)$: Bijl–Feynman formula for the excitation energy [Eq. (4.2)]. $\varepsilon(k)$: Upper limit on the excitation energy from the moment formula [Eq. (A. 41)]. $100b^2/a^2 + b^2$: % statistical weight of the $|b\rangle$ state. Δ: Dispersion parameter [Eq. (A.26)]. $\langle b|H - E_0|b\rangle$ Excitation energy of the $|b\rangle$ state [Eq. (A.43)].

in evaluating the matrix elements. Both determinations yield excitation energies in the general neighborhood of the curves based on the second-order Brillouin–Wigner perturbation formula. In detail, $\varepsilon(k|\mathrm{MW})$ is somewhat closer that $\varepsilon(k|\mathrm{SV})$ to the experimental dispersion curve, possibly because the general procedure followed by Massey and Woo (cf. Chapter 6) determines more structure in the correlation function $u(r)$.

The close concordance between calculations based on the Brillouin–Wigner perturbation formula and those using first, second, and third moments of $H - E_0 - \varepsilon_0(k)$ must signify that the incorrect components in the Bijl–Feynman state function are largely concentrated in a limited region of the energy eigenvalue space.

Equation (A.41) yields a formula for the coefficient γ in Eq. (4.50):

$$\gamma = \lim_{k\to 0}\left[\frac{mc\,\Delta(k)}{\hbar k}\right]^2 \frac{(\hbar ck)^3}{\langle \mathbf{k}|[H - E_0 - \varepsilon_0(k)]^3|\mathbf{k}\rangle} \qquad \text{(A.44)}$$

Since γ is known, the formula can be used to evaluate $\Delta(k)$. With help from Eq. (A.37) the remaining factor in the right-hand member of Eq. (A.44) is computed from the statement

$$\begin{aligned}\Gamma &\equiv \frac{\langle \mathbf{k}|[H - E_0 - \varepsilon_0(k)]^3|\mathbf{k}\rangle}{(\hbar ck)^3} \\ &= -1 + \frac{2\langle 0|\mathrm{K.E.}|0\rangle}{mc^2 N} + \frac{\rho}{30mc^2}\int g(r)\left[2r\frac{dv}{dr} + 3r^2\frac{d^2v}{dr^2}\right] d\mathbf{r} \qquad \text{(A.45)}\end{aligned}$$

A completely explicit statement in terms of the pressure and the mean kinetic and potential energies of the ground state becomes possible if $v(r)$ has the Lennard-Jones form. In particular, employing the 6–12 potential, the identity

$$2r\frac{dv}{dr} + 3r^2\frac{d^2v}{dr^2} = -216v(r) - 55r\frac{dv(r)}{dr} \qquad \text{(A.46)}$$

and the virial theorem [Eq. (6.36)] allow Eq. (A.45) to be rewritten as

$$\begin{aligned}\Gamma = -1 &+ \frac{2\langle 0|\mathrm{K.E.}|0\rangle}{mc^2 N} \\ &+ \frac{1}{30mc^2}\left[-220\langle 0|\mathrm{K.E.}|0\rangle - 432\langle 0|\mathrm{P.E.}|0\rangle + 330P\Omega\right] \qquad \text{(A.47)}\end{aligned}$$

I draw on Chapter 6 for numbers and insert the theoretical and experimental values:

$$\langle 0|\text{P.E.}|0\rangle \approx -21.5°\text{K}, \qquad \langle 0|\text{K.E.}|0\rangle \approx 14.3°\text{K},$$
$$mc^2 = 27.5°\text{K}, \qquad P = 0$$

at $\rho = 0.0218$ Å^{-3} to obtain

$$\Gamma \approx 7.5 \tag{A.48}$$

Equations (4.49)–(4.50), (A.44), and (A.48) now yield

$$\begin{aligned}\Delta(k) &= (\gamma\Gamma)^{1/2}\hbar k/mc \\ &\approx 2.37\ \hbar k/mc, \qquad k \ll 2\pi\rho^{1/3}\end{aligned} \tag{A.49}$$

Also, in the phonon region,

$$\begin{aligned}\frac{b^2}{a^2+b^2} &= \left(\frac{\gamma^3}{\Gamma}\right)^{1/2}\left(\frac{\hbar k}{mc}\right)^3 \\ &\approx 0.24\left(\frac{\hbar k}{mc}\right)^3\end{aligned}$$

$$\begin{aligned}\langle b|H-E_0|b\rangle &= \varepsilon_0(k)\left[1+\frac{\langle \mathbf{k}|(H-E_0-\varepsilon_0)^3|\mathbf{k}\rangle}{(\hbar ck)^3\Delta(k)}\right] \\ &\approx \left(\frac{\Gamma}{\gamma}\right)^{1/2} mc^2 \sim 87°\text{K}\end{aligned} \tag{A.50}$$

These results locate the incorrect component in the Bijl–Feynman function for a single phonon state in the neighborhood of 87°K (for $k \ll 2\pi\rho^{1/3}$) and also exhibit the extreme purity of the BF wave function.

APPENDIX 4-B

Evaluation of the Overlap Integral $\langle \mathbf{k}-\boldsymbol{l}, \boldsymbol{l}|1|\mathbf{k}\rangle$ *and the Interaction Matrix element* $\langle \mathbf{k}-\boldsymbol{l}, \boldsymbol{l}|\delta H|\mathbf{k}\rangle$ *Eqs. (4.39) and (4.40)*

In the integrand of the overlap integral the products of two and three $\rho_{\mathbf{k}}$ functions can be replaced by simple equivalent forms:

$$\begin{aligned}\rho_{\mathbf{k}-\boldsymbol{l}}^*\rho_{\boldsymbol{l}}^* &\to \rho_{\mathbf{k}}^* + N(N-1)\exp -i\mathbf{k}\cdot\mathbf{r}_1 \exp i\boldsymbol{l}\cdot\mathbf{r}_{12} \\ \rho_{\mathbf{k}-\boldsymbol{l}}^*\rho_{\boldsymbol{l}}^*\rho_{\mathbf{k}} &\to |\rho_{\mathbf{k}}|^2 + |\rho_{\boldsymbol{l}}|^2 + |\rho_{\mathbf{k}-\boldsymbol{l}}|^2 - 2N + N(N-1)(N-2) \\ &\quad\times \exp i(\mathbf{k}\cdot\mathbf{r}_{31} + \boldsymbol{l}\cdot\mathbf{r}_{12})\end{aligned} \tag{B.1}$$

Equation (2.3), giving a cluster-type representation of $p^{(3)}(1, 2, 3)$, allows a partial explicit evaluation of the overlap integral, with the result

$$\langle \mathbf{k}-\boldsymbol{l}, \boldsymbol{l}|1|\mathbf{k}\rangle = \frac{1}{[NS(k)S(l)S(\mathbf{k}-\boldsymbol{l})]^{1/2}}\Big\{-2+S(k)+S(l)+S(\mathbf{k}-\boldsymbol{l})$$
$$+[S(k)-1][S(l)-1]+[S(k)-1][S(\mathbf{k}-\boldsymbol{l})-1]$$
$$+[S(l)-1][S(\mathbf{k}-\boldsymbol{l})-1]$$
$$+\frac{1}{N}\int \delta p^{(3)}(1, 2, 3)\exp i(\mathbf{k}\cdot\mathbf{r}_{31}+\boldsymbol{l}\cdot\mathbf{r}_{12})\,d\mathbf{r}_{1,2,3}\Big\} \tag{B.2}$$

To estimate the remaining integral term, we observe that the identities

$$\mathbf{k}\cdot\mathbf{r}_{31}+\boldsymbol{l}\cdot\mathbf{r}_{12}=\mathbf{k}\cdot\mathbf{r}_{32}+(\mathbf{k}-\boldsymbol{l})\cdot\mathbf{r}_{21}$$
$$=\boldsymbol{l}\cdot\mathbf{r}_{32}+(\boldsymbol{l}-\mathbf{k})\cdot\mathbf{r}_{13}$$

signify that the integral is a symmetrical function of $\mathbf{k}$, $-\boldsymbol{l}$, $\boldsymbol{l}-\mathbf{k}$. Also, since $\delta p^{(3)}$ is a short-range function [large only when $r_{ij}\lesssim O(\rho^{-1/3})$, $1\leq i<j\leq 3$], the integral can be evaluated accurately when any one of the wave vectors, say k, is small compared to $2\pi\rho^{1/3}$. Equation (2.4) then implies

$$(1/N)\int \delta p^{(3)}(1, 2, 3)\exp i\boldsymbol{l}\cdot\mathbf{r}_{12}\,d\mathbf{r}_{1,2,3}$$
$$=-(\rho^3/N)\int h(r_{13})h(r_{23})\exp i\boldsymbol{l}\cdot\mathbf{r}_{13}\exp -i\boldsymbol{l}\cdot\mathbf{r}_{23}\,d\mathbf{r}_{1,2,3}$$
$$=-[S(l)-1]^2 \tag{B.3}$$

The simplest form meeting all conditions is

$$(1/N)\int\delta p^{(3)}(1, 2, 3)\exp i(\mathbf{k}\cdot\mathbf{r}_{31}+\boldsymbol{l}\cdot\mathbf{r}_{12})\,d\mathbf{r}_{1,2,3}$$
$$\approx[S(k)-1][S(\boldsymbol{l})-1][S(\mathbf{k}-\boldsymbol{l})-1] \tag{B.4}$$

Exactly this form is in fact, generated by $\delta p_c(1, 2, 3)$, the remainder function in the convolution approximation for $p^{(3)}$ [Eq. (2.6)]. Finally putting Eq. (B.4) into (B.2) produces the simple formula

$$\langle\mathbf{k}-\boldsymbol{l}, \boldsymbol{l}|1|\mathbf{k}\rangle=[(1/N)S(k)S(l)S(\mathbf{k}-\boldsymbol{l})]^{1/2} \tag{B.5}$$

The superposition approximation for $p^{(3)}$ yields

$$\frac{1}{N}\int\delta p_K^{(3)}(1, 2, 3)\exp i(\mathbf{k}\cdot\mathbf{r}_{31}+\boldsymbol{l}\cdot\mathbf{r}_{12})\,d\mathbf{r}_{1,2,3}$$
$$=(1/N)\rho^3\int h(r_{12})h(r_{23})h(r_{31})\exp i(\mathbf{k}\cdot\mathbf{r}_{31}+\boldsymbol{l}\cdot\mathbf{r}_{12})\,d\mathbf{r}_{1,2,3}$$
$$=[1/(2\pi)^3\rho]\int[S(k')-1][S(\mathbf{k}'-\mathbf{k})-1][S(\mathbf{k}'-\boldsymbol{l})-1]\,d\mathbf{k}' \tag{B.6}$$

Appropriate displacements of the origin in $\mathbf{k}'$ space can be used to show that the final integral in Eq. (B.6) is a symmetrical function of $\mathbf{k}$, $-\boldsymbol{l}$, $\boldsymbol{l}-\mathbf{k}$.

Matrix elements of the phonon–phonon interaction involve

$$\begin{aligned}\int \psi_0\, \rho_{\mathbf{k}-\boldsymbol{l}}^{*}\, \rho_{\boldsymbol{l}}^{*}(H-E_0)\psi_0\, \rho_{\mathbf{k}}\, d\mathbf{r}_{1,2,\ldots,N} &= (\hbar^2 N/2m)\int \psi_0^{\,2}(\nabla_1\, \rho_{\mathbf{k}-\boldsymbol{l}}\, \rho_{\boldsymbol{l}})^* \cdot \nabla_1\, \rho_{\mathbf{k}}\, d\mathbf{r}_{1,2,\ldots,N} \\ &= (\hbar^2 N/2m)\{k^2 + k\cdot(k-l)[S(l)-1] + k\cdot l[S(\mathbf{k}-\boldsymbol{l})-1]\} \qquad \text{(B.7)}\end{aligned}$$

with the results

$$\begin{aligned}\langle \mathbf{k}-\boldsymbol{l}, \boldsymbol{l}|\delta H|\mathbf{k}\rangle_{\mathrm{c}} = \frac{-1}{[NS(k)S(l)S(\mathbf{k}-\boldsymbol{l})]^{1/2}}\frac{\hbar^2}{2m}[k\cdot lS(|\mathbf{k}-\boldsymbol{l}|) \\ + k\cdot(k-l)S(l) - k^2 S(l)S(\mathbf{k}-\boldsymbol{l})] \qquad \text{(B.8)}\end{aligned}$$

and

$$\begin{aligned}\langle \mathbf{k}-\boldsymbol{l}, \boldsymbol{l}|\delta H|\mathbf{k}\rangle_{\mathrm{K}} &= \langle \mathbf{k}-\boldsymbol{l}, \boldsymbol{l}|\delta H|\mathbf{k}\rangle_{\mathrm{c}} \\ &\quad + \frac{\varepsilon_0(k)}{[NS(k)S(l)S(\mathbf{k}-\boldsymbol{l})]^{1/2}} \\ &\quad \times \Big\{[S(k)-1][S(l)-1][S(\mathbf{k}-\boldsymbol{l})-1] \\ &\quad - \frac{1}{(2\pi)^3\rho}\int [S(k')-1][S(\mathbf{k}'-\mathbf{k})-1][S(\mathbf{k}'-\boldsymbol{l})-1]\, d\mathbf{k}'\Big\} \qquad \text{(B.9)}\end{aligned}$$

Both forms vanish if k is large ($k \gg 2\pi\rho^{1/3} \sim 1.75$ Å^{-1}). In the range $k \ll 2\pi\rho^{1/3}$, $k \ll l$ the convolution form reduces to

$$\begin{aligned}\langle \mathbf{k}-\boldsymbol{l}, \boldsymbol{l}|\delta H|\mathbf{k}\rangle_{\mathrm{c}} \approx \frac{mc^2}{(2N)^{1/2}}\left(\frac{\hbar k}{mc}\right)^{3/2} \\ \times\left[1 - S(l) - \frac{l}{S(l)}\frac{\partial S(l)}{\partial l}\cos^2(\mathbf{k}, \boldsymbol{l})\right] \qquad \text{(B.10)}\end{aligned}$$

It is clear from Eq. (B.10) that virtual processes of free-phonon splitting and recombination reduce the phonon energy by a term of order k^3. The perturbation correction does not modify the velocity of sound (c for $k \to 0$).

The numerical differences between the two approximate formulas of Eqs. (B.6) and (B.9) can be traced in large part to the failure of $p_{\mathrm{K}}^{(3)}$ to meet the requirements of the sequential relation [Eq. (2.2)] connecting $p^{(2)}$ and $p^{(3)}$; consequently, the convolution form must be considered the more reliable of the two.

References

1. L. D. Landau, *Phys. Rev.* **60**, 356 (1941).
2. A. Bijl, *Physica*, **7**, 869 (1940).
3. R. P. Feynman, *Phys. Rev.* **94**, 262 (1954).
4. K. Huang and A. Klein, *Ann. Phys.* (*N.Y.*) **30**, 203 (1964).
5. R. P. Feynman and M. Cohen, *Phys. Rev.* **102**, 1189 (1956).
6. C. G. Kuper, *Proc. Roy. Soc.* (*London*) **A233**, 223 (1955).
7. H. W. Jackson and E. Feenberg, *Rev. Mod. Phys.* **34**, 686 (1962).
8. D. K. Lee, unpublished doctoral dissertation, Washington University, 1967; *Phys. Rev.* **162**, 134 (1967).
9. P. Goldhammer and E. Feenberg, *Phys. Rev.* **101**, 1233 (1956).
10. R. C. Young, L. C. Biedenharn, and E. Feenberg, *Phys. Rev.* **106**, 115 (1957).
11. S. Eckstein and B. B. Varga, *Phys. Rev. Letters* **21**, 1311 (1968).
12. J. de Boer, *in* "Phonons and Phonon Interactions" (T. A. Bak, ed.), p. 379. Benjamin, New York, 1967.
13. T. B. Davison and E. Feenberg, *Phys. Rev.* **171**, 221 (1968).
14. J. E. Enderby, T. Gaskell, and N. H. March, *Proc. Phys. Soc.* (*London*) **85**, 917 (1965).
15. N. Mihara and R. D. Puff, *Phys. Rev.* **174**, 221 (1968).
16. R. D. Puff and N. S. Gillis, *Ann. Phys.* (*N.Y.*) **46**, 364 (1968).
17. D. Hall, research in progress at Washington University (1968).

CHAPTER 5

Paired Phonon States in the Free-Phonon Approximation*

5.1. INTRODUCTION

The wave function

$$\begin{aligned} \psi(1, 2, \ldots, N \mid \mathbf{k}_1, \ldots, \mathbf{k}_\nu) &= \prod_1^\nu F_j \psi_0(1, 2, \ldots, N) \\ F_j &= \sum_l \mathscr{X}_j(\mathbf{r}_l - \mathbf{R}_j) \exp i\mathbf{k}_j \cdot \mathbf{r}_l \end{aligned} \tag{5.1}$$

describes a multiple free-phonon state of the boson liquid. If the wave-packet factors $\mathscr{X}_j(\mathbf{r} - \mathbf{R}_j)$ are essentially nonoverlapping for different values of j, the total excitation energy can be evaluated without difficulty and, as expected, is exactly the sum of single-phonon energies. The possibility of multiple phonons with the same wave vector ($\mathbf{k}_j = \mathbf{k}_{j'}$, for a range of j, j' values) is included.

The picture is not so simple when wave packets are replaced by plane waves, as in Eq. (4.1). An excitation then occupies the entire box, with the consequence that the functions defined by Eq. (4.1) do not form an orthogonal set; in addition, the additive property of the elementary excitation energies is not transparently obvious. For example, a factor $|\rho_\mathbf{k}|^2$ generates both a ground-state component and a two-phonon component. These remarks serve to introduce the basic problem: to determine the correct linear combinations of plane wave states representing multiple

* See Jackson and Feenberg [1]; also Jackson [2].

free-phonon states and, in the same context, determine the optimum BDJ-type trial function [Eqs. (2.12), (2.32)] for the description of the ground state.

5.2. THE GENERALIZED NORMALIZATION INTEGRAL

The analysis is based on the generalized normalization integral

$$I(\beta) = \Omega^{-N} \int \exp[u(1, 2, \ldots, N) + \beta V^*(1, 2, \ldots, N)] \, d\mathbf{r}_{1, 2, \ldots, N} \quad (5.2)$$

We distinguish two special cases: (1) A BDJ-type trial function ψ_0 describing the ground state,

$$\begin{aligned} u(1, 2, \ldots, N) &= \sum_{i<j} u(r_{ij}) = \ln \psi_0^2 \\ V^*(1, 2, \ldots, N) &= \sum_{i<j} V^*(r_{ij}) \\ V^*(r) &= v(r) - (\hbar^2/4m)\, \Delta u(r) \end{aligned} \quad (5.3)$$

and (2) an exact ground-state wave function ψ_0 as the correlation factor,

$$\begin{aligned} u(1, 2, \ldots, N) &= \ln \psi_0^2 \\ V^*(1, 2, \ldots, N) &= \sum_{i<j} v(r_{ij}) - \frac{\hbar^2}{8m} \sum_l \Delta_l \ln \psi_0^2 \\ &= \sum_{i<j} v(r_{ij}) - \frac{\hbar^2}{4m} \sum_l \left[\frac{\Delta_l \psi_0}{\psi_0} - \left(\frac{\nabla_l \psi_0}{\psi_0} \right)^2 \right] \end{aligned} \quad (5.4)$$

In both cases V^* is chosen so that the expectation value of H with respect to the normalized ground-state eigenfunction or trial function is given by

$$\begin{aligned} (0|H|0) &= \left[\frac{d}{d\beta} \ln I(\beta) \right]_{\beta=0} \\ &= \frac{1}{I(0)} \int \psi_0^2 V^* \, d\mathbf{r}_{1, 2, \ldots, N} \end{aligned} \quad (5.5)$$

Equation (5.4) also appears in the discussion of the dynamical consistency condition [Eq. (2.52)].

To see the significance of V^* in case (1), observe that the kinetic energy operator in H can be transformed by the identity

$$-\frac{\hbar^2}{8m}[(F_1\psi_0)^*\,\Delta_1 F_2\psi_0+(\Delta_1 F_1\psi_0)^*(F_2\psi_0)-2(\nabla_1 F_1\psi_0)^*\cdot\nabla_1(F_2\psi_0)]$$
$$=\frac{\hbar^2}{2m}\left[(\nabla_1 F_1)^*\cdot(\nabla_1 F_2)-\frac{1}{4}\Delta_1(F_1{}^*F_2)-\frac{1}{4}(F_1{}^*F_2)\sum_2^N\Delta_1 u(r_{1j})\right]\psi_0{}^2 \tag{5.6}$$

into a convenient form exhibiting well-defined model function and correlation factor components. No three-particle operators occur in this formulation. The left-hand member of Eq. (5.6) gives a convenient form to the kinetic energy density. When integrated over the fundamental volume it can be transformed into conventional forms by the application of Green's theorem. Surface integrals occurring in this transformation all vanish because of the periodic boundary condition.

5.3. GENERALIZED DISTRIBUTION FUNCTIONS

Since surface effects are suppressed by the periodic boundary condition, the single-particle distribution function is simply the constant ρ. A generalized two-particle distribution function is defined by

$$p^{(2)}(r_{12},\beta)=\rho^2 g(r_{12},\beta)=[N(N-1)/I(\beta)]\int(\exp\beta V^*)\psi_0{}^2\,d\mathbf{r}_{3,4,\ldots,N} \tag{5.7}$$

This definition imposes the conditions

$$\begin{aligned} &g(r,\beta)\geq 0, \qquad g(0,\beta)=0\\ &g(r,\beta)\to 1-O(1/N), \qquad r\to\infty\\ &\rho\int[g(r,\beta)-1]\,d\mathbf{r}=-1 \end{aligned} \tag{5.8}$$

The range of integration in the last line of Eq. (5.8) is limited to the fundamental cube Ω. In addition, the origin from which r is measured may be any point within or on the surface of the cube [again a consequence of the periodic boundary condition (Eq. (1.7))].

We also need the generalized liquid structure function

$$S(k, \beta) = 1 + \rho \int [g(r, \beta) - g(\infty, \beta)] \exp i\mathbf{k} \cdot \mathbf{r} \, d\mathbf{r} \tag{5.9}$$

For later use we need the notation

$$\begin{aligned} g(r) &\equiv g(r, 0), \qquad S(k) \equiv S(k, 0) \\ I &\equiv I(0), \qquad I' = \left[\frac{d}{d\beta} I(\beta)\right]_{\beta=0} \\ S'(k) &= \left[\frac{d}{d\beta} S(k, \beta)\right]_{\beta=0}, \qquad W = \exp \beta V^* \end{aligned} \tag{5.10}$$

5.4. $\rho_{\pm\mathbf{k}}$ MODEL SPACE AND MATRIX ELEMENTS

The basis functions

$$|m, n) = N^{-(m+n)/2} \rho_{\mathbf{k}}{}^m \rho_{-\mathbf{k}}^n \psi_0 \tag{5.11}$$

are eigenfunctions of the total linear momentum operator $\mathbf{P}$ with eigenvalue $\mathbf{P}' = \hbar\mathbf{k}(m - n)$. Conservation of linear momentum requires

$$(m', n'|W|m, n) = 0 \qquad \text{unless} \quad m' - n' = m - n \tag{5.12}$$

From the definitions of $I(\beta)$ and $S(k, \beta)$

$$\begin{aligned} &(0, 0|W|0, 0) = I(\beta) \\ &(0, 1|W|0, 1) = (1, 0|W|1, 0) = (0, 0|W|1, 1) \\ &\qquad = I(\beta)S(k, \beta) \end{aligned} \tag{5.13}$$

Equation (3.38) gives directly the general formula

$$(m', n'|W|m, n) = \delta_{m'+n-m-n'}(m' + n)! \; S(k, \beta)^{m'+n} I(\beta) \tag{5.14}$$

This simple result depends on letting N increase without limit. The normalized basis functions

$$|m, n\rangle = [I(0)(m + n)! \; S(k)^{m+n}]^{-1/2} |m, n) \tag{5.15}$$

now yield

$$\langle m', n' |1| m, n\rangle = \delta_{m+n'-m'-n} \frac{(m'+n)!}{[(m+n)!\,(m'+n')!]^{1/2}} \tag{5.16}$$

The matrix elements of H are evaluated in two steps. First, by Eq. (5.14)

$$\begin{aligned}(m', n'|V^*(1, 2, \ldots, N)|m, n) &= \left\{\frac{d}{d\beta}(m', n'|W|m, n)\right\}_{\beta=0} \\ &= (m', n'|1|m, n)\left[\frac{I'}{I} + (m'+n)\frac{S'(k)}{S(k)}\right] \\ &= (m', n'|1|m, n)\left[\langle 0|H|0\rangle + (m'+n)\frac{S'(k)}{S(k)}\right]\end{aligned} \tag{5.17}$$

Equation (5.6) defines the matrix elements of a remainder operator $H - V^*$. These matrix elements are evaluated in Appendix 5-A, with the result

$$\begin{aligned}\langle m'n'|H - V^*|mn\rangle = \frac{\hbar^2k^2}{2m}\Bigg[&\frac{mm'+nn'}{(m+n')S(k)} \\ &+ \frac{1}{2}(m+n')\left(1 - \frac{1}{S(k)}\right)\Bigg]\langle m'n'|1|mn\rangle\end{aligned} \tag{5.18}$$

Equations (5.17) and (5.18) yield a complete explicit evaluation of the matrix elements of H in the "**k**" function space:

$$\begin{aligned}\langle m'n'|H - \langle 0|H|0\rangle|mn\rangle &= \langle m'n'|1|mn\rangle \\ &\quad\times\left[\frac{mm'+nn'}{(m+n')}\varepsilon_0(k) + (m+n')\omega(k)\right] \\ \varepsilon_0(k) &= \frac{\hbar^2k^2}{2mS(k)} \\ \omega(k) &= \frac{S'(k)}{S(k)} + \frac{\hbar^2k^2}{4m}\left(1 - \frac{1}{S(k)}\right)\end{aligned} \tag{5.19}$$

In case (2), where ψ_0 is the exact ground-state eigenfunction, $\omega(k)$ vanishes [Eq. (2.61)].

5.5. A NORMALIZED ORTHOGONAL BASIS IN "k" FUNCTION SPACE

The matrix elements of H [Eq. (5.19)] cannot be given an immediate physical interpretation because the functions $|m, n\rangle$ do not form an orthogonal basis. It is therefore necessary to construct an orthonormal basis system in the $|m, n\rangle$ function space. In this construction we are guided by the picture of independent "free" phonons. We introduce new functions $|e; s, p\rangle$ defined by the real linear transformation

$$|e; s, p\rangle = \sum_{l=0}^{p} a_{sp;\, l}\, |l + s, l\rangle$$
$$a_{sp;\, l} = 0,\ l > p; \qquad s \geq -p, \quad p = 0, 1, 2, \ldots \tag{5.20}$$

and require the normalization-orthogonality property

$$\langle e; s, p|1|e; s, q\rangle = \sum_{h,\, l} a_{sp;\, h} a_{sq;\, l} \langle h + s, h|1|l + s, l\rangle$$
$$= \delta_{pq} \tag{5.21}$$

The physical object described by $|e; s, p\rangle$ is a system of $s + p$ "phonons" with momentum $\hbar\mathbf{k}$ and p "phonons" with momentum $-\hbar\mathbf{k}$. The total momentum is $\hbar\mathbf{k}s$, $s = -p, -p + 1, \ldots$. Analogous states with momentum $-\hbar\mathbf{k}s$ are described by the complex conjugate basis functions. Conservation of momentum ensures the orthogonality of $|l + s, l\rangle$ and $|l + s, l\rangle^*$ for $s \neq 0$. In addition, states with different values of s, p are orthogonal. The quotation marks call attention to the fact that these functions are not eigenfunctions of the Hamiltonian, even with neglect of the phonon–phonon interaction.

Equation (5.21) is not convenient for determining the expansion coefficients. An equivalent, but more tractable, set of condition is given in part by

$$\langle h + s, h|1|e; s, p\rangle = \sum_{l=0}^{p} a_{sp;\, l} \frac{(l + h + s)!}{[(2l + s)!\,(2h + s)!]^{1/2}}$$
$$= 0, \qquad h < p \tag{5.22}$$

signifying that $|h+s, h\rangle$ can be expressed as a linear combination of $|e; s, q\rangle$ with $q \leq h$. This property permits writing Eq. (5.20) as

$$|e; s, p\rangle = a_{sp;\,p}|p+s, p\rangle + \sum_{q=0}^{p-1} C_q|e; s, q\rangle \tag{5.23}$$

and yields the condition

$$1 = a_{sp;\,p}\langle e; s, p|1|p+s, p\rangle \tag{5.24}$$

Equations (5.22)–(5.24) yield

$$\begin{aligned}\langle h+s, h|1|e; s, p\rangle &= \sum_{l=0}^{p} a_{sp;\,l} \frac{(l+h+s)!}{[(2l+s)!\,(2h+s)!]^{1/2}} \\ &= \delta_{hp}/a_{sp;\,p}, \qquad h \leq p\end{aligned} \tag{5.25}$$

a system of inhomogeneous linear equations for the unknowns $a_{sp;\,p} \times a_{sp;\,l}$. The explicit solution is developed in Appendix 5-B with the result

$$a_{sp;\,h} = (-1)^{p+h} \frac{[(s+2h)!(s+p)!\,p!]^{1/2}}{h!\,(s+h)!\,(p-h)!} \tag{5.26}$$

An alternative form of Eq. (5.25) proves useful in the evaluation of matrix elements of the Hamiltonian operator. Write $(l+h+s)! = (l+h+s)(l+h+s-1)!$ and observe that

$$(h+s) \sum_{l=0}^{p} a_{sp;\,l} \frac{(l+h-1+s)!}{[(2l+s)!\,(2h+s)!]^{1/2}} = 0 \tag{5.27}$$

for $0 \leq h \leq p$. The factor $(h+s)$ makes the statement perfectly general (including the special case $h+s=0$). Consequently, Eq. (5.25) implies

$$\sum_{l=0}^{p} a_{sp;\,l} \frac{l(l+h+s-1)!}{[(2l+s)!\,(2h+s)!]^{1/2}} = \frac{\delta_{h,\,p}}{a_{sp;\,p}} \tag{5.28}$$

for $0 \leq h \leq p$.

5.6. EVALUATION OF $\langle e; s, q\,|H|\,e; s, p\rangle$

The linear transformation of Eq. (5.20) converts Eq. (5.19) into

$$\langle e; s, q|H|e; s, p\rangle = \langle 0|H|0\rangle\, \delta_{pq}$$
$$+\, \varepsilon_0 \sum_{lh} a_{sq,\,h} a_{sp;\,l} \frac{(l+h+s)!}{[(2l+s)!\,(2h+s)!]^{1/2}} \left[s + \frac{2lh}{l+h+s}\right]$$
$$+\, \omega \sum_{lh} a_{sq;\,h} a_{sp;\,l} \frac{(l+h+s)!}{[(2l+s)!\,(2h+s)!]^{1/2}} (l+h+s) \qquad (5.29)$$

Consider first the coefficient of ε_0, and suppose $0 \leq q \leq p$; from Eqs. (5.25) and (5.28) and the relation $h \leq q \leq p$ we conclude that this coefficient vanishes unless $q = p$, and in that case has the value $s + 2p$.

To evaluate the coefficient of ω, consider two special cases. First, $q = p$:

$$\sum_{lh} a_{sp;\,h} a_{sp;\,l} \frac{(l+h+s)!}{[(2l+s)!\,(2h+s)!]^{1/2}} (l+h+s)$$
$$= s + 2 \sum_h h a_{sp;\,h} \sum_l a_{sp;\,l} \frac{(l+h+s)!}{[(2l+s)!\,(2h+s)!]^{1/2}}$$
$$= s + 2p \qquad (5.30)$$

Next, $q < p$:

$$\sum_{lh} a_{sq;\,h} a_{sp;\,l} \frac{(l+h+s)!}{[(2l+s)!\,(2h+s)!]^{1/2}} (l+h+s)$$
$$= -\sum_{lh} a_{sq;\,h} a_{sp;\,l} \frac{(l+h+s)!}{[(2l+s)!\,(2h+s)!]^{1/2}}$$
$$+ \sum_h a_{sq;\,h} [(2h+1+s)(2h+2+s)]^{1/2}$$
$$\times \sum_l a_{sp;\,l} \frac{(l+h+1+s)!}{[(2l+s)!\,(2(h+1)+s)!]^{1/2}} \qquad (5.31)$$

Equations (5.20) and (5.25) and the condition $q<p$ eliminate the first sum on the right in Eq. (5.31); the second sum reduces to

$$\begin{aligned}\sum_h a_{sq;\,h}[(2h+1+s)(2h+2+s)]^{1/2}\,\delta_{h+1,\,p}/a_{sp;\,p}\\ &=(a_{sq;\,p-1}/a_{sp;\,p})[(2p+s-1)(2p+s)]^{1/2}\\ &=\delta_{q,\,p-1}(a_{sp-1;\,p-1}/a_{sp;\,p})[(2p+s-1)(2p+s)]^{1/2}\\ &=\delta_{q,\,p-1}[p(p+s)]^{1/2}\end{aligned} \tag{5.32}$$

since $q<p$ and $q\geq p-1$ require $q=p-1$.

These results may be summarized in the formulas

$$\begin{aligned}\langle e;s,p|H|e;s,p\rangle&=\langle 0|H|0\rangle+(s+2p)(\varepsilon_0+\omega)\\ \langle e;s,p-1|H|e;s,p\rangle&=[p(p+s)]^{1/2}\omega\\ \langle e;s,p+1|H|e;s,p\rangle&=[(p+1)(p+1+s)]^{1/2}\omega\end{aligned} \tag{5.33}$$

All other matrix elements $\langle e;t,q|H|e;s,p\rangle$ vanish.

5.7. EIGENVALUES OF H IN THE "k" FUNCTION SPACE

The matrix elements of Eq. (5.33) define a Bogoliubov-type eigenvalue problem. First canonical creation and annihilation operators are defined by

$$\begin{aligned}a_{\mathbf{k}}^{\dagger}|e;s,p\rangle&=(s+p+1)^{1/2}|e;s+1,p\rangle,\\ a_{\mathbf{k}}|e;s,p\rangle&=(s+p)^{1/2}|e;s-1,p\rangle\\ a_{-\mathbf{k}}^{\dagger}|e;s,p\rangle&=(p+1)^{1/2}|e;s-1,p+1\rangle,\\ a_{-\mathbf{k}}|e;s,p\rangle&=p^{1/2}|e;s+1,p-1\rangle\end{aligned} \tag{5.34}$$

with the terminal condition $|e;s,p\rangle=0,\ s<-p$.

Equations (5.33) and (5.34) completely determine an equivalent Hamiltonian operator in the occupation number space of the $\hbar k$ and $-\hbar k$ phonons:

$$H_{\mathbf{k}}+H_{-\mathbf{k}}=(a_{\mathbf{k}}^{\dagger}a_{\mathbf{k}}+a_{-\mathbf{k}}^{\dagger}a_{-\mathbf{k}})[\varepsilon_0(k)+\omega(k)]+(a_{\mathbf{k}}a_{-\mathbf{k}}+a_{\mathbf{k}}^{\dagger}a_{-\mathbf{k}}^{\dagger})\omega(k) \tag{5.35}$$

The transformation of $H_{\mathbf{k}}+H_{-\mathbf{k}}$ to diagonal form is accomplished by introducing new canonical creation and annihilation operators [3]

$$\begin{aligned} A_{\mathbf{k}} &= \lambda a_{\mathbf{k}} - \mu a_{-\mathbf{k}}^{\dagger}, \qquad & A_{\mathbf{k}}^{\dagger} &= \lambda a_{\mathbf{k}}^{\dagger} - \mu a_{-\mathbf{k}} \\ A_{-\mathbf{k}} &= \lambda a_{-\mathbf{k}} - \mu a_{\mathbf{k}}^{\dagger}, \qquad & A_{-\mathbf{k}}^{\dagger} &= \lambda a_{-\mathbf{k}}^{\dagger} - \mu a_{\mathbf{k}} \end{aligned} \tag{5.36}$$

subject to the condition

$$\lambda = [1 - D(k)^2]^{-1/2}, \qquad \mu = D(k)[1 - D(k)^2]^{-1/2} \tag{5.37}$$

with

$$\begin{aligned} D(k) &= \frac{-\omega}{\varepsilon_0 + \omega + (\varepsilon_0{}^2 + 2\varepsilon_0\,\omega)^{1/2}} \\ &= -1 - \frac{\varepsilon_0}{\omega} + \frac{1}{\omega}(\varepsilon_0{}^2 + 2\varepsilon_0\,\omega)^{1/2} \\ &= 0 \qquad \text{for} \quad \omega = 0 \quad \text{(case 2)} \end{aligned} \tag{5.38}$$

The postulated reality of the transformation (λ, μ real numbers) requires

$$\varepsilon_0(k) + 2\omega(k) \geq 0 \tag{5.39}$$

Equation (5.39) also ensures $D^2(k) \leq 1$.

Our analysis up to this point is incomplete in that we have actually considered explicitly model states involving only the wave vectors **k** and $-$**k**. To avoid this artificial restriction, we must consider the general product function space defined by

$$|\cdots m_{\mathbf{k}} \cdots) = \left[\prod_{\mathbf{k}} N^{-m_{\mathbf{k}}/2} \rho_{\mathbf{k}}^{m_{\mathbf{k}}}\right] \psi_0 \tag{5.40}$$

Nonvanishing matrix elements, for which the constraint $m_{\mathbf{k}}' + m_{-\mathbf{k}} = m_{\mathbf{k}} + m'_{-\mathbf{k}}$ fails, occur, but are neglected in the present analysis. A simple example is the coupling of the three-phonon state $|\mathbf{k}, \boldsymbol{l}, -\mathbf{k} - \boldsymbol{l}\rangle$ to $|0\rangle$ (the theory is developed in Appendix 5-C; numerical results appear in Table 6-7). This approximation (or neglect) limits the range of trial functions to the paired space (for the description of the ground state); however, the paired space includes all possible BDJ-type trial functions and much more.

I defer the analysis of those complications to a later occasion, and proceed here by introducing a separability approximation in the evaluation of $\langle \cdots n_{\mathbf{k}} \cdots |A| \cdots m_{\mathbf{k}} \cdots \rangle$ expressed by the statement that the matrix element in the product function space is replaced by a suitable sum and product of the elementary matrix elements:

$$\langle \cdots n_{\mathbf{k}} \cdots | 1 | \cdots m_{\mathbf{k}} \cdots \rangle \to \prod_{\mathbf{k},\, k_x > 0} \langle n_{\mathbf{k}}, n_{-\mathbf{k}} | 1 | m_{\mathbf{k}}, m_{-\mathbf{k}} \rangle$$

$$\langle \cdots n_{\mathbf{k}} \cdots | H - E_0 | \cdots m_{\mathbf{k}} \cdots \rangle \to \sum_{\mathbf{l},\, l_x > 0} \langle n_{\mathbf{l}}, n_{-\mathbf{l}} | H - E_0 | m_{\mathbf{l}}, m_{-\mathbf{l}} \rangle \quad (5.41)$$

$$\times \prod_{\mathbf{k} \neq \mathbf{l},\, k_x > 0} \langle n_{\mathbf{k}}, n_{-\mathbf{k}} | 1 | m_{\mathbf{k}}, m_{-\mathbf{k}} \rangle$$

the right-hand member differing from zero only if $n_{\mathbf{k}} + m_{-\mathbf{k}} = m_{\mathbf{k}} + n_{-\mathbf{k}}$. The replacement makes sense only in a limited function space characterized by the inequalities

$$\left.\begin{matrix} \sum_{\mathbf{k}} n_{\mathbf{k}} \\ \sum_{\mathbf{k}} m_{\mathbf{k}} \end{matrix}\right. < \cdots < N \quad (5.42)$$

This condition implies separability in the required sense (a related question is discussed in Chapter 3).

Using Eq. (5.41), product transformations on the product function space bring a substantial part of the Hamiltonian operator to the diagonal form

$$H_{\mathrm{D}} = E_0 + \frac{1}{2} \sum_{\mathbf{k}} [-\varepsilon_0(k) - \omega(k) + e(k)] + \sum_{\mathbf{k}} A_{\mathbf{k}}{}^{+} A_{\mathbf{k}}\, e(k) \quad (5.43)$$

in which $A_{\mathbf{k}}{}^{+} A_{\mathbf{k}}$ is an occupation number operator (with eigenvalues 0, 1, 2, ...), and

$$e(k) = [\varepsilon_0(k)^2 + 2\varepsilon_0(k)\omega(k)]^{1/2} \quad (5.44)$$

is the energy of a phonon of momentum $\hbar\mathbf{k}$. In case (2) $\omega(k) = 0$, and $e(k)$ reduces to the Bijl–Feynman formula. Also, in this case the correction to the ground-state energy vanishes, as it should, since $\langle 0|H|0\rangle$ is then the exact ground-state energy. In any case, the inequality

$$e(k) \leq \varepsilon_0(k) + \omega(k) \quad (5.45)$$

follows immediately from Eq. (5.44), showing that the correction to the estimated ground-state energy either vanishes or is negative.

The preceding analysis establishes a parallelism between the theoretical terms and descriptions of two distinct computational procedures, one developed by Bogoliubov for treating a boson system with weak interactions, the other adapted to a boson system with strong interactions. Corresponding statements in Table 5-1 exhibit the parallel terms and relations.

TABLE 5-1

Feature	Weak interaction	Strong Interaction
Zeroth-order description of the ground state	$\lvert N\rangle_0 = a_0^{\dagger N}\lvert vac\rangle$	$\psi_0 =$ BDJ trial function
First-order description of excited states	$\prod_{\mathbf{k}}(a_{\mathbf{k}}{}^{\dagger}a_0)^{n_{\mathbf{k}}}\lvert N\rangle_0$	$\prod_{\mathbf{k}} \rho_{\mathbf{k}}^{n_{\mathbf{k}}}\psi_0 \rightarrow$ Linear combinations to form orthonormal "free" phonon states.
Corresponding elements of the Hamiltonian operators	$\dfrac{\hbar^2k^2}{2m}$, Free-particle energy	$\varepsilon_0(k) = \dfrac{\hbar^2k^2}{2mS(k)}$ Free phonon energy
	$\rho h(k)$, Direct, exchange, and pairing interaction	$\omega(k)$, Effective interaction
Energy of an elementary excitation	$\left[\left(\dfrac{\hbar^2k^2}{2m}\right)^2 + 2\rho h(k)\dfrac{\hbar^2k^2}{2m}\right]^{1/2}$	$[\varepsilon_0(k)^2 + 2\varepsilon_0(k)\omega(k)]^{1/2}$
Energy of the ground state	$N\rho h(0) - \dfrac{1}{2}\sum' \times \left[\dfrac{\hbar^2k^2}{2m} + \rho h(k) - e(k)\right]$	$(0\lvert H\rvert 0) - \dfrac{1}{2}\sum' [\varepsilon_0(k) + \omega(k) - e(k)]$
Neglected interactions	Two-particle collisions with different values of initial and final momenta.	Free-phonon splitting and coalescing processes, inelastic collisions of two or more free phonons

5.8. REPRESENTATION OF $\rho_{\mathbf{k}}$ IN TERMS OF CREATION AND ANNIHILATION OPERATORS*

Equations (5.15) and (5.20) imply

$$\begin{aligned} \rho_{\mathbf{k}}\lvert e; s, p\rangle &= \sum_{l=0}^{p} a_{s,\,p;\,l}[NS(k)(s+2l+1)]^{1/2}\lvert s+l+1, l\rangle \\ \langle e; s+1, q\rvert\rho_{\mathbf{k}} &= \sum_{h=0}^{q} a_{s+1,\,q;\,h}[NS(k)(s+2h+2)]^{1/2}\langle s+h+1, h+1\rvert \end{aligned} \tag{5.46}$$

* See Campbell [4].

with the consequence

$$\begin{aligned}\langle e; s+1, q|\rho_{\mathbf{k}}|e; s, p\rangle &= \sum_{h=0}^{q} a_{s+1,q;h}[NS(k)(s+2h+2)]^{1/2} \\ &\quad\times\langle s+h+1, h+1|1|e; s, p\rangle \\ &= \sum_{l=0}^{p} a_{s,p;l}[NS(k)(s+2l+1)]^{1/2} \\ &\quad\times\langle e; s+1, q|1|s+l+1, l\rangle \end{aligned} \tag{5.47}$$

The orthogonality relations

$$\begin{aligned}\langle s+h+1, h+1|1|e; s, p\rangle &= 0, \qquad h+1<p \\ \langle e; s+1, q|1|s+l+1, l\rangle &= 0, \qquad l<q\end{aligned} \tag{5.48}$$

require

$$\langle e; s+1, q|\rho_{\mathbf{k}}|e; s, p\rangle = 0 \tag{5.49}$$

unless $q=p$ or $q=p-1$ [since nonvanishing elements occur in Eq. (5.47) only for $p \le h+1 \le q+1$ and $q \le l \le p$; hence $q \le p \le q+1$]. The two nonvanishing matrix elements of $\rho_{\mathbf{k}}$ are easily evaluated with the help of Eqs. (5.25) and (5.26):

$$\begin{aligned}\langle e; s+1, p|\rho_{\mathbf{k}}|e; s, p\rangle &= [NS(k)(s+2p+1)]^{1/2}\,\frac{a_{s,p;p}}{a_{s+1,p;p}} \\ &= [NS(k)]^{1/2}(s+p+1)^{1/2} \\ \langle e; s+1, p-1|\rho_{\mathbf{k}}|e; s, p\rangle &= [NS(k)(s+2p)]^{1/2}\,\frac{a_{s+1,p-1;p-1}}{a_{s,p;p}} \\ &= [NS(k)]^{1/2}p^{1/2}\end{aligned} \tag{5.50}$$

Comparison with Eq. (5.34) shows that these vanishing and nonvanishing matrix elements of $\rho_{\mathbf{k}}$ imply the operator equivalence

$$\rho_{\mathbf{k}} = [NS(k)]^{1/2}(a_{\mathbf{k}}^{\dagger} + a_{-\mathbf{k}}) \tag{5.51}$$

and, in consequence of Eqs. (5.36)–(5.38),

$$\rho_{\mathbf{k}} = [NS(k)\varepsilon_0(k)/e(k)]^{1/2}[A_{\mathbf{k}}^{\dagger} + A_{-\mathbf{k}}] \tag{5.52}$$

With the help of Eq. (5.52) the liquid structure function generated by the ground state of H_D is easily found to be

$$\hat{S}(k) = \frac{S(k)\varepsilon_0(k)}{e(k)} = \frac{\hbar^2 k^2}{2me(k)}$$
$$= \frac{S(k)}{[1 + 2\omega(k)/\varepsilon_0(k)]^{1/2}} \qquad (5.53)$$

Notice that Eq. (5.53) can be interpreted as a Bijl–Feynman formula for $e(k)$. It is also clear that the normalization condition on $\hat{S}(k)$ implied by $\hat{g}(0) = 0$ can be used to test the adequacy of approximate procedures for evaluating $\omega(k)$.

The limiting forms $\varepsilon_0(k) = \hbar kc$ and $e(k) = \hbar k\hat{c}$ $(k \ll 2\pi\rho^{1/3})$ define two evaluations of the velocity of sound in the long-wavelength region. Equation (5.53) implies

$$\hat{c}^2 = c^2[1 + 2(\omega/\varepsilon_0)_{k=0}] \qquad (5.54)$$

while Eq. (5.19) defining $\omega(k)$ give us

$$[S'/S^2]_{k=0} = mc^2[1 + 2(\omega/\varepsilon_0)_{k=0}] \qquad (5.55)$$

Consequently,

$$\lim_{k\to 0} [S'(k)/S^2(k)] = m\hat{c}^2 \qquad (5.56)$$

5.9. THE GROUND-STATE EIGENFUNCTION

Let Ψ_D denote the ground-state eigenfunction of the operator H_D defined by Eq. (5.43). This function is completely determined by the conditions

$$A_{\mathbf{k}}^{\dagger} A_{\mathbf{k}} \Psi_D = 0, \qquad k \neq 0 \qquad (5.57)$$

It is clear that Eq. (5.57) can be satisfied by taking Ψ_D as a product of the correlation factor ψ_0 and independent model function factors, one for each wave-vector pair **k**, —**k**. The form

$$\Psi_D = \left[\prod_{\mathbf{k},\, k_x > 0} F_{\mathbf{k}}\right] \psi_0 \qquad (5.58)$$

permits writing Eq. (5.57) as a condition on $F_{\mathbf{k}}\psi_0$

$$\{(1+D(k)^2)(a_{\mathbf{k}}{}^\dagger a_{\mathbf{k}} + a_{-\mathbf{k}}{}^\dagger a_{-\mathbf{k}}) + 2D(k)^2 - 2D(k)(a_{\mathbf{k}}{}^\dagger a_{-\mathbf{k}}{}^\dagger + a_{\mathbf{k}} a_{-\mathbf{k}})\}F_{\mathbf{k}}\psi_0 = 0 \quad (5.59)$$

The function $F_{\mathbf{k}}\psi_0$ is a linear combination of normalized, orthogonal free-phonon states generated by polynomials in $\rho_{\mathbf{k}}\rho_{-\mathbf{k}}$ multiplying the correlation function ψ_0:

$$F_{\mathbf{k}}\psi_0 = \sum_0^\infty C_p(k)|e; o, p\rangle \quad (5.60)$$

With the help of Eq. (5.34) the defining condition on $F_{\mathbf{k}}$ reduces to a system of linear homogeneous equations in the coefficients $C_p(k)$:

$$\{p[1+D^2(k)] + D^2(k)\}C_p(k) - pD(k)C_{p-1}(k) - (p+1)D(k)C_{p+1}(k) = 0 \quad (5.61)$$

The normalized solution of Eq. (5.61) is

$$C_p(k) = D(k)^p[1-D(k)^2]^{1/2} \quad (5.62)$$

Equations (5.11), (5.15), (5.26), and (5.62) now yield a completely explicit formula for Ψ_{D} as a power series in $|\rho_{\mathbf{k}}|^2$:

$$\Psi_{\mathrm{D}} = \prod_{\mathbf{k},\, k_x>0} \left\{[1-D(k)^2]^{1/2} \sum_{l=0}^\infty \frac{1}{l!^2}\left[\frac{1}{S(k)}\frac{|\rho_{\mathbf{k}}|^2}{N}D(k)\right]^l \times \sum_{p=0}^\infty \frac{(p+l)!}{p!}[-D(k)]^p\right\}\psi_0 \quad (5.63)$$

The condition $D^2(k) \leq 1$ imposed on $D(k)$ by Eq. (5.38) permits the sum over p to be expressed in closed form:

$$\sum_0^\infty \frac{(p+l)!}{p!}(-D)^p = \frac{l!}{(1+D)^{l+1}} \quad (5.64)$$

with the result

$$\begin{aligned} \Psi_{\mathrm{D}} &= \prod_{\mathbf{k},\, k_x>0}\left\{\left[\frac{1-D(k)}{1+D(k)}\right]^{1/2} \sum_{l=0}^\infty \frac{1}{l!}\left[\frac{1}{S(k)}\frac{D(k)}{1+D(k)}\frac{|\rho_{\mathbf{k}}|^2}{N}\right]^l\right\}\psi_0 \\ &= \left\{\prod_{\mathbf{k},\, k_x>0}\left[\frac{1-D(k)}{1+D(k)}\right]^{1/2}\right\}\left\{\exp\left[\frac{1}{2N}\sum_l{}' \frac{1}{S(l)}\frac{D(l)}{1+D(l)}|\rho_l|^2\right]\right\}\psi_0 \\ &= \left[\prod_{\mathbf{k},\, k_x>0}\frac{e(k)}{\varepsilon_0(k)}\right]^{1/2}\left\{\exp\left[-\frac{1}{2N}\sum_l{}' \frac{e(k)-\varepsilon_0(l)}{2S(l)\varepsilon_0(l)}|\rho_l|^2\right]\right\}\psi_0 \end{aligned} \quad (5.65)$$

The last line of Eq. (5.65) is a consequence of Eqs. (5.37)–(5.38) in the form

$$D/(1+D)=(\varepsilon_0-e)/2\varepsilon_0\,, \qquad (1-D)/(1+D)=e/\varepsilon_0 \tag{5.66}$$

The attentive reader will note that Eqs. (5.53), (5.65), and (5.66) conform to the requirements of Eqs. (3.51) and (3.52). However, the analysis is valid only within the limits set by the separability condition of Eq. (5.42). In the context of the derivation of the explicit formula for Ψ_{D} an equivalent necessary condition is

$$\sum_{\mathbf{k}} (\Psi_{\mathrm{D}}, a_{\mathbf{k}}{}^{\dagger} a_{\mathbf{k}} \Psi_{\mathrm{D}}) \equiv \xi N \ll N \tag{5.67}$$

Equations (5.34), (5.60), and (5.62) require

$$\begin{aligned}(\Psi_{\mathrm{D}}, a_{\mathbf{k}}{}^{\dagger} a_{\mathbf{k}} \Psi_{\mathrm{D}}) &= [1-D(k)^2] \sum_0^\infty p D(k)^{2p} \\ &= \frac{D(k)^2}{1-D(k)^2} \\ &= \frac{\omega(k)^2}{2e(k)[e(k)+\varepsilon_0(k)+\omega(k)]} \\ &\sim \left[\frac{\omega(k)}{2e(k)}\right]^2 \end{aligned} \tag{5.68}$$

The necessary condition becomes

$$\xi \approx \frac{1}{2\pi^2\rho} \int_0^\infty \left[\frac{\omega(k)}{2e(k)}\right]^2 k^2\, dk \ll 1 \tag{5.69}$$

In summary, the multiple free-phonon processes, with neglect of inelastic collisions, transform an initial BDJ-type description of the ground state into a final improved description of the same type. If the initial trial function ψ_0 is the optimum choice (in the sense that $\langle 0|H|0\rangle$ is the lowest possible expectation value of H within the BDJ-type function space), then $\omega(k)$ must vanish and $S'(k)=(\hbar^2k^2/4m)[1-S(k)]$ must hold for the liquid structure function defined by the trial function, just as for the exact ground-state solution. If the initial trial function is not optimum, the procedure leading to Ψ_{D} can be repeated until no further changes occur in the ground-state description and the associated diagonal operator H_{D}.

To complete the theoretical description, let $\delta u(r)$ represent the change in $u(r)$ defined by the ratio Ψ_D/ψ_0:

$$\frac{\Psi_D}{\psi_0} = \left[\prod_{\mathbf{k},\, k_x>0} \frac{e(k)}{\varepsilon_0(k)}\right]^{1/2} \exp\left[\frac{1}{4} N\, \delta u(0)\right] \exp\left[\frac{1}{2} \sum_{i<j} \delta u(r_{ij})\right] \tag{5.70}$$

Equation (5.65) requires

$$\begin{aligned}\delta u(r) &= -\frac{1}{N} \sum_{\mathbf{k}}{}' \frac{e(k) - \varepsilon_0(k)}{S(k)\varepsilon_0(k)} \exp i\mathbf{k}\cdot\mathbf{r} \\ &= -\frac{1}{N} \sum_{\mathbf{k}}{}' \left[\frac{1}{\hat{S}(k)} - \frac{1}{S(k)}\right] \exp i\mathbf{k}\cdot\mathbf{r} \\ &= -\frac{1}{(2\pi)^3 \rho} \int \left[\frac{1}{\hat{S}(k)} - \frac{1}{S(k)}\right] \exp i\mathbf{k}\cdot\mathbf{r}\, d\mathbf{k}\end{aligned} \tag{5.71}$$

5.10. EVALUATION OF $S'(k)$

In case (1) (BDJ-type trial function) the practical usefulness of the formalism depends on the evaluation of $S'(k)$. The basic formula is

$$\begin{aligned}S'(k) &= [dS(k, \beta)/d\beta]_{\beta=0} \\ &= (1/N) \int \psi_0^2 |\rho_{\mathbf{k}}|^2 [V^*(1, 2, \ldots, N) - \langle 0|H|0\rangle]\, d\mathbf{r}_{1,2,\ldots,N} \\ &= (1/N) \int \psi_0^2 [|\rho_{\mathbf{k}}|^2 - N][V^*(1, 2, \ldots, N) - \langle 0|H|0\rangle]\, d\mathbf{r}_{1,2,\ldots,N} \\ &= (N-1) \int \psi_0^2 (\exp i\mathbf{k}\cdot\mathbf{r}_{12}) \\ &\quad \times [V^*(1, 2, \ldots, N) - \langle 0|H|0\rangle]\, d\mathbf{r}_{1,2,\ldots,N}\end{aligned} \tag{5.72}$$

The last integral in Eq. (5.72) can be reduced to integrals over the two-, three-, and four-particle distribution functions. However, the available approximate forms for $p^{(3)}$ and $p^{(4)}$ prove inadequate in the evaluation of these integrals. This inadequacy of the superposition and other simple approximations shows up in the apparent result $S'(0+) \neq 0$, implying $e(0+) \neq 0$, in contradiction with the correspondence-principle interpretation of the long-wavelength excitations in liquid ^{4}He. In principle, the condition $S'(0+) = 0$ can be used as a necessary condition to test approximate forms for $p^{(3)}$ and $p^{(4)}$. The unsymmetrical forms $p^{(3)}(12|3)$

and $p^{(4)}(12|34)$ defined in Appendix 2-A meet this qualitative test, but fail to acheive semi-quantitative accuracy.

Alternative procedures are based on approximate formulas expressing $u(r)$ as a functional in $g(r)$: the (a) hypernetted-chain, (b) Percus–Yevick, and (c) BBGKY procedure.

Under (a) the evaluation of $S'(k)$ starts from

$$u_{\mathrm{HNC}}(r) + \beta V^*(r|u_{\mathrm{HNC}}) = \ln g(r, \beta) - \frac{1}{(2\pi)^3\rho}\int (\exp i\mathbf{k}\cdot\mathbf{r})\frac{[S(k,\beta)-1]^2}{S(k,\beta)}\,d\mathbf{k} \tag{5.73}$$

The classical counterpart of Eq. (5.73) (with $\beta = 0$) has been tested in studies of liquid argon, krypton, and zenon (reference 11, chapter II) and appears to be at least moderately accurate. We therefore expect sensible, and possibly semiquantitative, results from the application to compute $S'(k)$. Differentiation with respect to β followed by setting $\beta = 0$ transforms Eq. (5.73) into

$$\rho g(r) V^*(r) = \rho g'(r) + \frac{g(r)}{(2\pi)^3}\int (\exp i\mathbf{k}\cdot\mathbf{r})[1 - S^2(k)]\frac{S'(k)}{S^2(k)}\,d\mathbf{k} \tag{5.74}$$

To secure a simpler statement, equivalent to Eq. (5.74), but containing only one unknown function, let

$$\begin{aligned} L(k) &= S'(k)/S^2(k) \\ V_{\mathbf{h}}^* &= \rho\int (\exp i\mathbf{h}\cdot\mathbf{r}) g(r) V^*(r)\,d\mathbf{r}, \end{aligned} \tag{5.75}$$

multiply both members of Eq. (5.74) by $\exp i\mathbf{h}\cdot\mathbf{r}$, and integrate over the fundamental volume to obtain

$$V_{\mathbf{h}}^* = S'(h) + [1 - S^2(h)]L(h) + \frac{1}{(2\pi)^3\rho}\int [S(\mathbf{k}+\mathbf{h}) - 1][1 - S^2(k)]L(k)\,d\mathbf{k} \tag{5.76}$$

or

$$L(h) = V_h^* + \frac{1}{(2\pi)^3\rho}\int [1 - S(\mathbf{k}+\mathbf{h})][1 - S^2(k)]L(k)\,d\mathbf{k} \tag{5.77}$$

Equation (5.77) is a linear, inhomogeneous integral equation for the unknown function $L(h)$. At the origin ($h = 0$) it reduces to a mixed point and integral type boundary condition on $L(h)$. The physical meaning of $L(0)$ is made clear by Eq. (5.56), which states that $L(0) = m\hat{c}^2$.

The solution of Eq. (5.77) determines the sound velocity directly by Eq. (5.56) and indirectly through the compressibility computed from the corrected energy formula of Eq. (5.43). Consistency requires that the two determinations agree within resonable limits.

Something can be said about uniqueness. Consider the homogeneous eigenvalue equation

$$\mathscr{L}(h) = \Lambda \frac{1}{(2\pi)^3 \rho} \int [1 - S(|\mathbf{k} + \mathbf{h}|)][1 - S^2(k)]\mathscr{L}(k)\, d\mathbf{k} \tag{5.78}$$

subject to the condition that $\int |1 - S^2(k)| \mathscr{L}^2(k)\, d\mathbf{k}$ exists. The solution of the inhomogeneous equation is unique if $\Lambda = 1$ is not an eigenvalue. Equation (5.78) implies a lower limit on $|\Lambda|$ independent of $L(h)$. To see this, multiply both terms of Eq. (5.78) by $|1 - S^2(h)|\mathscr{L}(h)$ and integrate:

$$\begin{aligned}\int |1 - S^2(h)| \mathscr{L}^2(h)\, d\mathbf{h} &\leq |\Lambda| \frac{1}{(2\pi)^3 \rho} \int |1 - S(|\mathbf{k} + \mathbf{h}|)| \\ &\quad \times |[1 - S^2(h)][1 - S^2(k)]|\, |\mathscr{L}(h)\mathscr{L}(k)|\, d\mathbf{k}\, d\mathbf{h} \\ &< |\Lambda| \frac{1}{(2\pi)^3 \rho} \int |1 - S(k)|\, d\mathbf{k} \int [1 - S^2(h)]^2 \mathscr{L}^2(h)\, d\mathbf{h}\end{aligned} \tag{5.79}$$

Also, $|1 - S^2(h)| \geq |1 - S^2(h)|^2$ if $S^2(h) \leq 2$, which appears to hold for liquid ^{4}He. Consequently,

$$1 < |\Lambda| [1/(2\pi)^3 \rho] \int |1 - S(h)|\, d\mathbf{h} \tag{5.80}$$

In the special case that $S(k) \leq 1$ Eq. (5.80) requires $|\Lambda| > 1$. In the case of the ^{4}He system the several inequalities employed in deriving Eq. (5.80) may be strong enough to more than compensate for the occurrence of $|1 - S(k)|$ in Eq. (5.80) rather than $1 - S(k)$. Thus the conclusion $|\Lambda| > 1$ in the ^{4}He problem is plausible, but not proved.

A first step in the direction of understanding Eq. (5.77) in the ^{4}He problem is the observation that the physical interpretation of $L(0)$ requires $L(0) > -V_0^* = -2E_0/N$. If the actual solution reproduces this relation, it is clear that V_h^* is not a good starting approximation for a solution by iteration. The integral term must be large, and this indicates that the weight of the region in the integrand defined by $S(k) \leq 1$ must be considerably greater than 1. To estimate the integral

$$X = \frac{1}{2\pi^2 \rho} \int_0^{k_0} [1 - S(k)][1 - S^2(k)] k^2\, dk \tag{5.81}$$

[in which k_0 is the smallest solution of $S(x)=1$], we introduce the quadratic approximation $S(k) \approx B(k/k_F)^2$ with $B=0.20$ [Eq. (8.49)] and obtain

$$X \approx (3/2B^{3/2})0.103 \approx 1.73 \tag{5.82}$$

The value of the integral term in Eq. (5.77) at $h=0$ is enhanced if $L(k)$ changes sign near $k=k_0$, so that the interference effects in the integrand are constructive. These qualitative arguments indicate that the solution of Eq. (5.77) may conform to the physical requirements.

Useful information for choosing a starting approximation can be extracted from moment equations generated by Eq. (5.77). The function $V_h{}^*$ does not appear in the even moment equations, since

$$\begin{aligned}
\int h^{2n} V_h{}^* \, d\mathbf{h} &= (-1)^n \rho \int (\Delta^n \exp i\mathbf{h}\cdot\mathbf{r}) g(r) V^*(r) \, d\mathbf{r} \, d\mathbf{h} \\
&= (-1)^n \rho \int (\exp i\mathbf{h}\cdot\mathbf{r}) \, \Delta^n g(r) V^*(r) \, d\mathbf{h} \, d\mathbf{r} \\
&= (-1)^n (2\pi)^3 \rho [\Delta^n g(r) V^*(r)]_{r=0} \\
&= 0
\end{aligned} \tag{5.83}$$

[$g(r)$ and all its derivations vanish at the origin]. Also,

$$\begin{aligned}
\int h^{2n} [1 - S(h)] \, d\mathbf{h} &= (-1)^n \rho \int (\exp i\mathbf{h}\cdot\mathbf{r}) \, \Delta^n g(r) \, d\mathbf{r} \, d\mathbf{h} \\
&= (-1)^n (2\pi)^3 \rho [\Delta^n g(r)]_{r=0} \\
&= 0
\end{aligned} \tag{5.84}$$

These relations reduce the even moment equations generated by Eq. (5.77) to the simple statement

$$\int h^{2n} S^2(h) L(h) \, d\mathbf{h} = 0 \tag{5.85}$$

Equation (5.85) is already implied by the definition of $S'(k)$ and the fact that $g(r, \beta)$ and all the derivatives with respect to r vanish at $r=0$. An immediate inference from Eq. (5.85) is that $L(h)$ is an oscillatory function with an infinite number of zeros and, presumably, a rapidly decreasing amplitude beyond the first few cycles.

Procedure (b), based on the PY relation, leads to the inhomogeneous integral equation

$$L(h) = V_h^* + \frac{1}{(2\pi)^3 \rho} \int R(\mathbf{k} + \mathbf{h})[1 - S^2(k)]L(k)\, dk \tag{5.86}$$

in which $V^*(r) \equiv V^*(r|u_{\mathrm{PY}}) = v(r) - (\hbar^2/4m)\, \Delta u_{\mathrm{PY}}(r)$ and

$$R(k) = \rho \int (\exp i\mathbf{k} \cdot \mathbf{r})(1 - e^{u(r)})\, d\mathbf{r} \tag{5.87}$$

Procedure (c) leads to a complicated integral equation for $S'(k)$; it is omitted from further consideration here.

Further discussion of this topic is continued in the concluding section of Chapter 6, following the evaluation of $S(k)$ and V_k^*.

5.11. CONSEQUENCE OF $\omega(k) = 0$ IN THE HNC APPROXIMATION

The condition

$$\omega(k) \equiv \frac{S'(k)}{S(k)} + \frac{\hbar^2 k^2}{4m}\left[1 - \frac{1}{S(k)}\right] = 0 \tag{5.88}$$

characterizes the optimum BDJ-type trial function. The equivalent statements

$$S'(k) = (\hbar^2 k^2/4m)[1 - S(k)]$$
$$g'(r) = (\hbar^2/4m)\, \Delta g(r) \tag{5.89}$$

hold also for the liquid structure and radial distributions generated by the exact ground-state eigenfunction [Eqs. (2.57) and (2.60)]. These statements serve to motivate the investigation of the consequences of Eq. (5.88) in the context of the BDJ function space and explicit relations giving $u(r)$ as a functional in $g(r)$. In particular, the HNC relation can be used to derive a nonlinear differential-integral equation for the optimum radial distribution function.

The derivation of an equation for $g(r)$ begins with the application of the Laplacian operator to both members of Eq. (5.73). At $\beta = 0$ the result is

$$\Delta u(r) = \left[\frac{1}{g(r)} - 1\right] \Delta g(r) - \left[\frac{1}{g(r)} \frac{dg(r)}{dr}\right]^2 - \frac{1}{(2\pi)^3\rho} \int (\exp i\mathbf{k}\cdot\mathbf{r}) k^2 \left[1 - \frac{1}{S(k)}\right] d\mathbf{k} \tag{5.90}$$

Equations (5.74) and (5.89) yield directly

$$\frac{4m}{\hbar^2} v(r) - \Delta u(r) = \left[\frac{1}{g(r)} - 1\right] \Delta g(r) + \frac{1}{(2\pi)^3\rho} \int (\exp i\mathbf{k}\cdot\mathbf{r}) \frac{k^2}{S(k)^2} [1 - S(k)]\, d\mathbf{k} \tag{5.91}$$

Now $\Delta u(r)$ can be eliminated, leaving the equation satisfied by $g(r)$:

$$\frac{4m}{\hbar^2} v(r) = 2\left[\frac{1}{g(r)} - 1\right]\Delta g(r) - \left[\frac{1}{g(r)} \frac{dg(r)}{dr}\right]^2 + \frac{1}{(2\pi)^3\rho} \int (\exp i\mathbf{k}\cdot\mathbf{r}) \left[\frac{k}{S(k)}\right]^2 [1 - S^2(k)]\, d\mathbf{k} \tag{5.92}$$

Some implications of Eq. (5.92) are brought to the surface by introducing the notation

$$\frac{4m}{\hbar^2} \tilde{v}(r) \equiv \frac{1}{(2\pi)^3\rho} \int (\exp i\mathbf{k}\cdot\mathbf{r}) \left[\frac{k}{S(k)}\right]^2 [1 - S(k)^2]\, d\mathbf{k} = \Delta \frac{1}{(2\pi)^3\rho} \int (\exp i\mathbf{k}\cdot\mathbf{r}) \left[1 - \frac{1}{S(k)^2}\right] d\mathbf{k} \tag{5.93}$$

and writing Eq. (5.92) in the form

$$\frac{1}{g(r)} \left[\frac{dg(r)}{dr}\right]^2 + 2[g(r) - 1]\, \Delta g(r) = \frac{4m}{\hbar^2} g(r)[\tilde{v}(r) - v(r)] \tag{5.94}$$

A priori we do not know that Eq. (5.92) possesses a solution or that a solution, if it exists, behaves in a physically reasonable manner. To see some of the relations implied by reasonable behavior, suppose that $g(r) - 1$ is an oscillatory function of r with rapidly decreasing amplitude as $r \to \infty$. Then Eq. (5.94) requires that successive zeros of $g(r) - 1$ include at least two zeros of $\tilde{v}(r) - v(r)$; more precisely, an odd number of zeros of $\tilde{v}(r) - v(r)$ should occur between successive zeros and maxima or minima of $g(r) - 1$.

To continue the analysis, let $r_1, r_3, \ldots, r_{2n+1}, \ldots$ denote crossovers $[g(r_{2n+1}) = 1]$ and $r_2, r_4, \ldots, r_{2n}, \ldots$ stationary points $[dg/dr = 0$ at $r = r_{2n}$, $n = 1, 2, \ldots]$. At the crossover points

$$dg/dr = (-1)^n (2/\hbar)[m(\tilde{v} - v)]^{1/2}, \quad r = r_{2n+1} \tag{5.95}$$

At the stationary points

$$(g - 1)\, d^2g/dr^2 = (2m/\hbar^2) g(\tilde{v} - v), \quad r = r_{2n} \tag{5.96}$$
$$< 0$$

The experimental $g(r)$ conforms to these relations in a semiquantitative manner out to the second crossover ($r_3 \approx 4.5$ Å), indicating that Eqs. (5.93)–(5.94) possess a solution with physically reasonable properties.

APPENDIX 5-A

Matrix Elements of $\langle m', n'|H|m, n\rangle$

The derivation of Eq. (5.18) begins with Eq. (5.6) in the form

$$\begin{aligned}(m', n'|H - V^*|m, n) = {} & \delta_{m+n'-m'-n}(\hbar^2 N/2mN^{m+n'}) \\ & \times [(0|(\nabla_1 \rho_{\mathbf{k}}^{m'} \rho_{-\mathbf{k}}^{n'})^* \cdot (\nabla_1 \rho_{\mathbf{k}}^{m} \rho_{-\mathbf{k}}^{n})|0) \\ & - \tfrac{1}{4}(0|\Delta_1 |\rho_{\mathbf{k}}|^{2(m+n'-1)}|0)]\end{aligned} \tag{A.1}$$

The equivalent integrands

$$\begin{aligned}(\nabla_1 \rho_{\mathbf{k}}^{m'} \rho_{-\mathbf{k}}^{n'}) \cdot (\nabla_1 \rho_{\mathbf{k}}^{m} \rho_{-\mathbf{k}}^{n}) \to {} & k^2 [(mm' + nn')|\rho_{\mathbf{k}}|^{2(m+n'-1)} \\ & - (m'n + mn')(\exp -2i\mathbf{k} \cdot \mathbf{r}_1)\rho_{\mathbf{k}}^2 |\rho_{\mathbf{k}}|^{2(m+n'-2)}]\end{aligned} \tag{A.2}$$

$$\begin{aligned}(\exp -2i\mathbf{k} \cdot \mathbf{r}_1)\rho_{\mathbf{k}}^2 \to {} & (1/N)[|\rho_{2\mathbf{k}}|^2 + 2(|\rho_{\mathbf{k}}|^2 - N) \\ & + N(N-1)(N-2) \exp i\mathbf{k} \cdot (\mathbf{r}_{21} + \mathbf{r}_{31})]\end{aligned} \tag{A.3}$$

$$\begin{aligned}-\tfrac{1}{4} \Delta_1 |\rho_{\mathbf{k}}|^{2(m+n')} \to {} & (m + n')(k^2/2N)[(|\rho_{\mathbf{k}}|^2 - N)|\rho_{\mathbf{k}}|^2 \\ & - (m + n' - 1)N|\rho_{\mathbf{k}}|^2 + O(N)]|\rho_{\mathbf{k}}|^{2(m+n'-2)}\end{aligned} \tag{A.4}$$

lead to

$$(0|(\nabla_1 \rho_{\mathbf{k}}^{m'} \rho_{-\mathbf{k}}^{n'})^* \cdot (\nabla_1 \rho_{\mathbf{k}}{}^m \rho_{-\mathbf{k}}^{n})|0)$$

$$= N^{m+n'-1} k^2 \left[(m+n')! \frac{mm' + nn'}{m+n'} S(k)^{m+n'-1} + O\left(\frac{1}{N}\right) \right]$$

$$- \tfrac{1}{4}(0|\{\Delta_1 |\rho_{\mathbf{k}}|^{2(m+n')}\}|0)$$

$$= N^{m+n'-1} \frac{1}{2} k^2 \left\{ (m+n')!\, S(k)^{m+n'} (m+n') \left[1 - \frac{1}{S(k)} \right] + O\left(\frac{1}{N}\right) \right\} \tag{A.5}$$

from which Eq. (5.18) follows.

APPENDIX 5-B

Solution of Eq. (5.25)

We want to solve

$$\sum_{l=0}^{p} a_{sp;\,l}\, a_{sp;\,p} \frac{(l+h+s)!}{[(2l+s)!\,(2h+s)!]^{1/2}} = \delta_{hp}, \qquad 0 \le h \le p \tag{B.1}$$

for $a_{sp;\,l}$. Define

$$A_p(s) \equiv \det\{(l+h+s)!/[(2l+s)!\,(2h+s)!]^{1/2}\} \tag{B.2}$$

a $(p+1)$ by $(p+1)$ determinant with columns labeled by l and rows by h. Let $A_p{}^q$ denote the cofactor of the element in the bottom $[(p+1)\text{th}]$ row and qth column. These definitions apply for all integral p; in particular, for $p+1$. The square array representing A_{p+1} can be written as the square array for A_p bordered below by a $(p+2)$th row and on the right by a $(p+2)$th column. This picture yields immediately

$$A_p = A_{p+1}^{p+1} \tag{B.3}$$

Equation (B.3) enables us to write

$$a_{sp;\,p}^2 = A_p{}^p / A_{p+1}^{p+1}, \qquad a_{sp;\,q} A_{sp;\,p} = a_p{}^q / A_{p+1}^{p+1} (-1)^{p+q} \tag{B.4}$$

To evaluate $A_p{}^q$, observe that a factor $(s!)^{-1/2}$ can be removed from the first column, $[(s+2)!]^{-1/2}$ from the second column, and so on. The same factors can be removed from corresponding rows. Consequently,

$$A_p{}^q = [(s+2q)!\,(s+2p)!]^{1/2} \prod_{l=0}^{p} [1/(s+2l)!] B_p{}^q$$

$$B_p{}^q = \begin{vmatrix} s!\,(s+1)! & \cdots & (s+q-1)!\,(s+q+1)! & \cdots & (s+p)! \\ (s+1)!\,(s+2)! & \cdots & (s+q)!\,(s+q+2)! & \cdots & (s+p+1)! \\ \vdots & & & & \\ (s+p-1)!\,(s+p)! & \cdots & (s+p+q-2)!\,(s+p+q)! & \cdots & (s+2p-1) \end{vmatrix} \tag{B.5}$$

To evaluate $B_p{}^q(s)$, subtract the (p-1)th row $s+p-1$ times from the bottom row, and so on, finally subtracting the top row $s+1$ times from the second row. The result of this sequence of operations is

$$B_p{}^q(s) = (s!\,p!/q) B_{p-1}^{q-1}(s) \tag{B.6}$$

The q fold repetition of the procedure leading to Eq. (B.6) produces

$$B_p{}^q(s) = \frac{S!(s-1)!\cdots(s+q-1)!\,p!\,(p-1)!\cdots(p-q+1)!}{q!} B_{p-q}^{0}(s+q) \tag{B.7}$$

Continuing with the same procedure,

$$B_{p-q}^{0}(s+q) = (s+q+1)!\cdots(s+p)!\,(p-q-1)!\cdots O! \tag{B.8}$$

Eqs. (B.5)–(B.8) yield

$$A_p{}^q(s) = \frac{[(s+2q)!\,(s+2p)!]^{1/2}}{s!\,(s+2)!\cdots(s+2p)!} \frac{s!\,(s+1)!\cdots(s+p)!\,p!}{(s+q)!\,(p-q)!\,q!} \tag{B.9}$$

Using Eqs. (B.4) and (B.9), the final explicit solution is

$$\begin{aligned} a_{sp;\,p} &= \left[\frac{(s+2p)!}{(s+p)!\,p!}\right]^{1/2} \\ a_{sp;\,q} &= (-1)^{p+q} \frac{[(s+2q)!\,(s+p)!\,p!]^{1/2}}{(s+q)!\,(p-q)!\,q!} \end{aligned} \tag{B.10}$$

APPENDIX 5-C

*Contribution of the Three-Phonon Vertex to the Binding Energy of the Boson System**

Let ψ_0 denote the optimum BDJ-type trial function, in the sense that the expectation value of H takes on the lowest possible value in the BDJ function space. This choice of trial (and correlation) function permits use of the relation $\omega(k)=0$ in the useful form of Eq. (5.89).

Three-phonon basis functions,

$$|\mathbf{k}, \boldsymbol{l}, -\mathbf{k}-\boldsymbol{l}) = \psi_0 \rho_{\mathbf{k}} \rho_{\boldsymbol{l}} \rho_{-\mathbf{k}-\boldsymbol{l}} \tag{C.1}$$

with $kl|\mathbf{k}+\boldsymbol{l}| \neq 0$ can be used in linear combination with ψ_0 to generate an improved description of the ground state (outside of the BDJ function space) and a closer approach to the exact ground-state energy. To determine the normalized form of these functions, consider the relation

$$\int \psi_0^2 \exp\left(\frac{a}{N}|\rho_{\mathbf{k}}|^2\right) \exp\left(\frac{b}{N}|\rho_{\boldsymbol{l}}|^2\right) \exp\left(\frac{c}{N}|\rho_{\mathbf{h}}|^2\right) d\mathbf{r}_{1,2,\ldots,N}$$

$$= \frac{1}{[1-aS(k)][1-bS(l)][1-cS(h)]} \tag{C.2}$$

implied by Eqs. (3.37). The required quantity is just the third derivative of the integral with respect to a, b, and c evaluated at $a=b=c=0$. Thus the normalized three-phonon basis function is

$$|\mathbf{k}, \boldsymbol{l}, -\mathbf{k}-\boldsymbol{l}\rangle = \frac{|\mathbf{k}, \boldsymbol{l}, -\mathbf{k}-\boldsymbol{l})}{[N^3 S(k) S(l) S(|\mathbf{k}+\boldsymbol{l}|)]^{1/2}} \tag{C.3}$$

provided that $kl|\mathbf{k}+\boldsymbol{l}| \neq 0$. The second-order energy formula

$$\Delta E^{(2)} = \frac{1}{6} \sum_{\mathbf{k}, \boldsymbol{l}}' \frac{|\langle \mathbf{k}, \boldsymbol{l}, -\mathbf{k}-\boldsymbol{l}|H-E_0|0\rangle|^2}{E_0 - \langle \mathbf{k}, \boldsymbol{l}, -\mathbf{k}-\boldsymbol{l}|H|\mathbf{k}, \boldsymbol{l}, -\mathbf{k}-\boldsymbol{l}\rangle} \tag{C.4}$$

gives a reasonable estimate of the contribution from the three-phonon states to the ground-state energy.

* See Davison [5].

Equation (5.6) is used to evaluate the diagonal matrix element of H:

$$(\mathbf{k}, \boldsymbol{l}, -\mathbf{k}-\boldsymbol{l}|H|\mathbf{k}, \boldsymbol{l}, -\mathbf{k}-\boldsymbol{l})$$

$$=\frac{1}{2}N(N-1)\int \psi_0{}^2 V^*(r_{12})|\rho_{\mathbf{k}}\rho_{\boldsymbol{l}}\rho_{-\mathbf{k}-\boldsymbol{l}}|^2\, d\mathbf{r}_{1,2,\ldots,N}$$

$$+\frac{\hbar^2 N}{2m}\int \psi_0{}^2\left[|\nabla_1\rho_{\mathbf{k}}\rho_{\boldsymbol{l}}\rho_{-\mathbf{k}-\boldsymbol{l}}|^2-\frac{1}{4}\Delta_1|\rho_{\mathbf{k}}\rho_{\boldsymbol{l}}\rho_{-\mathbf{k}-\boldsymbol{l}}|^2\right] d\mathbf{r}_{1,2,\ldots,N} \quad \text{(C.5)}$$

In Eq. (C.2) the replacement of $\psi_0{}^2$ by $\psi_0{}^2 \exp(\beta V^*)$ allows the derivation of the formula

$$\langle\mathbf{k}, \boldsymbol{l}, -\mathbf{k}-\boldsymbol{l}|W|\mathbf{k}, \boldsymbol{l}, -\mathbf{k}-\boldsymbol{l}\rangle = I(\beta)\,\frac{S(k, \beta)S(l, \beta)S(|\mathbf{k}+\boldsymbol{l}|, \beta)}{S(k)S(l)S(|\mathbf{k}+\boldsymbol{l}|)} \quad \text{(C.6)}$$

For notation refer to Eq. (5.10). The derivative of both sides of Eq. (C.6) with respect to β evaluated at $\beta=0$ yields an explicit formula for the first integral in the right-hand member of Eq. (C.5):

$$\int \psi_0{}^2 \sum_{i<j} V^*(r_{ij})|\rho_{\mathbf{k}}\rho_{\boldsymbol{l}}\rho_{-\mathbf{k}-\boldsymbol{l}}|^2\, d\mathbf{r}_{1,2,\ldots,N}$$

$$=N^3\left[E_0+\frac{S'(k)}{S(k)}+\frac{S'(l)}{S(l)}+\frac{S'(|\mathbf{k}+\boldsymbol{l}|)}{S(|\mathbf{k}+\boldsymbol{l}|)}\right] \quad \text{(C.7)}$$

Then, taking $S'(k)$ from Eq. (5.89),

$$\langle\mathbf{k}, \boldsymbol{l}, -\mathbf{k}-\boldsymbol{l}|V^*|\mathbf{k}, \boldsymbol{l}, -\mathbf{k}-\boldsymbol{l}\rangle$$

$$=E_0+\frac{\hbar^2}{4m}\left[-k^2-l^2-|\mathbf{k}+\boldsymbol{l}|^2+\frac{k^2}{S(k)}+\frac{l^2}{S(l)}+\frac{|\mathbf{k}+\boldsymbol{l}|^2}{S(|\mathbf{k}+\boldsymbol{l}|)}\right] \quad \text{(C.8)}$$

The second integral in Eq. (C.5) can be reduced to an equally simple explicit formula. Starting from

$$\nabla_1\rho_{\mathbf{k}}\rho_{\boldsymbol{l}}\rho_{-\mathbf{k}-\boldsymbol{l}} = i\mathbf{k}(\exp i\mathbf{k}\cdot\mathbf{r}_1)\rho_{\boldsymbol{l}}\rho_{-\mathbf{k}-\boldsymbol{l}}$$

$$+\,i\boldsymbol{l}(\exp i\boldsymbol{l}\cdot\mathbf{r}_1)\rho_{\mathbf{k}}\rho_{-\mathbf{k}-\boldsymbol{l}} - i(\mathbf{k}+\boldsymbol{l})[\exp -i(\mathbf{k}+\boldsymbol{l})\cdot\mathbf{r}_1]\rho_{\mathbf{k}}\rho_{\boldsymbol{l}} \quad \text{(C.9)}$$

we get

$$|\boldsymbol{\nabla}_1 \rho_{\mathbf{k}}\rho_{\boldsymbol{l}}\rho_{-\mathbf{k}-\boldsymbol{l}}|^2 \to k^2|\rho_{\boldsymbol{l}}|^2|\rho_{-\mathbf{k}-\boldsymbol{l}}|^2 + l^2|\rho_{\mathbf{k}}|^2|\rho_{-\mathbf{k}-\boldsymbol{l}}|^2 + |\mathbf{k}+\boldsymbol{l}|^2|\rho_{\mathbf{k}}|^2|\rho_{\boldsymbol{l}}|^2$$
$$+ (2/N)[\mathbf{k}\cdot\boldsymbol{l}\,\rho_{\mathbf{k}-\boldsymbol{l}}\rho_{-\mathbf{k}}\rho_{\boldsymbol{l}}|\rho_{\mathbf{k}+\boldsymbol{l}}|^2$$
$$-\mathbf{k}\cdot(\mathbf{k}+\boldsymbol{l})\,\rho_{2\mathbf{k}+\boldsymbol{l}}\rho_{-\mathbf{k}-\boldsymbol{l}}\rho_{-\mathbf{k}}|\rho_{\boldsymbol{l}}|^2$$
$$-\boldsymbol{l}\cdot(\mathbf{k}+\boldsymbol{l})\,\rho_{\mathbf{k}+2\boldsymbol{l}}\rho_{-\mathbf{k}-\boldsymbol{l}}\rho_{-\boldsymbol{l}}|\rho_{\mathbf{k}}|^2] \qquad \text{(C.10)}$$

Also,

$$\Delta_1 \rho_{\mathbf{k}}\rho_{\boldsymbol{l}}\rho_{-\mathbf{k}-\boldsymbol{l}} \to -(1/N)(k^2 + l^2 + |\mathbf{k}+\boldsymbol{l}|^2)\rho_{\mathbf{k}}\rho_{\boldsymbol{l}}\rho_{-\mathbf{k}-\boldsymbol{l}}$$
$$+ (2/N)[\mathbf{k}\cdot(\mathbf{k}+\boldsymbol{l})|\rho_{\boldsymbol{l}}|^2 + \boldsymbol{l}\cdot(\mathbf{k}+\boldsymbol{l})|\rho_{\mathbf{k}}|^2 - \mathbf{k}\cdot\boldsymbol{l}|\rho_{\mathbf{k}+\boldsymbol{l}}|^2] \qquad \text{(C.11)}$$

The arrow signifies equivalence in evaluating the matrix elements. These results in Eq. (C.5) produce the explicit evaluation

$$\frac{\hbar^2 N}{2m}\int \psi_0{}^2\left[|\boldsymbol{\nabla}_1 \rho_{\mathbf{k}}\rho_{\boldsymbol{l}}\rho_{-\mathbf{k}-\boldsymbol{l}}|^2 - \frac{1}{4}\Delta_1|\rho_{\mathbf{k}}\rho_{\boldsymbol{l}}\rho_{-\mathbf{k}-\boldsymbol{l}}|^2\right] d\mathbf{r}_{1,2,\ldots,N}$$
$$= \frac{\hbar^2 N}{4m}\int \psi_0{}^2[|\boldsymbol{\nabla}_1 \rho_{\mathbf{k}}\rho_{\boldsymbol{l}}\rho_{-\mathbf{k}-\boldsymbol{l}}|^2 - \rho_{-\mathbf{k}}\rho_{-\boldsymbol{l}}\rho_{\mathbf{k}+\boldsymbol{l}}\,\Delta_1 \rho_{\mathbf{k}}\rho_{\boldsymbol{l}}\rho_{-\mathbf{k}-\boldsymbol{l}}]\, d\mathbf{r}_{1,2,\ldots,N}$$
$$= \frac{\hbar^2 N^3}{4m} S(k)S(l)S(|\mathbf{k}+\boldsymbol{l}|)\left[k^2 + l^2 + |\mathbf{k}+\boldsymbol{l}|^2 + \frac{k^2}{S(k)} + \frac{l^2}{S(l)} + \frac{|\mathbf{k}+\boldsymbol{l}|^2}{S(|\mathbf{k}+\boldsymbol{l}|)}\right] \qquad \text{(C.12)}$$

Equations (C.3), (C.8), and (C.12) combine to give

$$\langle \mathbf{k}, \boldsymbol{l}, -\mathbf{k}-\boldsymbol{l}|H|\mathbf{k}, \boldsymbol{l}, -\mathbf{k}-\boldsymbol{l}\rangle = E_0 + \varepsilon_0(k) + \varepsilon_0(l) + \varepsilon_0(|k+l|) \qquad \text{(C.13)}$$

just as if ψ_0 were the exact ground-state solution.

The interaction matrix element yields to the same type of analysis, with the complication that an approximation for the three-particle distribution function $p^{(3)}(1, 2, 3)$ is ultimately needed to complete the numerical evaluation. First

$$(\mathbf{k}, \boldsymbol{l}, -\mathbf{k}-\boldsymbol{l}|H - E_0|0) = (\mathbf{k}, \boldsymbol{l}, -\mathbf{k}-\boldsymbol{l}|H - V^*|0)$$
$$+\left[\frac{d}{d\beta}\frac{1}{I(\beta)}(\mathbf{k}, \boldsymbol{l}, -\mathbf{k}-\boldsymbol{l}|W|0)\right]_{\beta=0} \qquad \text{(C.14)}$$

and

$$(\mathbf{k}, \boldsymbol{l}, -\mathbf{k}-\boldsymbol{l}|H-V^*|0) = -(\hbar^2 N/8m) \int \psi_0{}^2 \, \Delta_1(\rho_{\mathbf{k}} \rho_{\boldsymbol{l}} \rho_{-\mathbf{k}-\boldsymbol{l}}) \, d\mathbf{r}_{1,2,\ldots,N} \tag{C.15}$$

The equivalence relation

$$\begin{aligned} \rho_{\mathbf{k}} \rho_{\boldsymbol{l}} \rho_{-\mathbf{k}-\boldsymbol{l}} \to |\rho_{\mathbf{k}}|^2 + |\rho_{\boldsymbol{l}}|^2 + |\rho_{\mathbf{k}+\boldsymbol{l}}|^2 - 2N \\ + N(N-1)(N-2) \exp i(\mathbf{k} \cdot \mathbf{r}_{13} + \boldsymbol{l} \cdot \mathbf{r}_{23}) \end{aligned} \tag{C.16}$$

is used to convert Eq. (C.15) into

$$\begin{aligned} \langle \mathbf{k}, \boldsymbol{l}, -\mathbf{k}-\boldsymbol{l}|H-V^*|0\rangle = \frac{\hbar^2}{8m} & \frac{1}{[NS(k)S(l)S(|\mathbf{k}+\boldsymbol{l}|)]^{1/2}} \\ & \times \Big\{(k^2 + l^2 + |\mathbf{k}+\boldsymbol{l}|^2) \\ & \times \Big[S(k) + S(l) + S(|\mathbf{k}+\boldsymbol{l}|) - 2 \\ & + \frac{1}{N} \int p^{(3)}(1, 2, 3) \\ & \times \exp i(\mathbf{k} \cdot \mathbf{r}_{13} + \boldsymbol{l} \cdot \mathbf{r}_{23}) \, d\mathbf{r}_{1,2,3} \Big] \\ & - 2\boldsymbol{l} \cdot (\boldsymbol{l} + \mathbf{k}) S(k) - 2\mathbf{k} \cdot (\boldsymbol{l} + \mathbf{k}) S(l) \\ & + 2\mathbf{k} \cdot \boldsymbol{l} \, S(|\mathbf{k}+\boldsymbol{l}|) \Big\} \end{aligned} \tag{C.17}$$

An explicit formula for $p^{(3)}$ (1, 2, 3) is required to convert Eq. (C.18) into a completely explicit function of $\mathbf{k}$, $\boldsymbol{l}$, $-\mathbf{k}-\boldsymbol{l}$; the convolution form of Eqs. (2.3) and (2.6) produces the result

$$\begin{aligned} \langle \mathbf{k}, \boldsymbol{l}, -\mathbf{k}-\boldsymbol{l}|H-V^*|0\rangle = \frac{\hbar^2}{8m} & \frac{1}{[NS(k)S(l)S(|\mathbf{k}+\boldsymbol{l}|)]^{1/2}} \\ & \times [(k^2 + l^2 + |\mathbf{k}+\boldsymbol{l}|^2) S(k) S(l) S(|\mathbf{k}+\boldsymbol{l}|) \\ & - 2\boldsymbol{l} \cdot (\mathbf{k}+\boldsymbol{l}) S(k) - 2\mathbf{k} \cdot (\mathbf{k}+\boldsymbol{l}) S(l) \\ & + 2\mathbf{k} \cdot \boldsymbol{l} \, S(|\mathbf{k}+\boldsymbol{l}|)] \end{aligned} \tag{C.18}$$

Exactly the same type of analysis applied to the matrix element of W yields

$$(\mathbf{k}, \boldsymbol{l}, -\mathbf{k}-\boldsymbol{l}|W|0) = N\mathrm{I}(\beta)S(k, \beta)S(l, \beta)S(|\mathbf{k}+\boldsymbol{l}|, \beta) \tag{C.19}$$

and, with help from Eq. (5.89),

$$\begin{aligned}\langle \mathbf{k}, \boldsymbol{l}, -\mathbf{k}-\boldsymbol{l}|V^* - E_0|0\rangle = \frac{\hbar^2}{4m}&\frac{1}{[NS(k)S(l)S(|\mathbf{k}+\boldsymbol{l}|)]^{1/2}}\\ &\times[-(k^2+l^2+|\mathbf{k}+\boldsymbol{l}|^2)S(k)S(l)S(|\mathbf{k}+\boldsymbol{l}|)\\ &+k^2S(l)S(|\mathbf{k}+\boldsymbol{l}|)+l^2S(k)S(|\mathbf{k}+\boldsymbol{l}|)\\ &+(k+l)^2S(k)S(l)]\end{aligned} \tag{C.20}$$

The complete off-diagonal matrix element is

$$\begin{aligned}\langle \mathbf{k}, \boldsymbol{l}, -\mathbf{k}-\boldsymbol{l}|H - E_0|0\rangle = \frac{\hbar^2}{8m}&\frac{1}{[NS(k)S(l)S(|\mathbf{k}+\boldsymbol{l}|)]^{1/2}}\\ &\times\{-(k^2+l^2+|\mathbf{k}+\boldsymbol{l}|^2)S(k)S(l)S(|\mathbf{k}+\boldsymbol{l}|)\\ &+2k^2S(l)S(|\mathbf{k}+\boldsymbol{l}|)+2l^2S(k)S(|\mathbf{k}+\boldsymbol{l}|)\\ &+2|\mathbf{k}+\boldsymbol{l}|^2S(k)S(l)-2\mathbf{k}\cdot(\mathbf{k}+\boldsymbol{l})\,S(l)-2\boldsymbol{l}\\ &\cdot(\mathbf{k}+\boldsymbol{l})\,S(k)+2\mathbf{k}\cdot\boldsymbol{l}\,S(|\mathbf{k}+\boldsymbol{l}|)\}\end{aligned} \tag{C.21}$$

One obvious condition must be satisfied by any approximate formula for the interaction matrix element: it must vanish when one variable, say $\mathbf{k}$, is allowed to become infinite. The factor in braces in Eq. (C.21) does indeed vanish when $S(k)$ and $S(|\mathbf{k}+\boldsymbol{l}|)$ are replaced by 1. Equation (C.21) fails if any one of the wave vectors vanishes; however, if one wave vector is small ($0 < |\mathbf{k}+\boldsymbol{l}| \ll 2\pi\rho^{1/3}$), the matrix element contains a factor $|\mathbf{k}+\boldsymbol{l}|^{1/2}$, and hence vanishes as $\mathbf{k}+\boldsymbol{l}$ approaches zero. The argument developed in Eqs. (B.2)–(B.4) of Chapter 4 based on the short-range property of $\delta p^{(3)}$ [as defined by Eq. (2.3)] yields the conclusion that Eqs. (C.18) and (C.21) are exact if any one of the magnitudes k, l, or $|\mathbf{k}+\boldsymbol{l}|$ approaches zero.

Numerical results for $\Delta E^{(2)}$ appear in Table (6-6).

References

1. H. W. Jackson and E. Feenberg, *Ann. Phys.* (*N.Y.*) **15**, 266 (1961).
2. H. W. Jackson, unpublished doctoral dissertation, Washington University, 1961.
3. N. N. Bogoliubov, *J. Phys. USSR* **11**, 23 (1947).
4. C. E. Campbell, private communication; H. W. Jackson and W. E. Massey report an independent derivation of the same relation.
5. T. B. Davison, unpublished doctoral dissertation, Washington University, 1968; T. B. Davison and E. Feenberg, *Ann. Phys.* (*N.Y.*) **53**, 559 (1969).

CHAPTER 6

The Boson System at Absolute Zero

6.1. INTRODUCTION

The ground-state properties of a uniform boson system can be studied by using a BDJ-type trial function to compute the expectation value of the Hamiltonian operator as a function of density. Several methods of evaluating the expectation value and determining optimum correlation factors have been developed lately, all giving results of a more or less semiquantitative character in the liquid ^{4}He problem [1]–[5]. These formulations have in common the basic hypothesis of a two-particle interaction operator conventionally represented by a Lennard-Jones type of potential function.

The two-particle interaction operator $v(r)$ involves implicitly two parameters, an energy and a range, which are determined to fit the observed properties of the many-body system as well as possible. In the ^{4}He problem these parameters are already closely fixed by the comparison of theory and experiment for the properties of the vapor phase over a wide range of temperature [6]–[8]. Little freedom remains for adjusting the parameters to fit other properties.

A Lennard-Jones potential

$$v(r) = \frac{\varepsilon^*}{n-6}\left[6\left(\frac{r^*}{r}\right)^n - n\left(\frac{r^*}{r}\right)^6\right] \tag{6.1}$$

with $n = 12$ has been the conventional choice in theoretical studies of the vapor and liquid phases of the ^{4}He system. The relation of the potential constants to the critical strength at which the two-particle system just fails to possess a bound state can be seen in a particularly clean manner by choosing $n = 10$. In the two-particle problem the radial wave function

$$\psi_2(r) = (1/r) \exp[-\mu(r^*/r)^4] \tag{6.2}$$

defines a 6–10 Lennard-Jones potential through the radial differential equation

$$\Delta\psi_2(r) = \left[-\frac{20\mu}{r^{*2}} \left(\frac{r^*}{r}\right)^6 + \frac{16\mu^2}{r^{*2}} \left(\frac{r^*}{r}\right)^{10} \right] \psi_2 \tag{6.3}$$

The identification of the bracketed factor with $(m/\hbar^2)v(r)$, requires

$$20\mu/r^{*2} = \tfrac{5}{2} m\varepsilon^*/\hbar^2 \tag{6.4}$$
$$16\mu^2/r^{*2} = \tfrac{3}{2} m\varepsilon^*/\hbar^2$$

or

$$\mu = \tfrac{3}{4}, \qquad m\varepsilon^* r^{*2}/\hbar^2 = 6 \tag{6.5}$$

The corresponding number for $n = 12$ is 7.05 (see [9]), close to theoretical estimates from the properties of the gas phase (Table 6-1). [The last statement has interesting implications for small molecules of ^{4}He and ^{3}He atoms. Since the force parameters put the diatomic ^{4}He molecule close to the limit of stability (on which side is uncertain) we can be confident that $(^4\text{He})^3$ possesses at least one bound state. Clearly, $(^3\text{He})^2$ is unbound and, because of the node required by the exclusion principle, the

TABLE 6-1

THEORETICAL DETERMINATIONS OF THE 6–12 POTENTIAL PARAMETERS

Calculated by	$\varepsilon^*(10^{-15}$ ergs)	r^* (Å)	$Q^* = \dfrac{m\varepsilon^* r^{*2}}{\hbar^2}$
* de Boer and Michels [6, 7][a]	1.411	2.869	6.94
* Haberlandt [8][a]	1.422	2.929	7.29
Massey [3][b]	1.419	2.975	7.51

[a] Based on the quantum theory of the second virial coefficient and the measured second virial coefficient.

[b] Based on fitting the experimental binding energy of the liquid at the equilibrium density (condition 2).

same statement holds for $(^3\mathrm{He})^3$. In this context the basic problem for ^{3}He molecules is just to determine the smallest value of n for which $(^3\mathrm{He})^n$ possesses a bound state. For larger values of n the structure of the discrete energy spectrum as a function of spin and rotational and vibrational quantum numbers is an untouched problem. The $(^4\mathrm{He})^n$ molecules are expected to show a significant correspondence with the properties of the alpha-particle-type nuclei (^{8}Be–^{40}Ca). A looser, but still interesting, correspondence can be expected between the properties of $(^3\mathrm{He})^n$ molecules and light nuclei].

The various computational procedures in the many-particle problem all involve the radial distribution and liquid structure functions and the expectation value of H:

$$\frac{1}{2\pi N\rho} E(\rho) \leq \frac{1}{2\pi N\rho} \mathscr{E}(\rho) = \frac{\hbar^2}{4m} \int_0^\infty \frac{dg}{dr} \frac{du}{dr} r^2\, dr + \int_0^\infty g(r) v(r) r^2\, dr \quad (6.6)$$

In references 1, 2, and 4, $g(r)$ is determined from simple parameterized forms of $u(r)$ by methods of numerical integration (Monte Carlo and molecular dynamics). Also needed in one or another of the procedures available to compute $g(r)$ and $u(r)$ are the three-particle distribution function and:

(a) the BBGKY relation

$$g(r_{12}) \frac{du(r_{12})}{dr_{12}} = \frac{dg(r_{12})}{dr_{12}} - \frac{1}{\rho^2} \int [p^{(3)}(1, 2, 3) - \rho^3 g(r_{12}) g(r_{13})] \times \frac{du(r_{13})}{dr_{13}} \cos(12, 13)\, d\mathbf{r}_3 \quad (6.7)$$

(b) the hypernetted-chain (HNC) relation [10], [11]

$$u_{\mathrm{HNC}}(r) = \ln g(r) - \frac{1}{(2\pi)^3 \rho} \int (\exp i\mathbf{k} \cdot \mathbf{r}) \frac{[S(k) - 1]^2}{S(k)}\, d\mathbf{k} \quad (6.8)$$

(c) the Percus–Yevick relation [12]

$$u_{\mathrm{PY}}(r) = \ln g(r) - \ln\left[1 + \frac{1}{(2\pi)^3 \rho} \int (\exp i\mathbf{k} \cdot \mathbf{r}) \frac{[S(k) - 1]^2}{S(k)}\, d\mathbf{k}\right] \quad (6.9)$$

The last two formulas are approximate, and the errors are not well characterized by the usual derivations. Nevertheless, the heuristic test has shown that both formulas are sensible and at least semiquantitative in applications to the liquid state. Also, both yield the correct asymptotic behavior of $u(r)$ when $S(k)$ satisfies the Feynman condition [Eqs. (1.80) and (3.24a)]. For $r \gg \rho^{-1/3}$ Eqs. (6.8) and (6.9) both reduce to

$$u(r) \approx -\frac{1}{2\pi^2 \rho r} \int_0^\infty \frac{\sin kr}{S(k)} [S(k) - 1]^2 k \, dk$$

$$= -\frac{1}{2\pi^2 \rho r^3} \int_0^\infty \frac{\sin x}{S(x/r)} \left[S\left(\frac{x}{r}\right) - 1\right]^2 x \, dx \tag{6.10}$$

The value of the integral in Eq. (6.10) is determined by the behavior of the integrand in the neighborhood of the origin. A simple explicit form of the integrand with correct behavior for $x \ll r\rho^{1/3}$ and qualitatively correct behavior for $x \gtrsim r\rho^{1/3}$ is

$$\frac{[1 - S(x/r)]^2}{S(x/r)} \approx \frac{2mcr}{\hbar x} \exp\left(-\frac{x}{rk_c}\right) \tag{6.11}$$

Putting this form in Eq. (6.10) yields

$$u(r) \approx -\frac{mc}{\pi^2 \hbar \rho} \frac{1}{r^2 + k_c^{-2}}, \qquad r \gg \rho^{-1/3} \tag{6.12}$$

in agreement with the more general derivation in Chapter 3.

The computational procedure based on the BBGKY relation [Eq. (6.7)] is developed in the following sections. The application to liquid helium occupies Sections 6.4 and 6.5. The charged boson system is treated in Chapter 7 by the same method. The method has also been applied by Clark and Wang [13] to study an alpha-particle model of low-density nuclear matter with interesting results on the probable number of alpha particles in the surface region of a heavy nucleus.

6.2. THE EXTREMUM PROPERTY OF THE KINETIC ENERGY

Equation (6.7) parallels a relation well known in the several BBGKY hierarchies of equations for the equilibrium properties of a classical imperfect fluid. The parallel arises from the formal correspondence between the BDJ $|\psi|^2$ and the classical equilibrium probability density in the N-particle configuration space.

Abe, who first applied Eq. (6.7) to the liquid ^{4}He problem [14], solved the equation by a formal iteration procedure and obtained an explicit approximate solution in closed form (actually just the HNC relation). The properties of the exact formal solution obtained by iteration are best studied in conjunction with the extremum problem associated with Eq. (6.7) by the observation that Eq. (6.7) is the Euler–Lagrange condition for the extreme value of the functional [15],

$$J(u) \equiv 2J_1 - J_{2a} - J_{2b} \tag{6.13}$$

in which

$$J_1 = 4\pi \int_0^\infty \frac{dg}{dr}\frac{du}{dr} r^2\, dr, \qquad J_{2a} = 4\pi \int_0^\infty \left(\frac{du}{dr}\right)^2 g(r) r^2\, dr$$

$$J_{2b} = \frac{1}{\rho^2} \int [p^{(3)}(1, 2, 3) - \rho^3(r_{12})g(r_{13})] \frac{du(r_{13})}{dr_{13}} \frac{du(r_{12})}{dr_{12}} \cos(12, 13)\, d\mathbf{r}_2\, d\mathbf{r}_3 \tag{6.14}$$

An equivalent homogeneous form can be constructed by substituting λu for u and computing the extreme value of $J(\lambda u)$ with respect to λ. The result is

$$\begin{aligned} &\lambda = J_1(u)/J_2(u), \qquad J_2 = J_{2a} + J_{2b} \\ &J = J_1^{\,2}/J_2 \end{aligned} \tag{6.15}$$

In the applications the extreme value of J, for reasonable trial forms for g, is found to be a maximum. Consequently, the kinetic energy per particle obeys the inequality

$$(1/N)\langle 0|\text{K.E.}|0\rangle \geq (\hbar^2\rho/8m)J_{\text{extremum}} \tag{6.16}$$

the equality holding only if $u(r)$ is a solution of Eq. (6.7). The subscript on J in Eq. (6.16) refers to the use of a trial function $u(r|\cdots\mu_l\cdots)$ in evaluating J with free parameters $\cdots\mu_l\cdots$ determined to give J an extreme value. If $u(k)$ is not a solution of Eq. (6.7), the quantity $(\hbar^2\rho/8m)J(u)$ is smaller than the accurate mean kinetic energy per particle.

Actual numerical work is possible only if the exact $p^{(3)}$ in Eq. (6.7) is replaced by a suitable explicit (and approximate) form. All calculations to date on the helium problem have been made with the Kirkwood superposition form $p_K(1, 2, 3)$ [Eq. (2.7)]. The impact of this approximation on the computed results is probably not great, since the inequality $J_{2a} \gg |J_{2b}|$ is verified in all available calculations. Alternative forms based on Abe's correction factor to p_K [Eq. (2.23)] are useful in the charged boson problem (Chapter 7). Serious, but not insuperable, computational difficulties stand in the way of applying these forms to the helium problem under realistic conditions.

To discuss the character of the extremum, let

$$\begin{aligned} \{1; 2, 3\} &= [p^{(3)}(1, 2, 3) - \rho^3 g(r_{12}) g(r_{13})]/\rho^2 g(r_{12}) g(r_{13}) \\ \omega(r) &\equiv g(r)\, du(r)/dr \end{aligned} \tag{6.17}$$

Then

$$\begin{aligned} |J_{2b}| &< \int |\{1; 2, 3\}|\, |\omega(r_{12})\omega(r_{13})|\, d\mathbf{r}_2\, d\mathbf{r}_3 \\ &< \int |\{1; 2, 3\}| \omega(r_{13})^2\, d\mathbf{r}_2\, d\mathbf{r}_3 \end{aligned} \tag{6.18}$$

For the Kirkwood form

$$\{1; 2, 3\} = \rho\, [g(r_{23}) - 1] \tag{6.19}$$

Using Eq. (6.19), the preceding inequality becomes

$$|J_{2b}| < \rho \int |g(r') - 1|\, d\mathbf{r}' \int \omega^2(r)\, d\mathbf{r} \tag{6.20}$$

The conclusion

$$|J_{2b}| < J_{2a} = \int [1/g(r)] \omega^2(r)\, d\mathbf{r} \tag{6.21}$$

does not follow rigorously for arbitrary ω, but is generally plausible considering the nature of the substitutions involved in arriving at the last term in Eq. (6.18). In the special case $g(r) \leq 1$ the conclusion does follow. Thus the arithmetical evidence for $J_2 > 0$ is supplemented by a plausible general argument.

Equations (6.13) and (6.15) are equivalent with respect to physical consequences. However, the homogeneous form possesses nonphysical extrema, with $J = J_1 = 0$. In particular, if the trial function is a linear combination of n functions, the eigenvalue problem for the extreme values generated by Eq. (6.15) possesses an $(n-1)$ fold multiple root $(J = J_1 = 0)$.

6.3. ITERATION–VARIATION PROCEDURE

The function $\omega(r)$ [Eq. (6.17)] gives a convenient expression for Eq. (6.7) and for J_{2b} when $p^{(3)}$ is replaced by p_K:

$$\omega(r) = \frac{dg(r)}{dr} - \rho g(r) \int [g(|\mathbf{r}' - \mathbf{r}|) - 1]\omega(r') \cos(\mathbf{r}', \mathbf{r})\, d\mathbf{r}' \tag{6.22}$$

$$J_{2b} = \rho \int [g(|\mathbf{r}' - \mathbf{r}|) - 1]\omega(r)\omega(r') \cos(\mathbf{r}', \mathbf{r})\, d\mathbf{r}\, d\mathbf{r}' \tag{6.23}$$

Equation (6.22) is solved by an iteration procedure starting from an assumed zeroth approximation $\omega_0(r)$. Usually, $\omega_0(r) = dg(r)/dr$ is suitable. The simplest possible connection between successive approximations is expressed by

$$\omega_{n+1}^{(0)}(r) = \frac{dg(r)}{dr} - \rho g(r) \int [g(|\mathbf{r}' - \mathbf{r}|) - 1]\omega_n^{(0)}(r') \cos(\mathbf{r}', \mathbf{r})\, d\mathbf{r}' \tag{6.24}$$

Somewhere along the line $\omega_{n+1}^{(0)}(r) \approx \omega_n^{(0)}(r)$ to the required degree of accuracy and the iteration process can be terminated. However, on occasion a large number of iterations have been necessary. Obviously, fewer iterations and a direct presentation of the required physical information is desirable. In the present analysis all the physical information is in J; ω is needed only to compute J. The clue to an improved iteration procedure is contained in the remark that an optimum linear combination of ω_n, $\omega_{n-1}, \ldots, \omega_0$ is superior as a trial function to any single function ω_l $(l \leq n)$ alone. The same optimum linear combination can serve, when inserted into the right-hand member of Eq. (6.24) in place of $\omega_n^{(0)}(r)$, to generate an improved $(n+1)$th approximation.

The evaluation of ω and J using a general linear combination may proceed as follows [3]. Introduce an arbitrary set of trial functions ω_0, $\omega_1, \ldots, \omega_n, \ldots$ and define the integral coefficients

$$A_\nu = 4\pi \int_0^\infty \omega_n(r)\left[\frac{d}{dr} \ln g(r)\right] r^2\, dr$$

$$B_{\mu\nu} = 4\pi \int_0^\infty \frac{1}{g(r)} \omega_\nu(r)\omega_\mu(r) r^2\, dr \tag{6.25}$$

$$+ \rho \int [g(|\mathbf{r}' - \mathbf{r}|) - 1]\omega_\mu(r)\omega_\nu(r') \cos(\mathbf{r}', \mathbf{r})\, d\mathbf{r}\, d\mathbf{r}'$$

At this point begin a systematic interation routine:

(a) Use ω_{n-1} and Eq. (6.24) to construct an nth approximation $\omega_{\bar{n}}$;
(b) Construct the function system ω_{n-1},

$$\omega_{\bar{n}} = \omega_{\bar{n}} - (B_{n-1,\bar{n}}/B_{n-1,n-1})\omega_{n-1} \tag{6.26}$$

(orthonormal in the sense that $B_{n-1,\bar{n}} = 0$);

(c) Introduce a trial function

$$\omega_n = (A_{n-1}/B_{n-1,n-1})\omega_{n-1} + a_{\bar{n}}\omega_{\bar{n}} \tag{6.27}$$

and the associated functional

$$J^{(n)} = J^{(n-1)} + 2a_{\bar{n}} A_{\bar{n}} - a_{\bar{n}}{}^2 B_{\bar{n},\bar{n}} \tag{6.28}$$

(d) Compute

$$\begin{aligned} a_{\bar{n}} &= A_{\bar{n}}/B_{\bar{n},\bar{n}} \\ J^{(n)} &= J^{(n-1)} + A_{\bar{n}}{}^2/B_{\bar{n},\bar{n}} \end{aligned} \tag{6.29}$$

(e) Return to (a) with ω_n replacing ω_{n-1}. Repeat all steps with $n-1$ replaced by n.

It is clear that this routine can be carried through as many stages as desired. Experience in physical problems shows that the iteration procedure stays within the function space for which $J_2(\omega) > 0$, and consequently $B_{\bar{n},\bar{n}} > 0$ and

$$J^{(n)} > J^{(n-1)} \tag{6.30}$$

The question of uniqueness can be discussed in the context of Eqs. (6.17)–(6.19). Consider the homogeneous eigenvalue problem

$$\omega_\Lambda(r_{12}) = -\Lambda g(r_{12}) \int \{1; 2, 3\} \omega_\Lambda(r_{13}) \cos(12, 13)\, d\mathbf{r}_3 \tag{6.31}$$

in the L^2 function space. The solution of the inhomogeneous equation is unique if $\Lambda = 1$ is not an eigenvalue of the homogeneous equation. Equation (6.31) implies

$$\int (1/g)\omega^2\, d\mathbf{r} < |\Lambda| \rho \int |g(r') - 1|\, d\mathbf{r}' \int \omega^2(r)\, d\mathbf{r} \tag{6.32}$$

If $g(r) \leq 1$, the inequality requires $|\Lambda| > 1$, which was to be proved. In the actual physical problem the conclusion $|\Lambda| > 1$ cannot be drawn, but there is no reason to doubt that it is in fact correct.

The program just described generates a function $\mathscr{E}(\rho, e^*, r^* | \cdots \mu_l \cdots)$ for the energy depending on the force parameters ε^* and r^*, on the density

ρ, and on the free parameters $\boldsymbol{\mu}$ in the trial form for g. The minimum value of $\mathscr{E}$ as a function of $\boldsymbol{\mu}$ defines a function $\mathscr{E}(\rho, e^*, r^*)$ giving the lowest upper bound on the true energy per particle consistent with the assumed form for g. The functions $g(r|\rho, e^*, r^*)$ and $J(\rho, \varepsilon^*, r^*)$ defined by inserting the optimum values of $\boldsymbol{\mu}$ into $g(r|\rho, \varepsilon^*, r^*, \boldsymbol{\mu})$ and $J(\rho, \varepsilon^*, r^*, \boldsymbol{\mu})$ provide a theoretical evaluation of the radial distribution function and of the kinetic energy.

In the application to liquid helium the potential parameters have been chosen in two different ways:

(1) The quantities ε^* and r^* in the 6–12 potential are taken to fit the properties of the vapor phase.

(2) The quantities ε^* and r^* are determined so that the minimum value of the computed energy as a function of density and the density at the minimum coincide with the experimental values

$$E_0/N = -7.20\ °\mathrm{K/atom}, \qquad \rho_0 = 2.18 \times 10^{22}/\mathrm{cc} \tag{6.33}$$

Under condition 1 we expect that both the equilibrium density and the binding energy generated by a BDJ-type trial function will be too small. This expectation is based on the argument that the trial function is (1) only an approximation to the true ground-state eigenfunction, and (2) departs more and more from the true eigenfunction as the density is increased.

6.4. THE VIRIAL THEOREM

Under condition 2 the virial theorem is needed to express the equilibrium condition $P=0$ in terms of known quantities. The derivation of the virial theorem for a pure state may start from a trial function $\psi(\lambda r_1, \ldots, \lambda \mathbf{r}_N|\rho/\lambda^3)$ defined in the region $(\lambda L)^3 = \lambda^3\Omega$ and scaled so that the expectation value of H attains a minimum value at $\lambda = 1$:

$$\begin{aligned}\mathscr{E}\left(\lambda, \frac{\rho}{\lambda^3}\right) &= \frac{\int \psi^*(\cdots\lambda\mathbf{r}_n\cdots|\rho/\lambda^3)\, H\psi(\cdots\lambda\mathbf{r}_n\cdots|\rho/\lambda^3)\, d\mathbf{r}_{1,2,\ldots,N}}{\int |\psi(\cdots\lambda\mathbf{r}_n\cdots|\rho/\lambda^3)|^2\, d\mathbf{r}_{1,2,\ldots,N}} \\ &= N\lambda^2 T\left(\frac{\rho}{\lambda^3}\right) + \frac{1}{2} N\rho \int g\left(\lambda r; \frac{\rho}{\lambda^3}\right) v(r)\, d\mathbf{r} \\ &= N\lambda^2 T\left(\frac{\rho}{\lambda^3}\right) + \frac{1}{2} N \frac{\rho}{\lambda^3} \int g\left(r; \frac{\rho}{\lambda^3}\right) v\left(\frac{r}{\lambda}\right) d\mathbf{r}\end{aligned} \tag{6.34}$$

$$\begin{aligned}(d\mathscr{E}/d\lambda)_{\lambda=1} &= (\partial\mathscr{E}/\partial\lambda)_{\lambda=1} - 3\rho(\partial\mathscr{E}/\partial\rho)_{\lambda=1} \\ &= 0\end{aligned} \tag{6.35}$$

The familiar statement of the virial theorem

$$\begin{aligned}\frac{3P\Omega}{N} &= \frac{3\rho}{N}\left(\frac{\partial\mathscr{E}}{\partial\rho}\right)_{\lambda=1} \\ &= \frac{1}{N}\left(\frac{\partial\mathscr{E}}{\partial\lambda}\right)_{\lambda=1} \\ &= 2T(\rho) - \tfrac{1}{2}\rho\int g(r;\rho)\, r\,\frac{dv}{dr}\, d\mathbf{r}\end{aligned} \tag{6.36}$$

follows immediately from Eqs. (6.34)–(6.35). In terms of $g(r|\rho, \varepsilon^*, r^*)$ and $J(\rho, \varepsilon^*, r^*)$,

$$\begin{aligned}\frac{1}{N}\mathscr{E}(\rho) &= \frac{\hbar^2\rho}{8m}J + 2\pi\rho\int_0^\infty g(r)v(r)r^2\, dr \\ \frac{3P\Omega}{N} &= \frac{\hbar^2\rho}{4m}J - 2\pi\rho\int_0^\infty g(r)r\,\frac{dv}{dr}\,r^2\, dr\end{aligned} \tag{6.37}$$

and, at $P=0$, $\rho=\rho_0$,

$$\frac{1}{N}\mathscr{E}(\rho_0) = \pi\rho_0\int_0^\infty g(r;\rho_0)[2v(r) + r\, dv/dr]r^2\, dr \tag{6.38}$$

The further discussion assumes a Lennard-Jones 6-n potential. The notation

$$C_l = \int_0^\infty g(r;\rho, \varepsilon^*, r^*)r^{-l+2}\, dr \tag{6.39}$$

in Eq. (6.37) at $P=0$ yields a pair of implicit equations for ε^* and r^*:

$$r^* = \left[\frac{2n}{3(n-2)}\frac{C_6}{C_n}\right]^{1/(n-6)}\left\{\frac{J - 12(m/\hbar^2\rho_0)[\mathscr{E}(\rho_0)/N]}{J - [8n/(n-2)](m/\hbar^2\rho_0)[\mathscr{E}(\rho_0)/N]}\right\}^{1/(n-6)} \tag{6.40}$$

$$\begin{aligned}\varepsilon^* = {} & \frac{\hbar^2}{12\pi m}\left(\frac{3(n-2)}{2n}\right)^{n/(n-6)}\left(\frac{C_n{}^6}{C_6}\right)^{1/(n-6)} \\ & \times\frac{\{J - [8n/(n-2)](m/\hbar^2\rho_0)[\mathscr{E}(\rho_0)/N]\}^{n/6}}{J - 12(m/\hbar^2\rho_0)[\mathscr{E}(\rho_0)/N]}\end{aligned} \tag{6.41}$$

These equations are solved by an iteration procedure. Starting values may be taken from the determination of ε^* and r^* to fit the properties of the vapor phase (as in condition 1 and Table 6-1). The resulting J, C_6, and C_n are used in Eqs. (6.25)–(6.36) to compute ε_1^* and r_1^*. These values are used in turn to compute J, C_6, and C_n, and the process continued until limiting values are defined with sufficient accuracy. In practice, the convergence is rapid.

6.5. NUMERICAL RESULTS

Following the determination of ε^* and r^* the radial distribution function and the energy can be determined as functions of density at masses 3 and 4. Computed quantities at mass 3 are used in Chapters 8–10 as auxiliary functions in evaluating the ground-state properties of the mass-3 fermion system (liquid ^{3}He).

Table 6-1 gives the potential parameters involved in conditions 1 and 2. Table 6-3 and 6-4 make possible a comparison of numerical results generated by the two potentials. We see that the mean kinetic and potential energies depend strongly on Q^*. An 8% increase in Q^* (involving an 11% increase in the effective hard-core volume) produces a 14% increase in mean kinetic energy at the experimental energy density. The behavior of

TABLE 6-2

COMPARISON[a] OF $\langle 0|\text{K.E.}|0\rangle$, $\langle 0|\text{P.E.}|0\rangle$, AND $\langle 0|H|0\rangle$ (IN UNITS OF °K/atom) FOR ^{4}He AT TWO DENSITIES[5a]

ρ/ρ_0[b]	Ref.	$N^{-1}\langle 0\|\text{K.E.}\|0\rangle$	$N^{-1}\langle 0\|\text{P.E.}\|0\rangle$	$N^{-1}\langle 0\|H\|0\rangle$	$-N^{-1}[E_0^B + \frac{1}{3}\langle 0\|\text{K.E.}\|0\rangle]$
0.9	Mc[1]	11.7	−17.6	−5.9	2.10
0.9	SV[4]	11.59	−17.55	−5.96	2.00
0.9	MW[5]	11.60	−17.15	−5.55	1.68
1.0	Mc[1]	14.16	−19.82	−5.66	0.94
1.0	SV[4]	13.73	−19.46	−5.73	1.15
1.0	MW[5]	14.06	−20.04	−5.97	1.28

[a] Based on the de Boer–Michels parameters (condition 1).
[b] $\rho_0 = 0.0218$ Å^{-2}.

TABLE 6-3

ENERGY QUANTITIES[a] FOR LIQUID ^{4}He AS FUNCTIONS OF DENSITY
(in units of °K/atom)[b]

ρ (Å^{-3})	$N^{-1}\langle 0\|\text{K.E.}\|0\rangle$	$N^{-1}\langle 0\|\text{P.E.}\|0\rangle$	E_0/N
0.0218	14.06	−20.04	−5.97
0.0226	14.98	−21.02	−6.03
0.0234	15.88	−21.91	−6.04
0.0242	16.85	−22.86	−6.00
0.0250	17.76	−23.67	−5.90
0.0258	18.70	−24.42	−5.72

[a] Based on the de Boer–Michels parameters (condition 1).
[b] Private communication from W. E. Massey.

$S(k)$ is also strongly influenced by the 8% increase in Q^*, the increase converting a point of inflexion near $k = 0.6$ Å^{-1} into a well-defined secondary maximum followed by a minimum at $k \sim 0.8$ Å^{-1}.

The close concordance seen in Table 6-2 among the several independent estimates of the mean kinetic and potential energies provides a welcome check on the consistency and accuracy of three quite different computational procedures. For liquid structure and radial distribution functions the agreement between theory and experiment is fairly good and the different theoretical versions are essentially indistinguishable. Theoretical

TABLE 6-4

ENERGY QUANTITIES FOR LIQUID ^{4}He AS FUNCTIONS OF DENSITY[a]
(in units of °K/atom)[b]

ρ (Å^{-2})	$N^{-1}\langle 0\|\text{K.E.}\|0\rangle$	$N^{-1}\langle 0\|\text{P.E.}\|0\rangle$	E_0/N
0.0218	16.06	−23.26	−7.20
0.0226	16.93	−24.11	−7.18
0.0234	17.87	−24.97	−7.10
0.0242	18.83	−25.82	−7.01
0.0250	19.88	−26.67	−6.79
0.0258	20.96	−28.52	−6.56

[a] Based on choosing the potential parameters to fit the experimental equilibrium density and energy (condition 2).
[b] See Massey [3].

and experimental determinations of $S(k)$ are plotted in Fig. 6-1. The last column in Table 6-2 exhibits numerical values of a quantity needed in the theory of a dilute solution of ^{3}He atoms in liquid ^{4}He (Chapter XI).

TABLE 6-5

ENERGY QUANTITIES FOR LIQUID ^{3}He (BOSON SOLUTION) AS FUNCTIONS OF DENSITY[a] (in units of °K/atom)[b]

ρ (Å^{-3})	$N^{-1}\langle 0\|\text{K.E.}\|0\rangle$	$N^{-1}\langle 0\|\text{P.E.}\|0\rangle$	E_0/N
0.0132	10.18	−12.98	−2.80
0.0140	10.96	−13.80	−2.84 (−2.06)
0.0148	11.77	−14.64	−2.87 (−2.10)
0.0156	12.60	−15.48	−2.88 (−2.11)
0.0164	13.44	−16.32	−2.88 (−2.09)
0.0172	14.31	−17.16	−2.85 (−2.06)
0.0180	15.23	−18.01	−2.78 (−2.00)
0.0188	16.19	−18.85	−2.66
0.0196	17.22	−19.72	−2.50
0.0204	18.28	−20.59	−2.31

[a] Based on choosing the potential parameters to fit the experimental equilibrium density and energy in liquid ^{2}He (condition 2). The numbers in parentheses in the last column are computed under condition 1.

[b] See Massey [3].

6.6. EXPLICIT TRIAL FUNCTIONS FOR $g(r)$ IN THE HELIUM PROBLEM*

We turn to the problem of choosing an appropriate family of trial functions for $g(r)$. "Appropriate" in this connection means $g(r|\boldsymbol{\mu}) \geq 0$, $g(r/\boldsymbol{\mu})v(r)$ is integrable, and $g(\infty|\boldsymbol{\mu}) = 1$ for all values of the parameters $\boldsymbol{\mu}$. Also, $g(r|\boldsymbol{\mu})$ must possess a well-defined nearest-neighbor peak over a subspace of the parameter space. The possibility of one or more following valleys and peaks is a desirable feature. Finally, the additional necessary conditions listed in Eq. (1.85) must be satisfied over all or part of the parameter space. The normalization condition

$$\rho \int [g(r|\boldsymbol{\mu}) - 1]\, d\mathbf{r} = -1 \tag{6.42}$$

* See Massy [3]; also Massey and Woo [5].

is especially important, since it fixes a scale parameter and thus permits an effective enlargement of the parameter space.

The several exact and approximate relations connecting $u(r)$ and $g(r)$ all give

$$u_0(r) = \ln g(r) \tag{6.43}$$

as a significant approximation for small r extending into the region of the first rising slope of $g(r)$. This observation is supported by two facts concerning the observed $g(r)$ and simple trial forms for $u(r)$ [15]. The first is that the observed behavior of $g(r)$ on the initial rising slope fits the form $A \exp[-(d/r)^{10}]$ quite well. The second is that the trial form $u(r) = -\Lambda(d/r)^n$ in conjunction with experimental $g(r)$ produces a maximum value of the functional $J(u)$ for $n = 10$. However it must be mentioned that $n = 5$ is required for small r ($r \ll \rho^{-1/3}$) to balance the inverse-twelfth-power term in the potential. McMillan [1] and also Schiff and Verlet [4] are guided by this condition in the construction of a parameterized $u(r)$ function.

Massey [3], considering that the fit to the rising slope of $g(r)$ is the physically significant condition, chooses the exponential function $\exp[-(d/r)^{10}]$ as the basic ingredient in constructing a family of trial functions. Following Massey's treatment [3], we write

$$g(r) = g_0(r) + \delta g_1(r) \tag{6.44}$$

subject to

$$\rho \int [g_0(r) - 1]\, d\mathbf{r} = -1, \qquad \int \delta g_1(r)\, d\mathbf{r} = 0 \tag{6.45}$$

and choose the explicit forms

$$g_0(r) = (1 + D) \exp\left[-\left(\frac{d}{r}\right)^{10}\right] - D \exp\left[-(1 + x)\left(\frac{d}{r}\right)^{10}\right]$$
$$\delta g_1(r) = A\left\{\left(\frac{d}{r}\right)^{m} \exp\left[-(1 + y)\left(\frac{d}{r}\right)^{10}\right] - B\left(\frac{d}{r}\right)^{n} \exp\left[-(1 + z)\left(\frac{d}{r}\right)^{10}\right]\right\} \tag{6.46}$$

The normalization condition on $g_0(r)$ requires

$$D = \frac{1 - 3/2(-0.3)!\,\eta}{(1 + x)^{0.3} - 1}, \qquad \eta = 2\pi\rho d^3 \tag{6.47}$$

leaving two parameters η and x in $g(r)$ to vary in the extremum problem for the total energy. The function $g_0(r)$ possesses a single peak value of magnitude

$$g_{0,\,\max} = \frac{x}{D^{1/x}} \left(\frac{1+D}{1+x}\right)^{1+(1/x)} \tag{6.48}$$

at the point

$$\left(\frac{r}{d}\right)_{0,\,\max} = \left[\frac{1}{x} \ln \frac{(1+x)D}{1+D}\right]^{-1/10} \tag{6.49}$$

In general, $g_0(r)$ is not sufficiently flexible to allow a good representation of the nearest-neighbor peak, The second function $\delta g_1(r)$ is capable of generating a broad range of nearest-neighbor peaks and one following valley. Equation (6.45) requires

$$B = \frac{[(m-13)/10]!\,(1+z)^{(n-13)/10}}{[(n-13)/10]!\,(1+y)^{(m-13)/10}} \tag{6.50}$$

leaving five parameters to locate and shape the nearest-neighbor peak and valley.

Massey's search of the parameter space began with $m = 16$ and $n = 8$ because these values were favored slightly by a direct fit of $g_0(r) + \delta g_1(r)$ to the observed radial distribution function. Succeeding trials with smaller values of m produced a slightly lower energy at $m = 6$ for n fixed at 8. Readers interested in the detailed search program and the extensive numerical results should consult Massey's paper and his Washington University thesis. These calculations are all based on the potential parameters determined by condition 2. In general, the agreement between theory and experiment is moderately good (this statement covers the equation of state, pressure, compressibility, velocity of first sound, liquid structure function, and radial distribution function).

Similar calculations under condition 1 by Massey and Woo [5] make possible a direct comparison with the analysis and results of McMillan [1] and Schiff and Verlet [4] (as exhibited in Table 6-2). For ^{4}He the differences between the MW and SV results are small; for ^{3}He, on the contrary, they are appreciable, and perhaps indicate that the use of the superposition approximation for $p^{(3)}$ in evaluating the kinetic energy overestimates that quantity by 0.5–1.0 °K/atom. Nevertheless, no comparable differences show up in the theoretical determinations of the liquid structure functions. Further clarification is desirable.

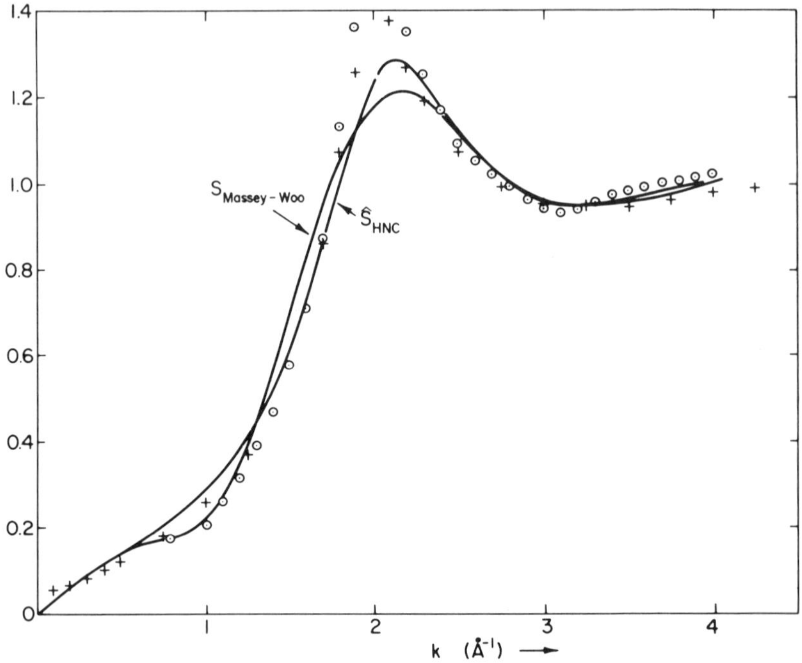

FIG. 6-1. Liquid structure function of liquid ^{4}He for the de Boer-Michels force parameters (condition 1) at the equilibrium density ($\rho = 0.0218$ Å^{-3}): $S(k)$—computed by Massey and Woo from a BDJ-type trial function; $\hat{S}(k)$—computed by Campbell using the paired-phonon analysis [Eq. (5.53)] and the hypernetted chain relation [Eq. (5.73)]. Experiment: ⊙ Neutron diffraction, 1.06°K, D. G. Henshaw, *Phys. Rev.* **119**, 9 (1960). + X-ray diffraction, 1.4°K, W. L. Gordon, C. H. Shaw, J. G. Daunt, *Phys. Chem. Solids* **5**, 117 (1958).

From a bystander's point of view it appears that the starting trial function $g_0(r)$ could be improved by adding a third exponential term which is negligible in the region of the nearest-neighbor peak:

$$g_0(r) = (1 + D) \exp - \left[- \left(\frac{d}{r} \right)^n \right] - D \exp \left[- \left(\frac{d'}{r} \right)^n \right]$$
$$- D' \left\{ \exp \left[- \left(\frac{d'}{r} \right)^n \right] - \exp \left[- \left(\frac{d''}{r} \right)^n \right] \right\} \tag{6.51}$$

with, very roughly, $d' \approx 2d$ and $d'' \approx 3d$. The modified $g_0(r)$ retains the advantage of simple explicit analytical formulas for the potential energy and the normalization condition. With more freedom in the parameter D, $g_0(r)$ should be capable of giving a good account of the initial rising slope and the first peak. The rigid constraints on $\delta g_1(r)$ would then be relaxed somewhat, allowing the extremum condition on the expectation value of H to generate a better representation of the first valley in $g(r)$ following the nearest-neighbor peak.

Before leaving this topic it is worth mentioning that the extremum property of $\langle H\rangle$ may get lost if approximate forms for $g(r)$ as a functional in u fail the normalization condition in an uncontrolled manner. The observation of this effect [16] motivated the development of the inverse procedure in which $u(r)$ in Eq. (6.6) is represented as a functional in $g(r)$.

6.7. CORRECTIONS TO $\langle 0|H|0\rangle$

The theoretical estimates of $E_0{}^{\mathrm{B}}$ are all given as expectation values of H with respect to directly or indirectly parameterized trial functions of the BDJ type. Several corrections are necessary before the comparison of $E_0{}^{\mathrm{B}}$ with experiment is meaningful, and these are now discussed.

A. Energy Generated by the Three-Phonon Vertex

This is a second-order energy correction generated by the matrix elements $\langle \mathbf{k}, \boldsymbol{l}, -\mathbf{k}-\boldsymbol{l}|H-\langle 0|H|0\rangle|0\rangle$ connecting a product-type trial function $|0\rangle$ with excited-state trial functions $\rho_{\mathbf{k}}\rho_{\boldsymbol{l}}\rho_{\mathbf{k}-\boldsymbol{l}}|0\rangle$. The matrix elements and energy correction are evaluated in Appendix 5-C in association with the paired-phonon analysis. Numerical results for ^{4}He estimated by Davison [16] appear in Table 6-6. These are based on the Massey-Woo [5] determination of the liquid structure function and tentative estimates by Campbell [18] of the correction to $S(k)$ produced by the paired-phonon analysis. Numerical results are not available for mass 3, but are expected to be of comparable magnitude (-0.5 to -1.0°K/atom).

B. Three Particle Polarization Energy

Consider three helium atoms with centers fixed at $\mathbf{r}_a$, $\mathbf{r}_b$, and $\mathbf{r}_c$, respectively. The potential energy of this system is

$$v(r_{ab}) + v(\mathbf{r}_{bc}) + v(r_{ca}) + \omega(\mathbf{r}_{ab}, \mathbf{r}_{bc}, \mathbf{r}_{ca}) \tag{6.52}$$

Here $v(r)$ includes the long-range two-particle polarization energy and the strong short-range repulsion produced by the promotion of two electrons

TABLE 6-6

THREE-PHONON AND THREE-PARTICLE POLARIZATION ENERGY CORRECTIONS (in °K/atom)

ρ (Å^{-3})	Three-phonon energy correction (Appendix 5-C)	Three-particle polarization Energy [Eq. (6.56)]
0.0218	−0.76	0.85
0.0226	−0.80	0.95
0.0234	−0.88	1.05
0.0242	−0.96	1.16
0.0250	−1.08	1.28
0.0258	−1.21	1.41

out of the K shells when the electron distributions of the two atoms overlap. The presence of a third particle modifies the induced polarization, which generates the two-particle polarization potential and leads to the three-particle polarization potential ω. This component has the form [19]–[21]

$$\omega_{abc} = \nu_3 \frac{3 \cos(ab, ac) \cos(ba, bc) \cos(ca, cb) + 1}{r_{ab}^{\,3}\, r_{bc}^{\,3}\, r_{ac}^{\,3}} \tag{6.53}$$

The best theoretical estimate of ν_3 for three helium atoms (in atomic units of energy and length) is 1.49 (see [20]). The equivalent coefficient when energy is expressed in degrees Kelvin and length in angstroms is 1530. Axelrod [19] has evaluated the total potential energy generated by ω_{abc} in static fcc and hcp lattices. The result is

$$\frac{1}{3!} \sum_{abc}' \omega_{abc} = N \frac{56.7 \times 1530}{3 r_0^{\,9}} \quad °\mathrm{K} \tag{6.54}$$

with r_0, the nearest-neighbor distance, expressed in angstroms. To convert Eq. (6.54) into a semiquantitative estimate of the three-particle polarization energy for the liquid, we observe that the relation between nearest-neighbor distance and number density for the face-centered-cubic lattice,

$$r_0 = (\sqrt{2}\rho)^{-1/3} \tag{6.55}$$

is also highly accurate for liquid ^{4}He if r_0 is identified with the location of the first maximum in the radial distribution function ($r_0 \approx 3.20$ Å, $\rho_0 = 0.0218$ Å^{-3}). This identification yields the estimate

$$(1/N)\left\langle (1/3!) \sum_{abc}{}' \, \omega_{abc} \right\rangle \approx 0.85(\rho/\rho_0)^3 \quad {}^\circ\mathrm{K} \tag{6.56}$$

Parallel columns in Table 6-6 show that the three-phonon correction to the energy and the three-particle polarization correction to the energy are opposite in sign and nearly equal in magnitude over the density range in which liquid ^{4}He exists. The fortuitous good cancellation has the consequence that the direct comparison of $E_0{}^{\mathrm{B}}$ and E_{exp} is meaningful. Equally good cancellation at mass 3 is extremely unlikely.

C. *Progress from the Available to the Optimum BDJ-type Trial Functions*

The available trial functions for the boson ground state, all of the BDJ product type, are certainly not the best of that type as measured by the expectation value of H. The paired-phonon analysis as developed in Chapter 5 transforms an initial BDJ-type trial function into an improved function of the same type. Campbell [18] has obtained tentative numerical estimates of the energy correction generated by the paired-phonon analysis in the ^{4}He problem starting from the Massey-Woo [5] trial function. At the equilibrium density the correction generated by both the HNC and the PY procedures amounts to -0.7 °K/atom, bringing the estimated total energy down to -6.7°K. Part of the remaining descrepancy can be blamed on the unrealistic shape of the repulsive term in the Lennard-Jones potential, but how much is uncertain. A more likely source of a substantial correction is the third-order energy shift generated by the three-phonon vertex. This quantity is neglected, not because of any objective argument that it should be small, but simply because it is difficult to evaluate.

A brief summary of high points in Campbell's analysis follows.

The HNC *Procedure* [Eqs. (5.73)–(5.77)]

The starting functions are $g(r)$, $S(k)$, and $u(r)$ determined by Massey and Woo using the de Boer–Michels force parameters. Equations (5.3), (5.73), and (5.75) yield $u_{\mathrm{HNC}}(r|g)$ and $V_k{}^*(g, u_{\mathrm{HNC}})$. The function $L(k|g, u_{\mathrm{HNC}})$ is computed and used to evaluate $\omega(k)$ [Eq. (5.19)], $\hat{S}(k)$ and $\hat{g}(r)$ [Eq. (5.53)], and $\delta u(r)$ [Eq. (5.71)]. The energy shift for the ground state at $\rho = 0.0218$ Å^{-3} is $(1/N)(H_{\mathrm{D}} - E_0) = -0.68$ °K/atom [Eq. (5.43)]. The associated separation parameter has the value $\xi = 0.03$ [Eq. (5.67)].

The HNC relation is not closed under the transformations of the paired-phonon analysis. Thus the function

$$\hat{u}_{\mathrm{HNC}}(r) = \ln \hat{g}(r) - \frac{1}{(2\pi)^3 \rho} \int (\exp i\mathbf{k}\cdot\mathbf{r}) \frac{[\hat{S}(k) - 1]^2}{\hat{S}(k)} \, d\mathbf{k} \tag{6.57}$$

is not expected to coincide with $u_{\mathrm{HNC}}(r) + \delta u(r)$, and it does not; however, the difference is not great.

A consistency test is provided by the equations

$$\begin{aligned} (1/N)E(g, u_{\mathrm{HNC}}) &= (\hbar^2\rho/8m)J_1(g, u_{\mathrm{HNC}}) + \tfrac{1}{2}\rho \int gv \, d\mathbf{r} \\ (1/N)E(\hat{g}, \hat{u}_{\mathrm{HNC}}) &= (\hbar^2\rho/8m)J_1(\hat{g}, \hat{u}_{\mathrm{HNC}}) + \tfrac{1}{2}\rho \int \hat{g}v \, d\mathbf{r} \end{aligned} \tag{6.58}$$

Numerical values of the matrix elements in Eq. (6.58) are listed in Table 6-7.

TABLE 6-7

ENERGY QUANTITIES (in °K/atom) AT $\rho = 0.0218$ Å^{-3}

Trial functions	$(\hbar^2\rho/8m)J_1$	$\frac{1}{2}\rho \int gv \, d\mathbf{r}$	E/N [Eq. (6.58)]
g, u_{HNC}	16.63	−20.03	−3.40
$\hat{g}$, $\hat{u}_{\mathrm{HNC}}$	16.64	−20.69	−4.05

The energy displacement is

$$(1/N)[E(\hat{g}, \hat{u}_{\mathrm{HNC}}) - E(g, u_{\mathrm{HNC}})] = -0.65 \quad °\mathrm{K/atom}$$

in close agreement with $(1/N)(H_D - E_0)$. The values in Table 6–7 indicate that the gain in energy produced by the paired-phonon analysis is mostly potential, with little change in the mean kinetic energy.

An iteration of the paired-phonon analysis starting from $\hat{S}(k)$ and $\hat{g}(r)$ yields an additional energy shift of −0.04 °K/atom, a separation parameter $\xi \approx 0.0005$, and essentially no change in the liquid structure function.

Figure 6-1 exhibits plots of $S(k)$ and $\hat{S}(k)$. These illustrate how the paired-phonon analysis smooths and sharpens the liquid structure function, raising the nearest-neighbor peak and reducing the hump on the first rising slope. Reference 18 contains tables and diagrams illustrating the manner in which successive iterations of the paired-phonon analysis converge to an optimum solution. Most striking are plots showing the large difference between $S'(k)$ and $(\hbar^2k^2/2m)[1 - S(k)]$ and the near equality of $\hat{S}'(k)$ and $(\hbar^2k^2/2m)[1 - \hat{S}(k)]$.

Quite similar numerical results are generated by the PY procedure with, however, only a qualitative check supplied by the analog of Eq. (6.58).

Still lacking is a direct verification by Monte Carlo or molecular-dynamics techniques that $u(r)+\delta u(r)$ generates a radial distribution function close to $\hat{g}(r)$ and an improved value for the energy. I suggest that the combination of molecular-dynamics techniques (for rigor) and the paired-phonon analysis (for systematic guidance) offers a practical route for a close approach in a rigorous context to the optimum pair-type trial function. In the present computer-oriented age, with rapidly increasing computer speed and capacity, it is relatively easy to use the computer to solve precisely defined numerical problems. To think in terms of optimum solutions is to enormously enhance the intellectual significance of the computer as well as the general usefulness of the results.

References

1. W. L. McMillan, *Phys. Rev.* **138**, A442 (1965).
2. D. Levesque, T. Khiet, D. Schiff, and L. Verlet, Orsay preprint (1965).
3. W. E. Massey, unpublished doctoral dissertation, Washington University, 1966; *Phys. Rev.* **151**, 153 (1966).
4. D. Schiff and L. Verlet, *Phys. Rev.* **160**, 208 (1967).
5. W. E. Massey and C. W. Woo, *Phys. Rev.* **164**, 256 (1967).
6. J. de Boer and A. Michels, *Physica* **5**, 945 (1938).
7. D. Hirschfelder, C. Curtiss, and R. Bird, "Molecular Theory of Gases and Liquids," Wiley, New York, 1964.
8. R. Haberlandt, *Phys. Letters* **14**, 197 (1965).
9. J. E. Kilpatrick and M. F. Kilpatrick, *J. Chem. Phys.* **19**, 930 (1951).
10. E. Meeron, *Phys. Fluids* **1**, 139 (1958).
11. T. Morita, *Progr. Theoret. Phys.* (*Kyoto*) **20**, 920 (1958).
12. J. K. Percus and G. J. Yevick, *Phys. Rev.* **110**, 1 (1958).
13. J. W. Clark and T. P. Wang, *Ann. Phys.* (*N.Y.*) **40**, 127 (1966).
14. R. Abe, *Progr. Theoret. Phys.* (*Kyoto*) **19**, 407 (1958).
15. F. Y. Wu and E. Feenberg, *Phys. Rev.* **122**, 739 (1961).
16. T. B. Davison, unpublished doctoral dissertation, Washington University, 1968; T. B. Davison and E. Feenberg, *Ann. Phys.* (*N.Y.*) **53,** 559 (1969).
17. C. D. Williams, unpublished doctoral dissertation, Washington University, 1961.
18. C. E. Campbell, unpublished doctoral dissertation, Washington University, 1968.
19. B. M. Axelrod, *J. Chem. Phys.* **19**, 724 (1951).
20. A. Dalgarno and G. A. Victor, *Molec. Phys.* **10**, 333 (1966).
21. H. Margenau and J. Stamper, *Advan. Quantum Chem.* **3**, 129 (1967).

CHAPTER 7

The Uniform Limit and the Charged Boson System

7.1. INTRODUCTION

The discussion in the preceding chapter is strongly oriented toward the numerical solution of real physical problems. However, something can be learned by considering extreme conditions far removed from the realities of the helium liquids. One such condition is the uniform limit already defined and analyzed in Chapter 2, where it was used to derive the HNC connection between u and g.

A physical basis for the uniform limit can be found in low density and weak interaction, as in the usual statement of conditions for the validity of the Bogoliubov treatment of the interacting boson system. Also, as pointed out by Foldy [1] and Lieb [2], uniform behavior is produced by high density in conjunction with some weak constraints on the potential. Here the theory is developed under the convenient assumption that the potential function $v(r)$ possesses a Fourier transform:

$$V(k) = \int (\exp i\mathbf{k} \cdot \mathbf{r}) v(r) \, d\mathbf{r} \tag{7.1}$$

7.2. EXPECTATION VALUE OF H IN THE UNIFORM LIMIT*

The definitions and notations of Eq. (2.20), (2.35), and (2.36) enable us to write for the expectation value of the potential energy

* See Lee [3].

$$\langle \text{P.E.} \rangle = \frac{1}{2} N\rho \int g(r)v(r)\, d\mathbf{r}$$

$$= \frac{1}{2} N\rho V(0) + \frac{1}{2} N\rho \int [g(r)-1]v(r)\, d\mathbf{r}$$

$$= \frac{1}{2} N\rho V(0) + \frac{1}{2}\frac{N}{(2\pi)^3} \int [S(k)-1]V(k)\, d\mathbf{k}$$

$$= \frac{1}{2} N\rho V(0) - \frac{\alpha\rho N}{4\pi^2} \int_0^\infty F(q)V(\alpha^{1/3}\rho^{1/3}q)q^2\, dq \tag{7.2}$$

Similarly, the expectation value of the kinetic energy (in the notation appropriate to discussing the uniform limit) is

$$\langle \text{K.E.} \rangle = N(\hbar^2\rho/8m) \int \nabla u \cdot \nabla g\, d\mathbf{r}$$

$$= -N[\hbar^2(\alpha\rho)^{2/3}/8m] \int \nabla\mathscr{Y}(s)\cdot\nabla G\, d\mathbf{s}$$

$$= -N[\hbar^2(\alpha\rho)^{2/3}/(4\pi)^3 m] \int q^2 Z(q)F(q)\, d\mathbf{q} \tag{7.3}$$

At this point the HNC connection between $u(r)$ and $g(r)$, Eq. (2.48), is used to reduce the expectation value of the kinetic energy to an explicit functional in $g(r)$. The total energy then appears as an explicit functional in $g(r)$:

$$\frac{1}{N}\left[\mathscr{E} - \frac{1}{2} N\rho V(0)\right] = \frac{\hbar^2(\alpha\rho)^{2/3}}{(4\pi)^3 m} \int q^2 F(q)\left[\frac{\alpha F(q)}{1-F(q)} + \frac{1}{2}\alpha^2(F_2(q) + \cdots\right] d\mathbf{q}$$

$$- \frac{\alpha\rho}{16\pi^3} \int F(q)V(\alpha^{1/3}\rho^{1/3}q)\, d\mathbf{q} \tag{7.4}$$

A third-order term in the power series for $Z(q)$ could be included, since the coefficient Z_3 is given explicitly by Eq. (2.45). To avoid undue complications, the discussion is continued retaining only linear and quadratic terms in α in the series formula for $Z(q)$. However, it must be emphasized that Z_1, Z_2, and Z_3 are given correctly as functionals in g, within the limitations imposed by the use of a BDJ-type trial function in computing the expectation values.

The structure of the integrands in Eq. (7.4) reveals that the optimum function $F(q)$ can depend on α only through the variable $k = (\alpha\rho)^{1/3}q$. Consequently, Eq. (7.4) can be expressed simply in terms of the variable

k and the liquid structure function $S(k) = 1 - F(q)$:

$$\frac{\mathscr{E}}{N} = \frac{1}{2}\rho V(0) + \frac{1}{N}[\mathscr{E}_0 + \mathscr{E}_1 + \cdots] \tag{7.5}$$

$$\frac{\mathscr{E}_0}{N} = \frac{\hbar^2}{(4\pi)^3 m\rho}\int\left[k^2\frac{[S(k)-1]^2}{S(k)} + 4m\rho[S(k)-1]V(k)\right] dk \tag{7.6}$$

$$\frac{\mathscr{E}_1}{N} = \frac{\hbar^2}{2(8\pi^2)^3 m\rho^2}\int k^2[1-S(k)][1-S(k')][1-S(\mathbf{k}'-\mathbf{k})]\, d\mathbf{k}\, d\mathbf{k}'$$

$$= \frac{\hbar^2\rho}{16m}\int [g(r)-1]^2\, \Delta g(r)\, d\mathbf{r} \tag{7.7}$$

The "smallness" parameter α is invisible in Eqs. (7.6) and (7.7). Nevertheless, it still occurs in the condition $|g(0)-1| \ll 1$ sufficient for the validity of physical results generated by the two equations. How far this condition is also necessary must be considered an open question in view of the usefulness of the HNC connection under realistic conditions on density and strength of interaction.

In the k, $S(k)$ notation the supplementary conditions

$$G(0) = (2\pi)^{-3}\int F(q)\, d\mathbf{q} = 1, \qquad F(0) = \int G(s)\, d\mathbf{s} = 1 \tag{7.8}$$

become

$$\alpha = [1/2\pi^2\rho]\int_0^\infty [1-S(k)]k^2\, dk, \qquad S(0) = 0 \tag{7.9}$$

7.3. OPTIMUM CHOICE OF THE LIQUID STRUCTURE FUNCTION

To the lowest order in α, the optimum liquid structure function is determined by the condition for minimum $\mathscr{E}_0$:

$$\int_0^\infty \delta S(k)\left\{\frac{\hbar^2k^2}{4m\rho}\left[1 - \frac{1}{S^2(k)}\right] + V(k) + \frac{\hbar^2k^2}{4m\rho}\frac{\delta S(k)}{S^3(k)}\right\}k^2\, dk \geq 0 \tag{7.10}$$

or

$$S_0(k) = \{1 + [4m\rho V(k)/\hbar^2k^2]\}^{-1/2} \tag{7.11}$$

provided that

$$2\rho V(k) + (\hbar^2 k^2/2m) \geq 0 \tag{7.12}$$

Equation (7.12) requires $V(0) > 0$; in addition, Eqs. (7.9) and (7.11) define α as a function of ρ:

$$\alpha = \frac{1}{2\pi^2 \rho} \int_0^\infty \left\{ 1 - \left[1 + \frac{4m\rho V(k)}{\hbar^2 k^2} \right]^{-1/2} \right\} k^2 \, dk \tag{7.13}$$

Now the density range in which $\alpha \ll 1$ can be computed when the interaction potential is known.

The energy formula reduces to

$$\begin{aligned} \frac{\mathscr{E}_0}{N} &= \frac{1}{2} \rho V(0) - \frac{\hbar^2}{16\pi^2 m\rho} \int_0^\infty \left[1 - \frac{1}{S(k)} \right]^2 k^4 \, dk \\ &= \frac{1}{2} \rho V(0) - \frac{1}{2\rho(2\pi)^3} \int \left\{ \frac{\hbar^2 k^2}{2m} + \rho V(k) - \left[\left(\frac{\hbar^2 k^2}{2m} \right)^2 \right. \right. \\ &\quad \left. \left. + 2 \frac{\hbar^2 k^2}{2m} \rho V(k) \right]^{1/2} \right\} d\mathbf{k} \end{aligned} \tag{7.14}$$

the second line reproducing the classical result of Bogoliubov. Equation (7.14) can be interpreted as giving the energy density $\rho\mathscr{E}_0/N$ as a function of particle density. Thus the compressibility K is easily computed:

$$\begin{aligned} K^{-1} &= \rho^2 \frac{\partial^2}{\partial \rho^2} \frac{\rho \mathscr{E}_0}{N} \\ &= \rho^2 V(0) - \frac{m\rho^2}{2\pi^2 \hbar^2} \int_0^\infty \frac{V(k)^2 \, dk}{\{1 + [4m\rho V(k)/\hbar^2 k^2]\}^{3/2}} \end{aligned} \tag{7.15}$$

Since the compressibility is necessarily positive, Eq. (7.15) implies the inequality

$$\int v(r) \, d\mathbf{r} > \frac{m}{2\pi^2 \hbar^2} \int_0^\infty \frac{V(k)^2 \, dk}{\{1 + [4m\rho V(k)/\hbar^2 k^2]\}^{3/2}} \tag{7.16}$$

which is satisfied in the limit $\rho \to 0$ if $v(r)$ is sufficiently weak. The opposite extreme, $\rho \to \infty$, places no restriction on $v(r)$ [beyond the necessary condition $V(0) > 0$].

The Bijl–Feynman formula for the energy of an elementary excitation (as derived in Chapter 5 for the BDJ-type trial function) yields

$$e(k) = \left[\left(\frac{\hbar^2 k^2}{2m}\right)^2 + 2\frac{\hbar^2 k^2}{2m}\rho V(k)\right]^{1/2} \tag{7.17}$$

in agreement with Bogoliubov and Zubarev [4]. Equation (7.17) defines the velocity of first sound as

$$c = [\rho V(0)/m]^{1/2} \tag{7.18}$$

consistent with Eqs. (7.15) only if the inequality in Eq. (7.16) is strong ($\gg$ rather than merely $>$).

To find a sufficient condition for associating uniform behavior with low density, observe that Eq. (7.13) reduces to

$$\alpha \approx (m/\pi^2\hbar^2)\int_0^\infty V(k)\,dk \tag{7.19}$$

as $\rho \to 0$. The inequality

$$(m/\pi^2\hbar^2)\int_0^\infty V(k)\,dk \ll 1 \tag{7.20}$$

implies $\alpha \ll 1$. The relative strengths of the inequalities (7.16) and (7.20) can be tested most simply by introducing a Gaussian form for $v(r)$. In this case Eq. (7.20) is a stronger condition on $v(r)$ by a factor $2^{3/2}$; consequently, it is safe to conclude that Eq. (7.16) is implied by Eq. (7.20) for a wide class of potential functions.

In the present context the first-order energy correction $\mathscr{E}_1$ (reduced by a factor α compared to $\mathscr{E}_0$) can be evaluated by introducing the zeroth-order liquid structure function $S_0(k)$ in the integral formula of Eq. (7.8). The result is correct to the required order because

$$\mathscr{E}_0(S_0 + \delta S) = \mathscr{E}_0(S_0) + O[(\delta S)^2] \tag{7.21}$$

and hence $\mathscr{E}_0(S_0 + \delta S)$ differs from $\mathscr{E}_0(S_0)$ by terms of order α^2.

The notion of a single-particle orbital has not been used in the preceding analysis. However, the occupation number $n(k)$ of the single-particle plane wave orbital with momentum $\hbar\mathbf{k}$ is implicit in the momentum-space evaluation of the kinetic energy integral [Eqs. (7.3)–(7.6)]. To obtain $n(k)$ from Eq. (7.6), first let N_0 denote the occupation number of the ground-state single-particle orbital ($k=0$). The relative depletion of the ground-state orbital is simply

$$\frac{N-N_0}{N}=\frac{1}{N}\sum_{\mathbf{k}\neq 0} n(k)=\frac{1}{(2\pi)^3\rho}\int n(k)\, d\mathbf{k} \tag{7.22}$$

and

$$\frac{1}{N}\langle \text{K.E.}\rangle=\frac{1}{(2\pi)^3\rho}\frac{\hbar^2}{2m}\int k^2 n(k)\, d\mathbf{k} \tag{7.23}$$

The comparison of Eqs. (7.6) and (7.23) gives us

$$n(k)=[S(k)-1]^2/4S(k), \qquad k>0 \tag{7.24}$$

subject to $\alpha \ll 1$ and $S(k)$ defined by Eq. (7.11). The same formula for $n(k)$ can be derived in the context of the Bogoliubov treatment of the boson system.

The identification of the coefficient of k^2 in Eq. (7.23) as $n(k)$ may be questioned on the ground that the integrand might include a term $\Delta_{\mathbf{k}}\varphi(\mathbf{k})$ which contributes nothing to the value of the integral. To overcome this objection, I compute the kinetic energy in a moving reference frame; this means (1) replacing k^2 in Eq. (7.23) by $[\mathbf{k}+(m\mathbf{v}_0/\hbar)]^2$, where $-v_0$ is the velocity of the moving frame, and (2) adding a term $\frac{1}{2}N_0 M v_0{}^2$ for the kinetic energy of the ground-state component. The coefficient of $v_0{}^2$ gives an unambiguous identification of $n(k)$ in agreement with Eq. (7.24).

7.4. THE YUKAWA POTENTIAL

The potential function is now specialized to

$$\begin{aligned} v(r) &= Z^2e^2\,(\exp - k_0 r)/r \\ V(k) &= 4\pi Z^2 e^2/(k_0{}^2+k^2) \end{aligned} \tag{7.25}$$

To simplify the notation, let

$$r_s=\left(\frac{3}{4\pi\rho}\right)^{1/3}, \qquad t=\left[\frac{1}{12Z^2}\frac{\hbar^2}{me^2}r_s{}^3\right]^{1/4}k, \qquad t_0=\left[\frac{1}{12Z^2}\frac{\hbar^2}{me^2}r_s{}^3\right]^{1/4}k_0 \tag{7.26}$$

and measure r_s and k_0^{-1} in Bohr units of length ($\hbar^2/me^2 = 0.5292 \times 10^{-8}$ cm if m and e are identified with the mass and charge of the electron respectively). Equation (7.13) for α becomes

$$\alpha = r_s^{3/4} Z^{3/2} \frac{4}{\pi} \left(\frac{4}{3}\right)^{1/4} \int_0^\infty \left\{1 - \frac{t(t^2 + t_0{}^2)^{1/2}}{[1 + t^2(t^2 + t_0{}^2)]^{1/2}}\right\} t^2\, dt$$

$$\leq r_s^{3/4} Z^{3/2} \frac{4}{\pi} \left(\frac{4}{3}\right)^{1/4} \int_0^\infty \left[1 - \frac{t^2}{(1 + t^4)^{1/2}}\right] t^2\, dt \tag{7.27}$$

Consider now a general potential $v(r)$ with Fourier transform $V(k)$ subject to the inequality of Eq. (7.12). Suppose a parameter Ze can be chosen so that $|V(k)|$ is dominated by $4\pi(Ze)^2/k^2$. Equations (7.13) and (7.27) show that α is dominated by an explicit upper bound of order $r_s^{3/4}$. Thus uniform limiting behavior occurs at sufficiently high density $[(r_s Z^2)^{3/4} \ll 1]$.

It will be noticed that a direct appeal to Eq. (7.13) in the limit $\rho \to \infty$ produces an indeterminant form ∞/∞ for the right-hand member; the advantage gained by introducing the dominating Coulomb potential is the replacement of the indeterminate form by a definite explicit function of density.

7.5. THE CHARGED BOSON SYSTEM*

The problem of the charged boson system at high density was first discussed by Foldy [1] in the context of the Bogoliubov approximation, and later by Girardeau [5] in the pair approximation. Lieb and Sakakura [6] derived the zeroth-order energy formula in configuration space. The following discussion is based largely on the uniform-limit analysis of Lee and Feenberg (Chapter 2) and the paired-phonon analysis of Jackson and Feenberg (Chapter 5).

The occurrence of $V(0)$ in Eq. (7.14) leads to an infinite energy when $V(k)$ is singular at the origin. To avoid this difficulty, the charged system is modified to include a uniform static charge distribution with total charge $-NZe$. The energy of assembly of the uniform background charge and the interaction energy of particles and background charge are included

* See Lee [3].

in the potential energy; thus

$$V(1, 2, \ldots, N) = \sum_{i<j} \frac{Z^2e^2}{r_{ij}} - \rho Z^2e^2 \sum_i \int \frac{d\mathbf{r}}{|\mathbf{r}_i - \mathbf{r}|} + \frac{1}{2}\rho^2 Z^2 e^2 \int \frac{d\mathbf{r}\, d\mathbf{r}'}{|\mathbf{r} - \mathbf{r}'|} \tag{7.28}$$

and

$$\begin{aligned} \langle \text{P.E.} \rangle &= \tfrac{1}{2}\rho^2 Z^2 e^2 \int [g(r_{12}) - 1](1/r_{12})\, d\mathbf{r}_1\, d\mathbf{r}_2 \\ &= \tfrac{1}{2} N\rho Z^2 e^2 \int [g(r) - 1](1/r)\, d\mathbf{r} \\ &= (1/\pi) N Z^2 e^2 \int_0^\infty [S(k) - 1]\, dk \end{aligned} \tag{7.29}$$

Equation (7.14) remains valid if the term in $V(0)$ is deleted.

Using the notation of Eq. (7.26), the zeroth-order energy formula reduces to

$$\begin{aligned} \frac{\mathscr{E}_0}{N} &= \frac{2}{\pi} 12^{1/4} \frac{Z^{5/2}}{r_s^{3/4}} \left\{ \int_0^\infty \left[1 - \frac{t^2}{(1+t^4)^{1/2}}\right]^2 (1+t^4)^{1/2} t^2\, dt \right. \\ &\qquad \left. - \int_0^\infty \left[1 - \frac{t^2}{(1+t^4)^{1/2}}\right] dt \right\} \\ &= -\frac{8}{\pi} 12^{1/4} \frac{Z^{5/2}}{r_s^{3/4}} \int_0^\infty \left[1 - \frac{t^2}{(1+t^4)^{1/2}}\right]^2 (1+t^4)^{1/2} t^2\, dt \end{aligned} \tag{7.30}$$

with energy in hydrogenic units ($me^4/2\hbar^2 = 13.60$ eV) and length in Bohr units.

The integrals occurring in Eqs. (7.27) and (7.30) can be reduced to beta functions and these in turn expressed in terms of gamma functions (Appendix 7.A). The numerical values are

$$\begin{aligned} &\int_0^\infty \left[1 - \frac{t^2}{(1+t^4)^{1/2}}\right] t^2\, dt = 0.6180 \\ &\int_0^\infty \left[1 - \frac{t^2}{(1+t^4)^{1/2}}\right] dt = 5 \int_0^\infty \left[1 - \frac{t^2}{(1+t^4)^{1/2}}\right]^2 (1+t^4)^{1/2} t^2\, dt \\ &\qquad = 0.8472 \end{aligned} \tag{7.31}$$

Equation (7.31) implies the physical statement

$$\langle \text{K.E.} \rangle_0 = -\tfrac{1}{5} \langle \text{P.E.} \rangle_0 \tag{7.32}$$

In other words, the negative of the mean potential energy equals five times the mean kinetic energy.

This statement bears a certain resemblance to the corresponding 2 : 1 ratio implied by the virial theorem for isolated charged systems (i.e., isolated atoms or molecules). Isolation means, of course, no external constraint, whereas the charged boson system is confined to a box, and hence is subject to an external pressure (in fact, a negative pressure).

The result stated in Eq. (7.32) cannot be accepted as an inexplicable gift from the theory of special functions. A physical basis must be sought in the extremum property of the expectation value and the special way in which the free parameters in the trial function enter the problem. Since α is the only free parameter, we examine the functional dependence of $\mathscr{E}_0$ on α when $V(\alpha^{1/3}\rho^{1/3}q)$ in Eq. (7.7) is replaced by $4\pi Z^2e^2/\alpha^{2/3}\rho^{2/3}q^2$:

$$\frac{\mathscr{E}_0}{N} = \alpha^{5/3}\frac{\hbar^2\rho^{2/3}}{4\pi^2 m}\int_0^\infty \frac{q^4F(q)\,dq}{1-F(q)} - \alpha^{1/3}\frac{Z^2e^2\rho^{1/3}}{\pi}\int_0^\infty F(q)\,dq \tag{7.33}$$

Now the function $F(q)$ is treated as given and only α is available as a variational parameter. Minimum energy with respect to α is found at

$$\alpha^{4/3} = \frac{16\pi}{5}\frac{Z^2e^2m}{\hbar^2\rho^{1/3}}\frac{\int_0^\infty F(q)\,dq}{\int_0^\infty \{q^4F(q)/[1-F(q)]\}\,dq} \tag{7.34}$$

and, because of the 5 : 1 ratio of exponents, Eq. (7.32) is satisfied. The resulting formula for the energy is

$$\frac{\mathscr{E}_0}{N} = -\frac{4}{5\pi}\rho^{1/3}Z^2e^2\left[\frac{16\pi Z^2e^2m}{5\hbar^2}\right]^{1/4}\frac{\left[\int_0^\infty F(q)\,dq\right]^{5/4}}{\left[\int_0^\infty \{q^4F(q)/[1-F(q)]\}\,dq\right]^{1/4}} \tag{7.35}$$

The optimum choice of $F(q)$ as defined by $F(q) = 1 - S_0(k)$ and Eq. (7.11) reduces Eq. (7.35) to Eq. (7.30). Under the same condition the formula for α [Eq. (7.34)] reduces to an identity, leaving Eq. (7.27) to determine α. This verification demonstrates the consistency of the two procedures for proving Eq. (7.32). Notice, however, that the second procedure [varying α for given and fixed $F(q)$] is more general.

Final results for α and $\mathscr{E}_0$ are

$$\alpha = 0.8456 Z^{3/2} r_s^{3/4} \tag{7.36}$$

$$\mathscr{E}_0/N = -0.8031\, Z^{5/2}/r_s^{3/4} \tag{7.37}$$

With $Z=1$, $r_s < \frac{1}{16}$ Bohr units appears to be safely within the range of useful accuracy of Eqs. (7.36)–(7.37).

The Fourier transform of $F(q)$ serves as an integral representation of the radial distribution function. A plot of $G(s)$ against s, computed by numerical integration, appears in [3].

For the charged boson system the relative depletion of the ground-state orbital is

$$\begin{aligned}\frac{N-N_0}{N} &= \frac{1}{8\pi^2\rho}\int_0^\infty \frac{[S(k)-1]^2}{S(k)}\, k^2\, dk \\ &= r_s^{3/4} Z^{3/2}\,\frac{1}{\pi}\left(\frac{4}{3}\right)^{1/4}\int_0^\infty\left[1-\frac{t^2}{(1+t^4)^{1/2}}\right]^2 (1+t^4)^{1/2}\, dt \\ &= 0.2114 Z^{3/2} r_s^{3/4} \qquad (7.38)\end{aligned}$$

in agreement with the result first derived by Foldy. An unexpected property of the Coulomb interaction appears in the relation

$$(N-N_0)/N = \tfrac{1}{4}\alpha = \tfrac{1}{4}[1-g(0)] \qquad (7.39)$$

required by the numerical coefficients in Eqs. (7.27), (7.36), and (7.38). Integration by parts applied to the integral in Eq. (7.38) produces the identity

$$\begin{aligned}\int_0^\infty\left[1-\frac{t^2}{(1+t^4)^{1/2}}\right]^2 (1+t^4)^{1/2}\, dt &= -\int_0^\infty\left[1-\frac{t^2}{(1+t^4)^{1/2}}\right] t^2\, dt \\ &\quad + \int_0^\infty [(1+t^4)^{1/2}-t^2]\, dt \\ &= \int_0^\infty\left[1-\frac{t^2}{(1+t^4)^{1/2}}\right] t^2\, dt \qquad (7.40)\end{aligned}$$

and thus demonstrates that Eq. (7.39) is an exact relation (in the extreme uniform limit).

7.6. FIRST-ORDER ENERGY CORRECTION FOR THE BOSON SYSTEM

The evaluation of $\mathscr{E}_1$ [Eq. (7.7)] has been accomplished by numerical integration. Using the notation of Eq. (7.26) and measuring energy in hydrogen units ($me^4/2\hbar^2$), the formula becomes

$$\frac{\mathscr{E}_1}{N}=\frac{Z^4}{2\pi^4}\int t^2\left[1-\frac{t^2}{(1+t^4)^{1/2}}\right]\left[1-\frac{t'^2}{(1+t'^4)^{1/2}}\right]$$
$$\times\left\{1-\frac{(\mathbf{t}'-\mathbf{t})^2}{[1+(\mathbf{t}'-\mathbf{t})^4]^{1/2}}\right\}d\mathbf{t}\,d\mathbf{t}'$$
$$=\frac{4Z^4}{\pi^2}\int_0^\infty\int_0^\infty tt'\left[1-\frac{t^2}{(1+t^4)^{1/2}}\right]\left[1-\frac{t'^2}{(1+t'^4)^{1/2}}\right]$$
$$\times\int_{|t-t'|}^{t+t'}\left[1-\frac{t''^2}{(1+t''^4)^{1/2}}\right]t''\,dt''\,dt'\,dt$$
$$=\frac{8Z^4}{\pi^2}\int_0^\infty\int_0^\infty tt'\left[1-\frac{t^2}{(1+t^4)^{1/2}}\right]\left[1-\frac{t'^2}{(1+t'^4)^{1/2}}\right]$$
$$\times\left[tt'-\frac{1}{4}\{[1+(t+t')^4]^{1/2}-[1+(t-t')^4]^{1/2}\}\right]dt\,dt'$$
$$=0.028025Z^4 \tag{7.41}$$

The formula for $\mathscr{E}_1$ can be decomposed into a sum of two terms, one generated by the Kirkwood form for $p^{(3)}$ and the other representing the correction introduced by the Abe form. The separate integrals have been evaluated, with the result that the Kirkwood form generates 70% of $\mathscr{E}_1$, the remaining 30% coming from the Abe correction. The complete formula for $\mathscr{E}$ in this order is

$$\mathscr{E}/N=-(0.8031/r_s^{3/4})Z^{5/2}+0.028025Z^4+O(r_s^{3/4}) \tag{7.42}$$

The constant in Eq. (7.42) is the best possible within the range of the BDJ-type trial functions. With inclusion of the remainder $O(r_s^{3/4})$, Eq. (7.42) is an exact expectation value, leaving only the limitations of the BDJ-type trial function to introduce errors into the computed energy.

At this point an informative comparison can be made with a result obtained by Bogoliubov and Zubarev [4]. Using a pairing-type trial function, he finds for $Z=1$

$$\left(\frac{\mathscr{E}}{N}\right)_G=-\frac{0.8031}{r_s^{3/4}}-\frac{1}{8}\ln r_s+O(r_s^{\,0}) \tag{7.43}$$

Notice that the logarithmic term raises the energy (since $r_s\ll 1$). The logarithmic term in Eq. (7.43) has been interpreted as the correct second term in an exact formula for the energy, with the corollary that the derivation of Eq. (7.42) involves an essential error. The logical situation was clarified by Brueckner [7], who showed that the logarithmic term is an artifact of the pairing approximation coupled with an incomplete perturbation calculation. Brueckner starts from the complete set of states defined by the Bogoliubov approximation and uses these states to evaluate first- and second-order terms in the perturbation series for the ground-state energy. The result is that the correct second term in the formula for the energy is a constant (independent of r_s), and, in fact, the same constant as appears in Eq. (7.42) to at least three significant figures. That the two constants are exactly equal has not been proved; if they differ, Brueckner's should be smaller (giving the lower energy).

At intermediate and low densities extensive calculations have been made by D. K. Lee using the functional J and the superposition form p_K to evaluate the kinetic energy [3]. The numerical results for the energy per particle are quite close to Eq. (7.12) over a wide range of r_s values, extending up to the boundary of the region within which $\alpha \leq 1$. At $r_s = 10$ (near where $\alpha = 1$ begins) the numerical procedure yields -0.120, while Eq. (7.42) gives -0.115. The difference is less than 5%.

The charged boson system continues to interest theorists by providing a testing ground for modern perturbation methods [8]–[10].

7.7. FIRST-ORDER CORRECTION TO THE LIQUID STRUCTURE FUNCTION

The function $S(k)$ may be chosen to minimize the total energy $\mathscr{E}_0 + \mathscr{E}_1$, with the result that $S(k)$ is determined by the implicit equation

$$\frac{1}{[S(k)]^2} = 1 + \frac{4m\rho V(k)}{\hbar^2 k^2} - \frac{1}{2(2\pi)^3\rho}\int\left(1 + 2\frac{k'^2}{k^2}\right)[1 - S(k')][1 - S(\mathbf{k}+\mathbf{k}')]\,d\mathbf{k}' \tag{7.44}$$

An obvious iteration procedure yields

$$S(k) = S_0(k) + \delta S(k) + \cdots$$

$$S_0(k) = \{1 + [4m\rho V(k)/\hbar^2 k^2]\}^{-1/2}$$

$$\begin{aligned}\delta S(k) &= \frac{[S_0(k)]^3}{4(2\pi)^3\rho}\int\left(1+2\frac{k'^2}{k^2}\right)[1-S_0(k')][1-S_0(\mathbf{k}+\mathbf{k}')]\,d\mathbf{k}' \\ &\to \alpha\frac{2m\rho V(k)}{\hbar^2k^2}, \qquad k\to\infty \\ &\to \frac{[S_0(k)]^3}{4\pi^2\rho k^2}\int_0^\infty k'^4[1-S_0(k')]^2\,dk', \qquad k\to 0\end{aligned} \tag{7.45}$$

Iterations beyond the first are not justified in the present context [use of p_{A1} of Eq. (2.17) for $p^{(3)}$]. The condition $\delta S(k) \ll S_0(k)$, implicit in the use of the iteration procedure, requires

$$\lim_{k\to 0}\left[\frac{S_0(k)}{2\pi k}\right]^2\frac{1}{\rho}\int_0^\infty k'^4[1-S_0(k')]^2\,dk' \ll 1 \tag{7.46}$$

In the Coulomb problem

$$\begin{aligned}\delta S(k) &= \frac{1}{4\pi^2}\left(\frac{4}{3}\right)^{1/4} Z^{3/2}\, r_s^{3/4}\left[\frac{t^2}{(1+t^4)^{1/2}}\right]^3\int\left(1+2\frac{t'^2}{t^2}\right) \\ &\quad\times\left[1-\frac{t'^2}{(1+t'^4)^{1/2}}\right]\left\{1-\frac{(t+t')^2}{[1+(\mathbf{t}+\mathbf{t}')^4]^{1/2}}\right\}d\mathbf{t}' \\ &\to \alpha/8t^4, \qquad t\gg 1 \\ &\to \alpha t^4\,\frac{2}{\pi}\left(\frac{4}{3}\right)^{1/4}\frac{1}{0.8456}\int_0^\infty t'^4\left[1-\frac{t'^2}{(1+t'^4)^{1/2}}\right]^2 dt' \\ &= 0.076\alpha t^4, \qquad t\ll 1\end{aligned} \tag{7.47}$$

7.8. CORRECTIONS FROM THE "PAIRED-PHONON" ANALYSIS

In the context of the uniform limit the integral equation [Eq. (5.71)] determining the function $S'(k)$ can be solved with sufficient accuracy by a single iteration. First the HNC connection is used in the form

$$u(r) = -\frac{1}{2}[g(r)-1]^2 + \frac{1}{(2\pi)^3\rho}\int(\exp i\mathbf{k}\cdot\mathbf{r})\left[1-\frac{1}{S(k)}\right]d\mathbf{k} + O(\alpha^3) \tag{7.48}$$

to evaluate $V_k{}^*$:

$$V_k{}^* \equiv U_k{}^* + \frac{1}{(2\pi)^3\rho} \int [S(\mathbf{k}' + \mathbf{k}) - 1] U_{k'}^* \, d\mathbf{k}' \tag{7.49}$$

$$\begin{aligned} U_k{}^* &\equiv \rho \int (\exp i\mathbf{k} \cdot \mathbf{r}) \left[v(r) - \frac{\hbar^2}{4m} \Delta u(r) \right] d\mathbf{r} \\ &= \rho V_k + \frac{\hbar^2 k^2}{4m} \left[1 - \frac{1}{S(k)} \right] \\ &\quad - \frac{\hbar^2 k^2}{8m} \frac{1}{(2\pi)^3 \rho} \int [S(k') - 1][S(\mathbf{k} + \mathbf{k}') - 1] \, d\mathbf{k}' + \cdots \end{aligned} \tag{7.50}$$

and, with the help of Eq. (7.44),

$$\begin{aligned} U_k{}^* &= \frac{\hbar^2 k^2}{4mS(k)^2} [1 - S(k)] \\ &\quad + \frac{1}{(2\pi)^3 \rho} \int \frac{\hbar^2 k'^2}{4m} [1 - S(k')][1 - S(\mathbf{k} + \mathbf{k}')] \, d\mathbf{k}' + O(r_s{}^0) \end{aligned} \tag{7.51}$$

$$\begin{aligned} V_k{}^* &= \frac{\hbar^2 k^2}{4mS(k)^2} [1 - S(k)] \\ &\quad + \frac{1}{(2\pi)^3 \rho} \int \frac{\hbar^2 k'^2}{4m} [1 - S(k')][1 - S(\mathbf{k} + \mathbf{k}')] \left[1 - \frac{1}{S^2(k')} \right] d\mathbf{k}' + O(r_s{}^0) \end{aligned} \tag{7.52}$$

Finally, Eq. (7.52) in the integral equation for $L(k)$ yields the simple result

$$L(k) = [\hbar^2 k^2 / 4mS(k)^2][1 - S(k)] + O(r_s{}^0) \tag{7.53}$$

and Eq. (5.19) for $\omega(k)$ reduces to

$$\begin{aligned} \omega(k) &\equiv S(k)L(k) + [\hbar^2 k^2 / 4mS(k)][S(k) - 1] \\ &= O(r_s{}^0) \end{aligned} \tag{7.54}$$

The absence of a component of order $r_s^{-3/4}$ in $\omega(k)$ means that the correction to the ground-state energy generated by the "free-phonon" analysis is extremely small:

$$\begin{aligned} \frac{1}{2} \sum_{\mathbf{k}} \{ -\varepsilon_0(k) - \omega(k) + [\varepsilon_0(k)^2 + 2\varepsilon_0(k)\omega(k)]^{1/2} \} &\approx - \frac{N}{4(2\pi)^3 \rho} \int \frac{\omega(k)^2}{\varepsilon_0(k)} \, d\mathbf{k} \\ &= NO(r_s^{9/4}) \end{aligned} \tag{7.55}$$

Furthermore, the modified dispersion relation for the phonon energy [Eq. (5.42)] reduces to the zeroth-order Bijl–Feynman form with

$$\begin{aligned} e(k) &= [\varepsilon_0(k)^2 + 2\varepsilon_0(k)\omega(k)]^{1/2} \\ &\approx \varepsilon_0(k) + \omega(k) \\ &= [\hbar^2 k^2/2mS(k)] + O(r_s{}^0) \end{aligned} \tag{7.56}$$

No new formulas emerge from the "paired"-phonon analysis in the uniform limit, but we learn that the optimum BDJ trial function is a remarkably good approximation to the correct ground-state wave function. Although the estimates of remainder terms are stated in the form appropriate to the Coulomb interaction, the analysis is perfectly general under the assumption that the two-particle interaction operator possesses a Fourier transform plus the constraint of Eq. (7.12).

APPENDIX 7-A

Evaluation of Certain Definite Integrals

The integrals in Eqs. (7.30) and (7.40) are readily evaluated with the aid of an identity in the theory of beta functions [11]:

$$\int_0^1 \frac{\xi^{x-1}(1-\xi)^{y-1}\, d\xi}{(a+x)^{x+y}} = \frac{B(x, y)}{(1+a)^x a^y} \tag{A.1}$$

With the change of variable

$$\xi = t^2/(1+t^4)^{1/2} \tag{A.2}$$

the integrals in Eqs. (7.30) and (7.40) reduce to

$$\begin{aligned} \int_0^\infty \left[1 - \frac{t^2}{(1+t^4)^{1/2}}\right] t^2\, dt &= \frac{1}{2}\int_0^1 \frac{\xi^{1/2}(1-\xi)^{-3/4}}{(1+\xi)^{7/4}}\, d\xi \\ &= 2^{-5/2} B(\tfrac{3}{2}, \tfrac{1}{4}) \\ &= \frac{1}{12\pi^{1/2}}\, \Gamma^2\!\left(\frac{1}{4}\right) \\ &= 0.6180248 \cdots \end{aligned} \tag{A.3}$$

$$\int_0^\infty \left[1 - \frac{t^2}{(1+t^4)^{1/2}}\right]^2 (1+t^4)^{1/2} t^2 \, dt = \tfrac{1}{2} \int_0^1 \frac{\xi^{1/2}(1-\xi)^{-1/4}}{(1+\xi)^{9/4}} \, d\xi$$
$$= 2^{-5/2} B(\tfrac{3}{2}, \tfrac{3}{4})$$
$$= \frac{1}{5\pi^{1/2}} \Gamma^2\left(\frac{3}{4}\right)$$
$$= 0.1694426 \cdots \tag{A.4}$$

$$\int_0^\infty \left[1 - \frac{t^2}{(1+t^4)^{1/2}}\right] dt = \tfrac{1}{2} \int_0^1 \frac{\xi^{-1/2}(1-\xi)^{-1/4}}{(1+\xi)^{5/4}} \, d\xi$$
$$= 2^{-3/2} B(\tfrac{1}{2}, \tfrac{3}{4})$$
$$= \pi^{-1/2} \, \Gamma^2(\tfrac{3}{4})$$
$$= 0.8472130 \cdots \tag{A.5}$$

References

1. L. L. Foldy, *Phys. Rev.* **124**, 649 (1961).
2. E. H. Lieb, *Phys. Rev.* **130**, 2518 (1963).
3. D. K. Lee, unpublished doctoral dissertation, Washington University, 1967; D. K. Lee and E. Feenberg, *Phys. Rev.* **137**, A731 (1965).
4. N. N. Bogoliubov and D. N. Zubarev, *Soviet Phys. —JETP* **1**, 83 (1955).
5. M. Girardeau, *Phys. Rev.* **127**, 1809 (1962).
6. E. H. Lieb and A. Y. Sakakura, *Phys. Rev.* **133**, A899 (1964).
7. K. A. Brueckner, *Phys. Rev.* **156**, 207 (1967).
8. S. K. Ma and C-W. Woo, *Phys. Rev.* **159**, 165 (1967).
9. C-W. Woo and S. K. Ma, *Phys. Rev.* **159**, 176 (1967).
10. M. Shick and T. M. Wu, *Phys. Rev.* **177**, 313 (1969).
11. W. Magnus and R. Oberhettinger, "Formulas and Theorems for Mathematical Physics," p. 4. Chelsea Publishing Company, New York, 1949.

CHAPTER 8

Correlated Basis Functions for Fermion Systems. Diagonal Matrix Elements

8.1. INTRODUCTION

The utility of correlated basis functions in the many-particle boson problem has been demonstrated in Chapters 4 and 5 on the elementary excitations in liquid ^{4}He. Here we begin the development of the same concept for the fermion system. Liquid ^{3}He, the electron gas in a metal, nuclear matter, and the degenerate neutron gas are examples of fermion fluids. The first two are real physical systems, the third is hypothetical, and the fourth may exist as a stellar object. The discussion in this and the next chapter is developed in terms appropriate to the ^{3}He system [1]–[4] and is probably best suited to that system; the corresponding treatment of nuclear matter differs mainly in a different choice of correlation factor [5]–[8] and recognition of the strong dependence of the interaction operator on the spin and isospin states of the interacting particles.

The theory begins with an antisymetrical function Φ describing a state of the N-particle system in the absence of interaction. The model is adapted to the presence of strong short-range repulsive interactions by introducing a symmetrical, positive-valued correlation factor $\psi^{B}(1, 2, \ldots, N)$ which vanishes when any two particles approach closely. The resulting trial function is

$$\Psi = \psi^{B}\Phi \tag{8.1}$$

The simplest type of model function is a Slater determinant constructed from products of plane wave orbitals and spin (or spin and isospin) functions. Construction of a suitable trial (or basis) system may start from a set of linearly independent model functions $\Phi(|\mathbf{n})$. In the applications the correlated functions $\Psi(|\mathbf{n})$ are used to evaluate matrix elements of the identity and the Hamiltonian operator. A suitable linear transformation of Ψ's then generates an orthonormal set of basis functions and the associated matrix representation of H.

The utility and accuracy of the theory depend critically on the choice of correlation function. This function should contain a large part of the physical effects produced by the interactions among the particles. These interactions generate strong short-range repulsive forces when two or more particles approach closely, and thus produce an excluded region of configuration space into which the particles penetrate with small probability. For liquid ^{3}He at the equilibrium density the excluded region is a large fraction of the total volume. Under these conditions it is plausible that correlations produced by the short-range repulsions depend little on the boundary conditions and type of permutation symmetry satisfied by the space part of the wave function. One is led to consider that the boson-type ground-state eigenfunction $\psi_0{}^{\mathrm{B}}$ of the Hamiltonian operator H possesses all the qualitative features demanded of a correlation factor and also includes almost all of the correlation effects generated by the short-range repulsive component in the interaction. On the basis of this argument the prescription for the correlation function is fixed: the eigenvalue equation,

$$H\psi_0{}^{\mathrm{B}} = E_0{}^{\mathrm{B}}\psi_0{}^{\mathrm{B}} \tag{8.2}$$

solved for the lowest state of the boson-type spectrum at the given density ρ, generates a function $\psi_0{}^{\mathrm{B}}$ which is identified with ψ^{B} in Eq. (8.1). This prescription possesses practical utility, first in the sense that $E_0{}^{\mathrm{B}}$ and the essential probability distributions defined by $\psi_0{}^{\mathrm{B}}$ can be computed reasonably well, and second in the sense of yielding a simple convenient formalism for computing the properties of the condensed fermion system. A detailed specification of $\psi_0{}^{\mathrm{B}}$ in the N-particle configuration space is of course impossible. However, only the two- and three-particle distribution functions are needed in the present development.

We have seen in Chapter 6 how the radial distribution function $\mathbf{g}(r)$ of the boson solution can be calculated. Numerical determinations by Massey [9], Massey and Woo [10] and Schiff and Verlet [11] are available for the evaluation of matrix elements and integrals occurring in the theory of the fermion liquid. It is necessary to stress that $g(r)$ has been computed only in the approximation in which $\psi_0{}^{\mathrm{B}}$ is represented by a BDJ-type trial function. This means that the theory of the fermion liquid based on $\psi_0{}^{\mathrm{B}}$ as the correlation factor involves, in practice, a systematic error generated by the presumed small, but essentially unknown error in g. The gain is a simple formalism well adapted to numerical evaluation.

The only practical alternative to $\psi_0{}^{\mathrm{B}}$ as a correlation factor is just the BDJ form, a symmetrical product of two-particle functions. This form has been applied extensively in nuclear problems following the pioneer study of Iwamoto and Yamada [5]. Clark and Westhaus [8] give a full development of the basic theory, including explicit formulas for diagonal and nondiagonal elements of H in a normalized-orthogonal representation. The BDJ form has also proved useful in the study of the solid helium systems [12]–[14].

In nuclear problems the special case of a charge-independent hard core (of diameter d) as part of the two-nucleon interaction operator suggests the introduction of the ground-state solution, $\psi_0{}^{\mathrm{B}}(1, 2, \ldots, N|\rho d^3)$, of the Schrödinger equation for a system of hard-core bosons to serve as the N-particle correlation function. In this formulation of the nuclear problem the matrix elements of H include matrix elements of the interaction operator in the region outside of the hard cores.

An obvious disadvantage of the suggested procedure is the reduced accuracy in the description of the ground state by a single configuration, because the correlation function is not adapted to the complete interaction operator, but only to the hard-core component. To offset this loss, two evident advantages can be mentioned. First, the difficult and tedious computational problem of adapting the correlation function to the complete interaction operator is avoided, and second, the method is well suited to comparing the consequences of a wide range of two-particle interaction operators. In any case, the inclusion of a second-order energy correction is desirable and can be expected to compensate for the reduced accuracy of a single-configuration description.

In the problem of the helium solids a modified Hamiltonian operator H' including only part of the attractive component of the interaction operator can be used to generate a liquid-type correlation factor $\psi_0^{\mathrm{B}'}$. In this formulation the calculation of the eigenvalues of liquid like and solid like states starts from the level $E_0^{\mathrm{B}'}$. By proper choice of H' the auxiliary eigenvalue can be made to satisfy the constraint $E_0^{\mathrm{B}'} \leq 0$. The obvious optimum choice requires a minimum value for $E_0^{\mathrm{B}'}$ while maintaining the liquidlike character of the state described by $\psi_0^{\mathrm{B}'}$.

8.2 THE GENERALIZED NORMALIZATION INTEGRAL

Model functions $\Phi(1, 2, \ldots, N|\mathbf{n})$ are constructed from a set of single-particle orbitals $u(\mathbf{r}, \sigma|n) \equiv u(|n)$. The discrete variables (spin or spin and isospin) are denoted by σ. Where particle l is in state n we write $u(\mathbf{r}_l, \sigma_l|n) \equiv u(l|n)$. A proliferation of multiple indices is avoided by writing $\mathbf{n} = 1, 2, \ldots, N$ without implying that $\mathbf{n}$ represents the ground-state configuration. Explicitly,

$$\Phi(|\mathbf{n}) = \sum_{\nu} (\pm) P_{\nu} \varphi(|\mathbf{n}), \qquad \varphi(|\mathbf{n}) = \prod_{l=1}^{N} u(l|l) \tag{8.3}$$

The immediate problem is the transformation of the diagonal matrix elements

$$\begin{aligned} (\mathbf{n}|1|\mathbf{n}) &= \int \psi_0^{\mathrm{B}^2} \Phi^* \varphi \, dv_{1,2,\ldots,N} \\ (\mathbf{n}|H|\mathbf{n}) &= \int \psi_0{}^{\mathrm{B}} \Phi^* H \psi_0{}^{\mathrm{B}} \varphi \, dv_{1,2,\ldots,N} \end{aligned} \tag{8.4}$$

into forms suitable for numerical evaluation. This requires a cluster-expansion procedure. Note that in Eq. (8.4) the symbol $\int dv$ denotes both integration over the space coordinate $\mathbf{r}$ and summation over the discrete variable σ.

A partial evaluation of the matrix elements of H is accomplished by introducing the eigenvalue $E_0{}^{\mathrm{B}}$ and the notation

$$\bar{k}_l{}^2 \equiv -(u(1|l), \Delta_1 u(1|l))/(u(1|l), u(1|l)) \tag{8.5}$$

Then

$$\begin{aligned} (\mathbf{n}|H|\mathbf{n}) = &\left[E_0{}^{\mathrm{B}} + \frac{\hbar^2}{2m} \sum_l \bar{k}_l{}^2\right] (\mathbf{n}|I|\mathbf{n}) \\ &+ \frac{\hbar^2}{2m} \int \psi_0^{\mathrm{B}^2} \left[-\Phi^* \varphi \sum_l \bar{k}_l{}^2 + \sum_l \nabla_l \Phi^* \cdot \nabla_l \varphi\right] dv_{1,2,\ldots,N} \end{aligned} \tag{8.6}$$

Equation (8.6) exhibits the Fermi energy of the model state in association with $E_0{}^{\mathrm{B}}$ as a zeroth approximation to the energy of the correlated state. The remainder integral represents contributions from exchange terms in the product $\Phi^* \varphi$. The simpler (but less explicit) form

$$(\mathbf{n}|H|\mathbf{n}) = E_0{}^{\mathrm{B}}(\mathbf{n}|1|\mathbf{n}) + \frac{\hbar^2}{2m} \sum_l \int \psi_0^{\mathrm{B}^2} \nabla_l \Phi^* \cdot \nabla_l \varphi \, dv_{1,2,\ldots,N} \tag{8.7}$$

is better suited to the cluster development procedures.

Equation (8.6) expresses the expectation value of H in a physically transparent way as a sum of three terms: (1) the eigenvalue of the boson solution, (2) the Fermi energy of a system of noninteracting particles, and

(3) the fermion correlation energy given by the ratio of two $3N$-fold integrals. Direct evaluation of the integrals occurring in Eq. (8.6) and (8.7) leads to a completely useless form, because the correct linear dependence of $\langle H \rangle$ on N is hidden in the ratio of two immensely complicated polynomials in N. This difficulty is familiar in both classical and quantum treatments of many-particle problems. To avoid the difficulty, we follow the lead of Iwamoto and Yamada [5] and introduce an appropriate generalized normalization integral, in this case

$$I(\beta) = \int \psi_0^{B^2} [\exp \beta K(1, 2, \ldots, N)] \Phi^* \varphi \, dv_{1,2,\ldots,N}$$
$$K(1, 2, \ldots, N) = \sum_l K(l), \qquad K(l) = \nabla_l^* \cdot \nabla_l \tag{8.8}$$

The starred and unstarred gradient factors operate on Φ^* and φ, respectively $\nabla^* \cdot \nabla \Phi^* \varphi = (\nabla \Phi)^* \cdot (\nabla \varphi)$. In terms of $I(\beta)$

$$(\mathbf{n}|1|\mathbf{n}) = I(0)$$
$$\langle H \rangle \equiv \frac{(\mathbf{n}|H|\mathbf{n})}{(\mathbf{n}|1|\mathbf{n})} \tag{8.9}$$
$$= E_0{}^{B} + \frac{\hbar^2}{2m} \left[\frac{d}{d\beta} \ln I(\beta) \right]_{\beta=0}$$

Thus the problem is reduced to the evaluation of ln $I(\beta)$. Equation (8.9) tells us directly that ln $I(\beta)$ is a linear function of N.

Another form of the exponential operator in Eq. (8.8) is useful for generating the radial distribution function $g_F(r)$. In this application

$$K(1, 2, \ldots, N) = \sum_{i<j} K(r_{ij}) \tag{8.10}$$

in which $K(r)$ is an arbitrary function.

A suitable cluster development is needed to evaluate the generalized normalization integral. Here we suffer happily from an embarrassment of riches. Three more or less distinct procedures are known, all based on the BDJ-type correlation factor. In the following sections these procedures are developed briefly in the context of $\psi_0{}^B$ as the correlation factor. It is worthwhile emphasizing that none of these procedures require subjecting the correlation factor itself to a cluster development; in the cluster integrals the factor ψ^{B^2} is always represented by the appropriate distribution functions generated by ψ^{B^2}.

8.3 ADDITIVE APPROXIMANTS AND CLUSTER INTEGRALS—IWAMOTO-YAMADA (IY) FORMALISM

Successive approximants to $I(\beta)$ are defined by the equations

$$I_m(\beta) = \int \psi_0^{B^2} e^{\beta K(1)} u^*(1|m) u(1|m)\, dv_1\, d\mathbf{r}_{2,3,\ldots,N}$$
$$= X_m(\beta)$$

$$I_{mn}(\beta) = \int \psi_0^{B^2} e^{\beta K(1,2)} u(1|m) u(2|n)[1 - P_{21}^{12}] u^*(1|m) u^*(2|n)\, dv_{12}\, d\mathbf{r}_{3,\ldots,N}$$
$$= X_m(\beta)\, X_n(\beta) + X_{mn}(\beta)$$

$$\begin{aligned} I_{mnp}(\beta) = \int \psi_0^{B^2} e^{\beta K(1,2,3)} & u(1|m) u(2|n) u(3|p) \\ & \times [1 - P_{21}^{12} - P_{32}^{23} - P_{13}^{31} + P_{312}^{123} + P_{231}^{123}] \\ & \times u^*(1|m) u^*(2|n) u^*(3|p)\, dv_{1,2,3}\, d\mathbf{r}_{4,\ldots,N} \qquad (8.11) \\ = X_m(\beta) & X_n(\beta) X_p(\beta) + X_m(\beta) X_{np}(\beta) + X_n(\beta) X_{pm}(\beta) \\ & + X_p(\beta) X_{mn}(\beta) + X_{mnp}(\beta) \end{aligned}$$

$$\begin{aligned} I_{mnpq}(\beta) = \int \psi_0^{B^2} e^{\beta K(1,2,3,4)} & u(1|m) u(2|n) u(3|p) u(4|q) \\ & \times [1 - P_{21}^{12} - \cdots + P_{312}^{123} + \cdots + P_{12}^{21} P_{43}^{34} + \cdots \\ & - P_{4123}^{1234} - \cdots] u^*(1|m) u^*(2|n) u^*(3|p) u^*(4|q)\, dv_{1,2,3,4}\, d\mathbf{r}_{5,\ldots,N} \\ = X_m X_n & X_p X_q + X_m X_{npq} + \cdots + X_q X_{mnp} + X_m X_n X_{pq} + \cdots \\ & + X_p X_q X_{mn} + X_{mn} X_{pq} + \cdots + X_{mq} X_{np} + X_{mnpq} \end{aligned}$$

and so on. Each approximant $I_{m \cdots q}$ is represented as well as possible by an additive cluster approximation formed from all the preceding cluster integrals (the X's). The difference between the approximant and the cluster approximation defines a new cluster $X_{m \cdots q}$. At each stage the cluster approximation is constructed so that detailed and strong cancellation occurs between the various exchange terms in $I_{m \cdots q}$ and the corresponding products of distinct cluster integrals in the cluster approximation, leaving always a remainder to be represented by $X_{m \cdots q}$. Clearly, the approximants and the cluster integrals do not depend on the order of the indices. Also, the first few approximants are not in any sense approximations to $I(\beta)$.

At the end of the chain of approximants

$$I(\beta) = \sum \{\cdots X_m \cdots\}\{\cdots X_{np} \cdots\}\{\cdots X_{qrs} \cdots\} \cdots \{X_{123 \cdots N} \quad \text{or} \quad 1\} \tag{8.12}$$

in which the indices on each product in the sum range over 1, 2, ..., N with no duplications and no omissions. To simplify the discussion of magnitudes, the plane wave orbitals are normalized to unit amplitude. Order-of-magnitude estimates of the products in Eq. (8.12) are based on the relations

$$X_m = 1 + O(\beta), \qquad X_{mn} = O(1/N), \qquad X_{mnp} = O(1/N^2) \tag{8.13}$$

and so on. The normalized cluster integrals

$$x_{m \cdots q} = X_{m \cdots q}/X_m \cdots X_q \tag{8.14}$$

are used to express I in the asymptotic ($N \to \infty$, $\rho = \text{const}$) exponential form

$$I(\beta) = \prod_1^N X_m(\beta) \exp G_{\mathrm{IY}}(\beta|\mathbf{n})$$

$$\begin{aligned} G_{\mathrm{IY}}(\beta|\mathbf{n}) = \sum_{m<n} x_{mn} &+ \sum_{m<n<p} (x_{mnp} - x_{mn}x_{np} - x_{mp}x_{pn} - x_{nm}x_{mp}) \\ &+ \sum_{m<n<p<q} [x_{mnpq} + (x_{mn}x_{np}x_{pq} + \cdots) \\ &+ (x_{mq}x_{nq}x_{pq} + \cdots) - (x_{mnp}x_{pq} + \cdots)] + \cdots \end{aligned} \tag{8.15}$$

The exponential form is useful because the exponent is proportional to N [as a consequence of the order-of-magnitude relations stated in Eq. (8.13)]. A simple derivation of Eq. (8.15) is developed in Appendix 8-A.

8.4. ADDITIVE APPROXIMANTS AND CLUSTER INTEGRALS—AVILES–HARTOGH–TOLHOEK (AHT) FORMALISM

The AHT formalism is based on the theorem that the product of two determinants can be written as a single determinant:

$$\Phi^*\Phi = \det(P_{ij}), \qquad P_{ij} = \sum_{n=1}^{N} u^*(i|n)u(j|n) \tag{8.16}$$

A cluster expansion for the radial distribution function $g_F(r)$ is then generated in terms of successively larger minors of $\det(P_{ij})$. The condition that the functions $u(|n)$ form an orthonormal set is needed at this point. At every stage of approximation the formula for $g_F(r_{12})$ possesses the property of invariance under a unitary transformation of the single-particle orbitals contained in **n** [denoted by $U(\mathbf{n})$]. Notice that the IY formula for G lacks this property of evident invariance. Invariance fails in the three-index addend (at $\beta = 0$) because the product term $x_{mn}x_{np}$ contains a repeated index. Repeated indices occur systematically for all p-index addends ($p \geq 3$), with the consequence that any truncated form for G_{IY} [produced by dropping all addends with $p+1$ or more indices ($p \geq 3$)] is not invariant under $U(\mathbf{n})$. The significance of a failure of evident invariance under $U(\mathbf{n})$ must be discussed (see Chapter 9). However, let us turn first to the task of generating an invariant cluster expansion for $I(\beta)$.

Invariant approximants $I^{(p)}$ and cluster integrals $x^{(p)}$ are generated by averaging $I_{m \cdots q}$ over all possible choices of $m, \ldots, q$ within **n**. Thus

$$\begin{aligned}
I^{(1)} &= \frac{1}{N}\sum_m I_m = X^{(1)} \\
I^{(2)} &= \frac{1}{N(N-1)}\sum_{m,n} I_{mn} \\
&= X^{(1)2} + X^{(2)} \\
I^{(3)} &= \frac{1}{N(N-1)(N-2)}\sum_{mnp} I_{mnp} \\
&= X^{(1)3} + 3X^{(1)}X^{(2)} + X^{(3)} \\
I^{(4)} &= \frac{1}{N(N-1)(N-2)(N-3)}\sum_{mnpq} I_{mnpq} \\
&= X^{(1)4} + 6X^{(1)2}X^{(2)} + 4X^{(1)}X^{(3)} + 3X^{(2)2} + X^{(4)}
\end{aligned} \tag{8.17}$$

and so on. The last step in this sequence is

$$I(\beta) = N! \sum_{(\cdots\nu_l\cdots)} \prod_{l=1}^{N} \frac{X^{(l)^{\nu_l}}}{l!^{\nu_l}\nu_l!} \tag{8.18}$$

the sum extending over all integral solutions of the equation $\sum l\nu_l = N$. Order-of-magnitude estimates of $I(\beta)$ are based on the general relation

$$X^{(l)} \sim 0(1/N^{l-1}) \tag{8.19}$$

A theorem from the equilibrium theory of the classical imperfect gas [15] can be invoked to convert Eq. (8.18) to the asymptotic exponential form

$$\begin{aligned} I(\beta) &= X^{(1)^N} \exp G_{\mathrm{AHT}}(\beta|\mathbf{n}) \\ G_{\mathrm{AHT}}(\beta|\mathbf{n}) &= \tfrac{1}{2}N^2x^{(2)} + \tfrac{1}{6}N^3(x^{(3)} - 3x^{(2)^2}) \\ &\quad + \tfrac{1}{24}N^4(x^{(4)} - 12x^{(2)}x^{(3)} + 20x^{(2)^3}) + \cdots \end{aligned} \tag{8.20}$$

in which $x^{(l)} = X^{(l)}/X^{(1)^l}$. Equation (8.20) exhibits a cluster expansion of the type developed by Aviles and Hartogh and Tolhoek.

The averaging process exhibited in the definition of $I^{(l)}$ serves the double function of giving equal weight to all possible configurations containing l orbitals belonging to $\mathbf{n}$ and, as a corollary, maintaining invariance under $U(\mathbf{n})$. Since $I(\beta)$ possesses the invariance property, it is not unreasonable to require that a procedure for computing $I(\beta)$ in terms of successive approximants should also possess it at each stage of approximation. This is not, however, a necessary condition for a satisfactory computational method. Just the fact that a truncated form for G_{IY} is not invariant under $U(\mathbf{n})$ means that the series of G_{IY} converges most rapidly for some particular choice of orthogonal basis functions in the function space. In this connection simple plane waves appear well suited to utilize effectively the opportunities for detailed internal cancellation implicit in the formulas for $X_{m\cdots q}$.

From the defining relations, Eqs. (8.11) and (8.17), we see that

$$X^{(2)} = \frac{1}{N(N-1)} \sum_{mn} X_{mn}, \qquad X^{(3)} = \frac{1}{N(N-1)(N-2)} \sum_{mnp} X_{mnp} \tag{8.21}$$

neglecting terms of order β^2/N^3. However, X_4 is not related to the average value of X_{mnpq} in the same direct manner. The presence of $X^{(2)^2}$ in the defining equation means that

$$X^{(4)} + 3X^{(2)^2} = \frac{(N-4)!}{N!} \sum_{mnpq}{}' (X_{mnpq} + 3X_{mn}X_{pq}) \tag{8.22}$$

the prime on the summation denoting absence of terms with two or more identical indices. Consequently,

$$\frac{1}{4!}N^4X^{(4)} - \sum_{m<n<p<q} X_{mnpq} = -\frac{N^2}{8(N-1)^2}\left(\sum_{mn} X_{mn}\right)^2 + \frac{N^2}{8(N-1)^2}\left(1+\frac{4}{N}\right)\sum_{mnpq}{}' X_{mn}X_{pq}$$

$$= \frac{1}{2}N^3X^{(2)^2} - \sum_{m<p<q} \times (X_{mn}X_{np} + X_{np}X_{pm} + X_{nm}X_{mp}) \quad (8.23)$$

Equations (8.21) and (8.23) are sufficient to verify the identity of G_{IY} and G_{AHT} up to and including terms in X_{mnpq} and $X^{(4)}$. Here the significant point is that corresponding orders in the two developments are not identical and, in fact, differ by terms of order N. The superiority of the IY form is demonstrated in Chapter 9, where a truncated form of G_{IY} meets a consistency test while G_{AHT} to the same order fails.

A simpler test is provided by two formulas for the radial distribution function generated by truncated forms of G_{IY} and G_{AHT} using Eq. (8.10) in defining $I_{m\cdots q}$ and $X_{m\cdots q}$. This means that in Eq. (8.11), $I_m = X_m = 1$ independent of β, $K(r_{12})$ occurs in $I_{mn}(\beta)$, and $K(r_{12}) + K(r_{23}) + K(r_{31})$ in $I_{mnp}(\beta)$. The appropriate single-particle orbitals are plane waves multiplied by functions of the discrete variables. A Fermi sphere containing all the allowed wave vectors in **n** (now the ground-state configuration) is defined by the radius

$$k_{\mathrm{F}} = (6\pi^2\rho/s)^{1/3} \quad (8.24)$$

where s denotes the number of spin (and isospin) orientations represented equally in **n** ($s = 1$, ferromagnetic state of ^{3}He; $s = 2$, paramagnetic state of ^{3}He; $s = 4$, ground-state of nuclear matter).

The function $g_{\mathrm{F}}(r)$ defined by

$$[\ln I(\beta)]' = \tfrac{1}{2}N\rho \int g_{\mathrm{F}}(r)K(r)\, d\mathbf{r} \quad (8.25)$$

now appears in the forms

$$g_{\mathrm{IY}}(r) = g(r)F_{\mathrm{IY}}(r), \qquad g_{\mathrm{AHT}}(r) = g(r)F_{\mathrm{AHT}}(r) \quad (8.26)$$

with

$$F(r) = 1 + F^{(2)}(r) + F^{(3)}(r) + \cdots$$

$$F^{(2)}(r) = -\frac{1}{s} l^2(k_F r)$$

$$\begin{aligned} F_{IY}^{(3)}(r) = &-\frac{2\rho}{s} \int g(r')[g(\mathbf{r}-\mathbf{r}') - 1] l^2(k_F r')\, d\mathbf{r}' \\ &+ \frac{2\rho}{s^2} l(k_F r) \int g(r')[g(\mathbf{r}-\mathbf{r}') - 1] l(k_F r') l(k_F|\mathbf{r}-\mathbf{r}'|)\, d\mathbf{r}' \end{aligned} \tag{8.27}$$

$$\begin{aligned} F_{AHT}^{(3)}(r) = &-\frac{2\rho}{s} \int g(r')[g(\mathbf{r}-\mathbf{r}') - 1] l^2(k_F r')\, d\mathbf{r}' \\ &+ \frac{2\rho}{s^2} l(k_F r) \int g(r') l(k_F r')[g(\mathbf{r}-\mathbf{r}') l(k_F|\mathbf{r}-\mathbf{r}'|) - l(k_F r) l(k_F r')]\, d\mathbf{r}' \end{aligned}$$

TABLE 8-1

VALUES OF $F^{(2)}(r)$, $F_{IY}^{(3)}(r)$, $F_{AHT}^{(3)}(r)$, $F_{IY}(r)$, AND $F_{AHT}(r)$ FOR $s = 2$[3, 4]

r (Å)	$F^{(2)}(r)$	$F_{IY}^{(3)}(r)$	$F_{AHT}^{(3)}(r)$	$F_{IY}(r)$	$F_{AHT}(r)$
1.8	−0.303	0.014	0.013	0.711	0.710
2.2	−0.233	0.027	0.025	0.749	0.793
2.6	−0.167	0.037	0.035	0.870	0.868
3.0	−0.111	0.044	0.043	0.934	0.932
3.4	−0.066	0.049	0.048	0.983	0.982
3.8	−0.035	0.051	0.049	1.016	1.015
4.2	−0.015	0.047	0.046	1.032	1.032
4.6	−0.004	0.038	0.038	1.034	1.034
5.0	0.000	0.024	0.024	1.024	1.024
5.4	0.000	0.008	0.008	1.007	1.007
5.8	−0.002	−0.004	−0.004	0.994	0.994
6.2	−0.003	−0.007	−0.006	0.990	0.990
6.6	−0.004	−0.003	−0.003	0.993	0.994
7.0	−0.003	0.002	0.002	0.999	0.999
7.4	−0.003	0.005	0.005	1.003	1.003
7.8	−0.002	0.006	0.006	1.005	1.004
8.2	−0.001	0.005	0.005	1.004	1.004
8.6	0.000	0.004	0.004	1.004	1.004
9.0	0.000	0.002	0.002	1.002	1.002

and

$$l(x) = (3/x^3)(\sin x - x \cos x) \tag{8.28}$$

A particular simple choice of $g(r)$ (g_0 in Chapter 6) is used to compute the results shown in Table 8-1 for the paramagnetic state of ^{3}He at the equilibrium density. It is clear that the two forms g_{IY} and g_{AHT} are essentially indistinquishable.

No attempt has been made to evaluate directly terms of order $1/N$ in $g_F(\infty)$, since terms of order N^0 are neglected in the evaluation of G_{IY} and G_{AHT}.

8.5. MULTIPLICATIVE APPROXIMANTS AND CLUSTER INTEGRALS

The additive procedures evaluate $I(\beta)$ as a formal series [Eqs. (8.12) or (8.18)] paralleling the classical cluster development of the partition function. Only after studying the structure of these series is it possible to recognize the possibility of the exponential representation and useful truncated forms. The multiplicative procedures avoid the intermediate step and go directly to useful formulas. Van Kampen [16] formulated the multiplicative procedure in the context of the classical equilibrium theory of the imperfect gas. Nosanow [12] and Nosanow and Mullin [13] applied the procedure to the ground state of solid ^{3}He with inclusion of exchange effects. Independently, Clark and Westhaus [8] developed the formalism as an alternative to the additive procedures for nuclear problems. All these treatments are based on the BDJ-type correlation factor.

The multiplicative procedure may start from the approximants $I_{m\cdots q}$ defined by Eq. (9.11). Multiplicative approximants $Z_{m\cdots q}$ are defined by the sequence

$$\begin{aligned}
I_{mn} &= I_m I_n Z_{mn} \\
I_{mnp} &= I_m I_n I_p Z_{mn} Z_{np} Z_{pm} Z_{mnp} \\
&= \frac{I_{mn} I_{np} I_{pm}}{I_m I_n I_p} Z_{mnp} \\
I_{mnpq} &= (I_m \cdots I_q)(Z_{mn} \cdots Z_{pq})(Z_{mnp} \cdots Z_{npq}) Z_{mnpq} \\
&= \frac{(I_m \cdots I_q)(I_{mnp} \cdots I_{npq})}{I_{mn} \cdots I_{pq}} Z_{mnpq}
\end{aligned} \tag{8.29}$$

$$I_{mnpqr} = (I_m \cdots I_q)(Z_{mn} \cdots Z_{qr})(Z_{mnp} \cdots Z_{pqr})(Z_{mnpq} \cdots Z_{npqr})Z_{mnpqr}$$
$$= \frac{(I_{mn} \cdots I_{qr})(I_{mnpq} \cdots I_{npqr})}{(I_m \cdots I_q)(I_{mnp} \cdots I_{pqr})} Z_{mnpqr}$$

and so on. The general law is evident and can be proved by induction. At the end of the sequence

$$I(\beta) = \left(\prod_l I_l\right)\left(\prod_{m<n} Z_{mn}\right)\left(\prod_{m<n<p} Z_{mnp}\right) \cdots (Z_{12 \cdots N-1} \cdots Z_{23 \cdots N})Z_{12 \cdots N} \tag{8.30}$$

The usefulness of the product representation in the treatment of the liquid state depends on the property $Z_{m_1 m_2 \cdots m_p} - 1 \sim O(1/N^{p-1})$, which holds for almost all independent values of the indices (terms of larger order occur for $p \geq 4$, but the larger magnitude is compensated by constraints on the index space). Equation (8.30) yields

$$\ln I(\beta) = \sum_1^N \ln I_l + \sum_{m<n} (Z_{mn} - 1)$$
$$+ \sum_{m<n<p} (Z_{mnp} - 1) + \sum_{m<n<p<q} (Z_{mnpq} - 1) + O(N^0) \tag{8.31}$$

each sum making a contribution proportional to N. The explicit representation of the Z's derived from Eqs. (8.11) and (8.29) gives

$$Z_{mn} = I_{mn}/I_m I_n = 1 + x_{mn}$$
$$Z_{mnp} = \frac{1 + x_{mn} + x_{np} + x_{pm} + x_{mnp}}{(1 + x_{mn})(1 + x_{np})(1 + x_{pm})} \tag{8.32}$$
$$Z_{mnpq} = [1 + x_{mn} + \cdots + x_{pq} + x_{mnp} + \cdots + x_{npq} + x_{mn} x_{pq} + \cdots$$
$$+ x_{mq} x_{pn} + x_{mnpq}][(1 + x_{mn}) \cdots (1 + x_{pq})]$$
$$\times [(1 + x_{mn} + x_{np} + x_{pm} + x_{mnp}) \cdots (1 + x_{np} + x_{pq} + x_{qn} + x_{npq})]^{-1}$$

and, retaining only the leading terms in powers of $1/N$,

$$Z_{mn} - 1 = x_{mn}$$
$$Z_{mnp} - 1 \approx x_{mnp} - x_{mn} x_{np} - x_{mp} x_{pn} - x_{nm} x_{mp} \tag{8.33}$$
$$Z_{mnpq} - 1 \approx x_{mnpq} - (x_{mnp} x_{mq} + \cdots) + (x_{mq} x_{nq} x_{pq} + \cdots)$$
$$+ (x_{mn} x_{np} x_{pq} + \cdots)$$

Equations (8.15), (8.31), and (8.33) verify the identity of the formulas for $I(\beta)$ given by the IY and the generalized Van Kampen procedures through four-index elements. Clark and Westhaus [8] give a general proof.

Equations (8.10), (8.25), and (8.30) can be used to determine $g_F(r_{12})$ by the multiplicative formalism. Equation (8.30) yields

$$[\ln I(\beta)]' = \sum_{m<n} (Z'_{mn}/Z_{mn}) + \sum_{m<n<p} (Z'_{mnp}/Z_{mnp}) + \cdots \tag{8.34}$$

With plane wave orbitals it is easily verified that the truncated form of $g_F(r_{12})$ given by the two-index summand in Eq. (8.34) exactly satisfies the normalization condition $\rho \int [g(r) - 1] \, d\mathbf{r} = -1$.

How do succeeding terms in Eq. (8.34) influence the normalization of g_F? The defining equation for Z_{mnp} makes it homogeneous of degree zero in the exponential factors $\exp \beta K(r_{ij})$. By induction, the same property holds for any $Z_{m \cdots t}$ with three or more indices. This property ensures that the component of g_F generated by the three-index summand in Eq. (8.34) contributes nothing to the normalization. The same statement holds for all summands with three or more indices. To illustrate this statement, observe that

$$\frac{Z'_{mnp}}{Z_{mnp}} = \frac{I'_{mnp}}{I_{mnp}} - \frac{I'_{mn}}{I_{mn}} - \frac{I'_{np}}{I_{np}} - \frac{I'_{pm}}{I_{pm}} \tag{8.35}$$

If now the factors $K(r_{ij})$ in the integrands of the primed quantities are all replaced by 1, the reduced ratios of integrals formed in this manner add up to zero (three from I'_{mnp}/I_{mnp} and one from each of the two-index ratios).

Let $g_{F\nu}(r_{12})$ denote the radial distribution function generated by the first $\nu - 1$ summands in Eq. (8.34). For each of these

$$\rho^2 \int [g_{F\nu}(r_{12}) - 1] \, d\mathbf{r}_1 \, d\mathbf{r}_2 = -1 \tag{8.36}$$

independent of ν. Unfortunately, the exact normalization of the truncated forms is associated with the asymptotic behavior

$$g_{F\nu}(\infty) = 1 + (\beta_\nu/N) \tag{8.37}$$

and, in general, there is no reason to expect $\beta_\nu = 0$ or even $\beta_\nu \to 0$ as $\nu \to \infty$. The asymptotic properties of the correct fermion ground state are not necessarily properties of a single-configuration approximation.

8.6. EXPLICIT FORMULAS FOR CLUSTER INTEGRALS AND GROUND-STATE-ENERGY QUANTITIES FOR LIQUID ³He

With plane wave orbitals the approximants defined by Eqs. (8.8) and (8.11) involve the functions

$$\prod_1^t \exp(\beta \boldsymbol{\nabla}_l{}^* \cdot \boldsymbol{\nabla}_l) \exp(i\mathbf{k}_l \cdot \mathbf{r}_l) \cdot \exp(-i\mathbf{k}_l \cdot \mathbf{r}_l) = \prod_1^t \exp(\beta k_l{}^2) \quad (8.38)$$

$$\begin{aligned}
&[\exp \beta(\boldsymbol{\nabla}_1{}^* \cdot \boldsymbol{\nabla}_1 + \boldsymbol{\nabla}_2{}^* \cdot \boldsymbol{\nabla}_2)][\exp i(\mathbf{k}_m \cdot \mathbf{r}_1 + \mathbf{k}_n \cdot \mathbf{r}_2)] \\
&\qquad \times P_{21}^{12} \exp -i(\mathbf{k}_m \cdot \mathbf{r}_1 + \mathbf{k}_n \cdot \mathbf{r}_2) \\
&\qquad = \exp(2\beta \mathbf{k}_m \cdot \mathbf{k}_n) \exp(i\mathbf{k}_{mn} \cdot \mathbf{r}_{12}) \\
&\qquad = \exp[\beta(k_m{}^2 + k_n{}^2)] \exp[-\tfrac{1}{2}\beta(k_{mn}^2 + k_{nm}^2] \exp(i\mathbf{k}_{mn} \cdot \mathbf{r}_{12}) \\
&\exp \beta(\boldsymbol{\nabla}_1{}^* \cdot \boldsymbol{\nabla}_1 + \boldsymbol{\nabla}_2{}^* \cdot \boldsymbol{\nabla}_2 + \boldsymbol{\nabla}_3{}^* \cdot \boldsymbol{\nabla}_3)[\exp i(\mathbf{k}_m \cdot \mathbf{r}_1 + \mathbf{k}_n \cdot \mathbf{r}_2 + \mathbf{k}_p \cdot \mathbf{r}_3)] \\
&\qquad \times P_{312}^{123} \exp -i(\mathbf{k}_m \cdot \mathbf{r}_1 + \mathbf{k}_n \cdot \mathbf{r}_2 + \mathbf{k}_p \cdot \mathbf{r}_3) \\
&\qquad = \exp \beta(k_m{}^2 + k_n{}^2 + k_p{}^2) \exp -\tfrac{1}{2}\beta[k_{mn}^2 + k_{np}^2 + k_{pm}^2] \\
&\qquad \times \exp i(k_{mn} \cdot \mathbf{r}_1 + \mathbf{k}_{np} \cdot \mathbf{r}_2 + \mathbf{k}_{pm} \cdot \mathbf{r}_3)
\end{aligned}$$

and so on. These formulas suggest the convenient notation

$$\begin{aligned}
\exp(12 \cdots \nu | mn \cdots t) = (-1)^{\nu-1}&[\exp \beta(k_m{}^2 + \cdots + k_t{}^2)] \\
&\times \langle mn \cdots t | P_{\nu 12 \cdots \nu-1}^{12 \cdots \nu} | mn \cdots t \rangle_s \\
&\times \sum \exp -\tfrac{1}{2}\beta(k_{mn}^2 + k_{np}^2 + \cdots + k_{tm}^2) \\
&\times \exp i(\mathbf{k}_{mn} \cdot \mathbf{r}_1 + \mathbf{k}_{np} \cdot \mathbf{r}_2 + \cdots + \mathbf{k}_{tm} \cdot \mathbf{r}_\nu) \quad (8.39)
\end{aligned}$$

in which the summation is over the set of $(\nu - 1)!$ cyclic permutations on $12 \cdots \nu$. A typical term is shown. The spin matrix elements are all equal, with the value 1 or 0, the first if all single-particle spin states denoted by the indices are identical, the second if both single-particle spin states are present. These matrix elements are written $\langle mn \cdots t \,|\, tmn \cdots t-1 \rangle$ in the following discussion. In terms of the $e(\cdots|\cdots)$ symbols the generalized normalization integral of Eq. (8.8) takes the form

$$I(\beta) = \int \psi_0^{B^2} \prod_1^N (\exp \beta k_n{}^2) \Big[1 + \sum_{m<n} e(12|mn) + \sum_{m<n<p} e(123|mnp) + \sum_{m<n<p<q} \{e(1234|mnpq) + e(12|mn)e(34|pq) + e(12|mp)e(34|qn) + e(12|mq)e(34|np)\} + \cdots \Big] d\mathbf{r}_{1,2,\ldots,N} \tag{8.40}$$

The first four additive cluster integrals are .

$$\begin{aligned} X_m &= (\exp \beta k_m{}^2) \int \psi_0^{B^2} \, d\mathbf{r}_{1,2,\ldots,N} \\ &= \exp \beta k_m{}^2 \\ X_{mn} &= \int \psi_0^{B^2} e(12|mn) \, d\mathbf{r}_{1,2,\ldots,N} \\ X_{mnp} &= \int \psi_0^{B^2} e(123|mnp) \, d\mathbf{r}_{1,2,\ldots,N} \\ X_{mnpq} &= \int \psi_0^{B^2} [e(1234|mnpq) + e(12|mn)e(34|pq) \\ &\qquad + e(12|mp)e(34|qn) + e(12|mq)e(34|pn)] \, d\mathbf{r}_{1,2,\ldots,N} \end{aligned} \tag{8.41}$$

No approximation is required to evaluate the one- and two-index cluster integrals. Equations (8.39) and (8.41) yield

$$X_{mn}(\beta) = -(1/N) X_m(\beta) X_n(\beta) (\exp -\beta k_{mn}^2)[S(k_{mn}) - 1]\langle mn|nm\rangle \tag{8.42}$$

The convolution form for $p^{(3)}(1, 2, 3)$ in the evaluation of the three-particle cluster integral produces the approximate formula

$$\begin{aligned} X_{mnp}(\beta) \approx 2N^{-2} X_m X_n X_p & \exp[-\tfrac{1}{2}\beta(k_{mn}^2 + k_{np}^2 + k_{pm}^2) \\ & \times \langle mnp|pmn\rangle \{[S(k_{mn}) - 1][S(k_{np}) - 1] + [S(k_{np}) - 1] \\ & \times [S(k_{pm}) - 1] + [S(k_{pm}) - 1][S(k_{mn}) - 1] \\ & + [S(k_{mn}) - 1][S(k_{np}) - 1][S(k_{pm}) - 1]\} \end{aligned} \tag{8.43}$$

A complete evaluation of the four-index cluster integral has not been attempted as yet. However, a special class of these integrals resembles the three-index cluster integral both in structure and in dependence on N. This class is distinguished by relations of linear dependence among the wave vectors $\mathbf{k}_m$, $\mathbf{k}_n$, $\mathbf{k}_p$, $\mathbf{k}_q$ (i.e., $\mathbf{k}_{mn} = \mathbf{k}_{pq}$) and can be evaluated accurately using only an asymptotic form for $p^{(4)}(1, 2, 3, 4)$ [i.e., $p^{(4)} \to \rho^4 g(r_{12}) g(r_{34})$ when $\mathbf{r}_1$ and $\mathbf{r}_2$ are remote from $\mathbf{r}_3$ and $\mathbf{r}_4$]. Varying appraisals of the significance of these terms has been given by Iwamoto and Yamada [5] and by C. W. Woo [4]. I follow Woo in the working hypothesis that only the complete contribution of the four-index cluster integrals to the evaluation of $I(\beta)$ has physical significance. This means essentially the assumption that the pattern of convergence suggested by the one-, two-, and three-index cluster integrals is not deceptive.*

Equations (8.9) and (8.34) require derivatives of the multiplicative approximants with respect to β evaluated at $\beta = 0$. The explicit formulas generated by Eq. (8.33) and Eqs. (8.41)–(8.43) are

$$\begin{aligned} Z_l' &= k_l^2 \\ Z'_{mn} &= (1/N)k_{mn}^2[S(k_{mn}) - 1]\langle mn\,|\,nm\rangle \\ Z'_{mnp} &= -(1/N^2)\langle mnp\,|\,pmn\rangle\{k_{mn}^2\, S(k_{mn})[S(k_{np}) - 1][S(k_{pm}) - 1] \\ &\quad + k_{np}^2\, S(k_{np})[S(k_{pm}) - 1][S(k_{mn}) - 1] \\ &\quad + k_{pm}^2\, S(k_{pm})[S(k_{mn}) - 1][S(k_{np}) - 1]\} \end{aligned} \tag{8.44}$$

The corresponding explicit formula for the expectation value of H is

$$E_0{}^{\mathrm{F}} \equiv \langle H\rangle = E_0{}^{\mathrm{B}} + E_1{}^{\mathrm{F}} + E_2{}^{\mathrm{F}} + E_3{}^{\mathrm{F}} + \cdots \tag{8.45}$$

in which

$$\begin{aligned} E_1{}^{\mathrm{F}} &= \frac{\hbar^2}{2m}\sum_1^N k_l^2 \\ E_2{}^{\mathrm{F}} &= \frac{\hbar^2}{4mN}\sum_{m,\,n} k_{mn}^2[S(k_{mn}) - 1]\langle mn\,|\,nm\rangle \\ E_3{}^{\mathrm{F}} &= -\frac{\hbar^2}{4mN^2}\sum_{m,\,n,\,p} k_{mn}^2\, S(k_{mn})[S(k_{np}) - 1][S(k_{pm}) - 1]\langle mnp\,|\,pmn\rangle \end{aligned} \tag{8.46}$$

I emphasize once more that the two-index cluster integrals are exact and the three-index cluster integrals are inexact only because of the necessity of introducing an approximate form for the three-particle distribution function generated by $\psi_0{}^{\mathrm{B}}$. The imperative that emerges from

* F. Y. Wu reports that he has evaluated the complete four-index term E_{04}^{F} using the convolution form $P_c(1, 2, 3, 4)$ of D. K. Lee (Appendix 2-C). He finds that E_{03}^{F} is even larger than E_{03}^{F}. Considering that $P_c(1, 2, 3, 4)$ fails badly when two or more points coincide or nearly coincide ($r_{ij} \lesssim \rho^{-3}$) no strong conclusion can be drawn safely at present from this result. It may become significant when some insight has been gained into the unknown error terms of the convolution forms of the three- and four-particle distribution functions.

the diagonal and nondiagonal matrix elements of H, given as simple functionals in $S(k)$, is simple and direct: determine $S(k)$ as well as possible using the best possible trial function for which the evaluation of $S(k)$ is feasible. The special properties of any particular choice of trial function need not and should not appear explicitly in the matrix elements of H.

In the ground-state configuration of zero spin the momentum distributions fill Fermi spheres of radii $\hbar k_F$. At the surface of the spheres the kinetic energy per particle is

$$e_F = \hbar^2 k_F{}^2/2m = (\hbar^2/2m)(3\pi^2\rho)^{2/3} \tag{8.47}$$

In terms of e_F

$$E_{01}^F = \tfrac{3}{5}Ne_F$$

$$\begin{aligned} E_{02}^F &= (\hbar^2/2mN)[\Omega^2/(2\pi)^6] \int (\mathbf{k}-\mathbf{h})^2[S(\mathbf{k}-\mathbf{h})-1]\, d\mathbf{k}\, d\mathbf{h} \\ &= Ne_F(3/8\pi)^2 \int x_{12}^2[S(k_F x_{12})-1]\, d\mathbf{x}_1\, d\mathbf{x}_2 \\ &= Ne_F\, 24 \int_0^1 [S(2k_F x)-1][1-\tfrac{3}{2}x+\tfrac{1}{2}x^3]x^4\, dx \end{aligned} \tag{8.48}$$

$$E_{03}^F = -Ne_F(3/8\pi)^3 \int x_{12}^2\, S(k_F x_{12})[S(k_F x_{23})-1][S(k_F x_{31})-1]\, d\mathbf{x}_1\, d\mathbf{x}_2\, d\mathbf{x}_3$$

The three-dimensional variables of integration $\mathbf{x}_\nu$ range over a unit sphere. A general integration formula derived in Appendix 8-B is used to reduce E_{02}^F to a one-dimensional integral.

The integrals occurring in Eq. (8.48) can be computed by standard methods of numerical integration for given $S(k)$. However, the fact that the theoretical liquid structure function is represented fairly well by a quadratic function of k on the range $0 \leq k \leq 2k_F$ makes possible an analytical evaluation. The formula

$$S(k) \approx B(k/k_F)^2, \qquad 0 \leq k \leq 2k_F \tag{8.49}$$

is used to estimate E_{03}^F with B determined to fit the accurate numerical evaluation of E_{02}^F. As a test, E_{03}^F was also evaluated at $\rho = 0.024$ Å^{-3} by numerical integration; the two evaluations differ by less than 2%.

The quadratic formula for $S(k)$ in Eq. (8.48) yields

$$\begin{aligned} E_{02}^F &\approx -\tfrac{3}{5}Ne_F(\tfrac{1}{2}-\tfrac{6}{7}B) \\ E_{03}^F &\approx -\tfrac{3}{5}Ne_F(\tfrac{3}{7}B-\tfrac{352}{315}B^2+\tfrac{472}{735}B^3) \end{aligned} \tag{8.50}$$

A detailed comparison between theory and experiment is deferred until Chapter 10, following the derivation and evaluation of a second-order correction generated by configuration interaction [4]. Although small, this correction is important because it materially improves the density dependence of the theoretical energy and also improves the statistical and transport properties. Numerical results computed by H. T. Tan are listed in Chapter 10, Table 10-1.

These results are encouraging in that the expectation value of H for a trial function constructed from a single configuration is actually negative, although the value is only 20% of the experimental energy. The rapid decrease in magnitude along the sequence E_{01}^{F}, E_{02}^{F}, E_{03}^{F} is also highly encouraging. Little is known about E_{04}^{F}, and we cannot assert with assurance that it must fit smoothly into the rapidly convergent behavior indicated by the preceding three fermion terms. However, a certain sanguine outlook is essential in the analysis and interpretation of many-particle problems. We therefore continue under the working hypothesis that the apparent rapid convergence seen in Chapter 10, Table 10-1 will not prove illusory when E_{04}^{F} and higher terms are evaluated accurately.*

APPENDIX 8-A

*Exponential Form of the Cluster Expansion for the Generalized Normalization Integrals**

Reduced cluster integrals are introduced through the definition

$$x_{ij\cdots hl} = X_{ij\cdots hl}/X_i X_j \cdots X_h X_l \tag{A.1}$$

Then

$$I(12\cdots N) = \left[\prod_1^N X_j\right] K(12\cdots N)$$

$$\begin{aligned} K(12\cdots N) = 1 &+ \sum_{m<n} x_{mn} + \sum_{m<n<p} x_{mnp} \\ &+ \sum_{m<n<p<q} (x_{mnpq} + x_{mn}x_{pq} + x_{mp}x_{nq} + x_{mq}x_{pn}) \\ &+ \sum_{m<n<p<q<r} (x_{mnpqr} + x_{mn}x_{pqr} + \cdots + x_{qr}x_{mnp}) + \cdots \end{aligned} \tag{A.2}$$

* See footnote, p. 182.
* See Wu and Feenberg [1] and Wu [2].

Next consider the functions generated from $K(12 \cdots N)$ by omitting all terms in Eq. (A.2) containing indices in the set $(ij \cdots k)$. The reduced K functions defined by this process are written

$$K_{(ij\cdots k)} = K[1,2\cdots(i-1)(i+1)\cdots(j-1)(j+1)\cdots(k-1)(k+1)\cdots N] \tag{A.3}$$

To simply the analysis, let $K \equiv K(12 \cdots N)$. The reduced functions $K_{(q)}$, $K_{(pq)}$, and $K_{(npq)}$ obtained by omitting first a single index q, then two indices including q, and so on, are easily seen to satisfy the equation

$$\begin{aligned} K = K_{(q)} &+ \sum_p x_{pq} K_{(pq)} + \sum_{n<p} x_{npq} K_{(npq)} \\ &+ \cdots + \sum_{h<l<\cdots<p} x_{hl\cdots pq} K_{(hl\cdots pq)} + \cdots \end{aligned} \tag{A.4}$$

As compared with Eq. (A.2), Eq. (A.4) has the advantage of associating terms of all orders in the cluster integrals with each summation, even the first. Also, all summations in Eq. (A.4) are of the same general order of magnitude in N, although forming a rapidly convergent numerical series. This property is brought to the surface by the substitutions

$$K = e^G, \qquad K_{(q)} = \exp(G - \delta G_q), \qquad K_{(pq)} = \exp(G - \delta G_p - \delta G_q), \quad \text{etc.} \tag{A.5}$$

which convert Eq. (A.4) into

$$\exp(\delta G_q) = 1 + \sum_p x_{pq} \exp(-\delta G_p) + \sum_{n<p} x_{npq} \exp(-\delta G_n - \delta G_p) + \cdots \tag{A.6}$$

We pause to note that δG_p is independent of N; also, that the exponent $G - \delta G_p - \delta G_g$ defined by Eq. (A.5) fails to be exact by terms of order $O(1/N)$. Equation (A.6) can be solved by an obvious iteration procedure. The result is

$$\begin{aligned} \exp(\delta G_q) = 1 &+ \sum_p x_{pq} - \sum_{np} x_{np} x_{pq} + \tfrac{1}{2} \sum_{np} x_{npq} + \tfrac{1}{6} \sum_{mnp} x_{mnpq} \\ &- \sum_{mnp} \left(\tfrac{1}{2} x_{qp} x_{pnm} + x_{qpn} x_{nm} + x_{qp} x_{pn} x_{nm} + x_{pq} x_{pn} x_{pm}\right) + \cdots \end{aligned} \tag{A.7}$$

A diagrammatic representation is found useful at this stage to characterize the different terms. The meaning of the diagrams is illustrated in
Fig. 8-1; the open circles refer to free dummy indices of a summation,
the solid circles to the index q. The following equation is a diagrammatic
representation of exp δG_q; the corresponding representation of δG_q
appears in Eq. (A.9).

$$\text{(diagram)} = \sum_{n,\,p} x_{np}\, x_{pq}$$

$$\text{(diagram)} = \sum_{m,\,n,\,p} x_{mn}\, x_{np}$$

$$\text{(diagram)} = \sum_{n,\,p} x_{npq}$$

$$\text{(diagram)} = \sum_{m,\,n,\,p} x_{mnp}$$

$$\exp(\delta G_q) = 1 + \text{(diagram)} - \text{(diagram)} + \frac{1}{2!}\,\text{(diagram)} + \frac{1}{3!}\,\text{(diagram)}$$

$$- \frac{1}{2}\,\text{(diagram)} - \text{(diagram)} + \text{(diagram)} + \text{(diagram)} \tag{A.8}$$

$$G\delta_q = \text{(diagram)} + \frac{1}{2!}\,\text{(diagram)} - \frac{1}{2}\left[\,\text{(diagram)} + 2\,\text{(diagram)}\,\right]$$

$$+ \frac{1}{3!}\,\text{(diagram)} + \frac{1}{2}\left[\,2\,\text{(diagram)} + 2\,\text{(diagram)}\,\right]$$

$$+ \frac{1}{3}\left[\,\text{(diagram)} + 3\,\text{(diagram)}\,\right]$$

$$- \frac{1}{2}\left[\,\text{(diagram)} + \text{(diagram)} + 2\,\text{(diagram)}\,\right] + \cdots \tag{A.9}$$

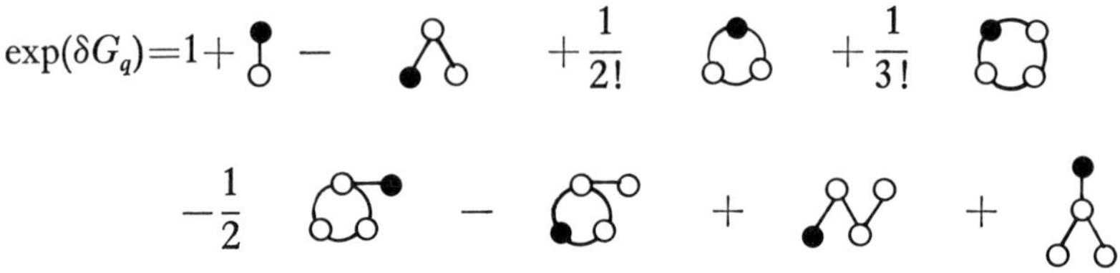

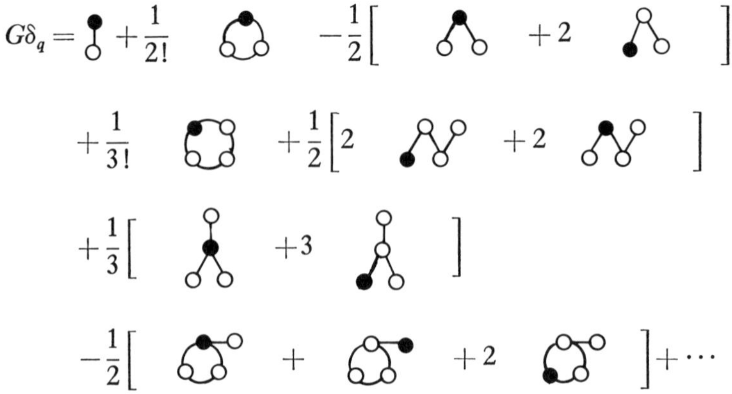

Equation (A.9) is essentially a difference equation for G. The solution as found by inspection is represented diagrammatically by

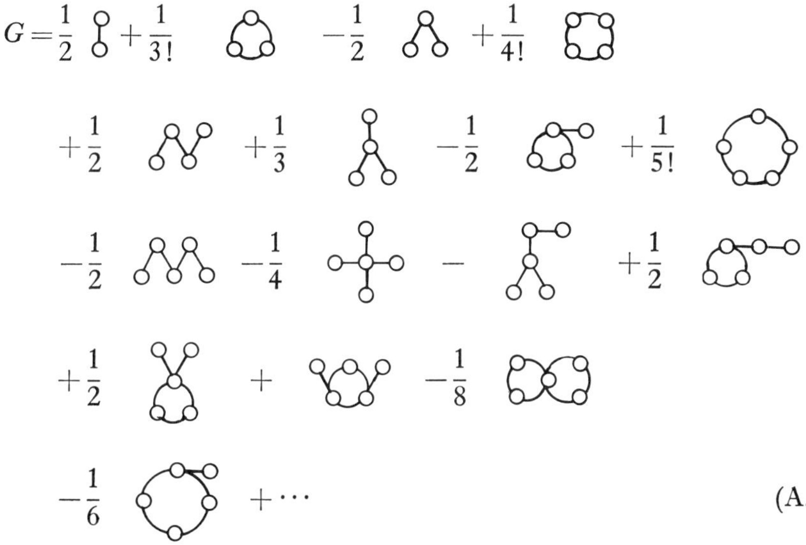

(A.10)

APPENDIX 8-B

Integration Formula for a Spherical Region

A function $f(|\mathbf{r}-\mathbf{r}'|)$ is integrated over concentric spherical regions of radii a in the variables $\mathbf{r}$ and $\mathbf{r}'$:

$$F(a)=\int_{r,r'\leq a} f(|\mathbf{r}-\mathbf{r}'|)\,d\mathbf{r}\,d\mathbf{r}' \tag{B.1}$$

Observe that $F(a)$ can be expressed as a one-dimensional integral

$$F(a)=\frac{16\pi^2}{3}a^3\int_0^{2a} f(s)P(s)s^2\,ds \tag{B.2}$$

in which the weight factor $P(s)$ is a universal function with a simple geometrical interpretation.

Let $n(r)$ take on the value 1 within the sphere and 0 outside. Then*

$$F(a) = \int n(r')n(r)\, f(s)\, \delta(\mathbf{s} - \mathbf{r} + \mathbf{r}')\, d\mathbf{r}\, d\mathbf{r}'\, d\mathbf{s}$$

$$= \int f(s)\left[\int n(r)n(|\mathbf{r} - \mathbf{s}|)\, d\mathbf{r}\right] d\mathbf{s} \qquad \text{(B.3)}$$

$$P(s) = (3/4\pi a^3) \int n(r)n(|\mathbf{r} - \mathbf{s}|)\, d\mathbf{r} \qquad \text{(B.4)}$$

The integral in Eq. (B.4) is simply the overlap volume of two spheres of radius a, one centered at the origin and the other centered at the point **s**. An elementary calculation yields

$$P(s) = 1 - \tfrac{3}{2}(s/2a) + \tfrac{1}{2}(s/2a)^3 \qquad \text{(B.5)}$$

* Procedure suggested by Dr. Fa Yueh Wu.

References

1. F. Y. Wu and E. Feenberg, *Phys. Rev.* **128**, 943 (1962).
2. F. Y. Wu, *J. Math. Phys.* **4**, 1438 (1963).
3. E. Feenberg and C. W. Woo, *Phys. Rev.* **137**, A391 (1965).
4. C. W. Woo, *Phys. Rev.* **151**, 138 (1966); unpublished doctoral dissertation, Washington University, 1966.
5. F. Iwamoto and M. Yamada, *Progr. Theoret. Phys.* (*Kyoto*) **17**, 543; *ibid.* **18**, 345 (1957).
6. J. B. Aviles, *Ann. Phys.* (*N.Y.*) **5**, 251 (1958).
7. C. D. Hartogh and H. A. Tolhoek, *Physica* **24**, 721, 875, 896 (1958).
8. J. W. Clark and P. Westhaus, *Phys. Rev.* **141**, 833 (1966).
9. W. E. Massey, *Phys. Rev.* **151**, 153 (1966).
10. W. E. Massey and C. W. Woo, *Phys. Rev.* **164**, 256 (1967).
11. D. Schiff and L. Verlet, *Phys. Rev.* **160**, 208 (1967).
12. L. H. Nosanow, *Phys. Rev. Letters* **13**, 270 (1964).
13. L. H. Nosanow and W. J. Mullin, *Phys. Rev. Letters* **14**, 133 (1965).
14. K. A. Brueckner, and J. Froberg, *Progr. Theoret. Phys.* (*Kyoto*) *Suppl.* 383 (1965).
15. T. L. Hill, "Statistical Mechanics," McGraw Hill, New York, 1956.
16. G. N. van Kampen, *Physica* **27**, 783 (1961).

CHAPTER 9

Correlated Basis Functions for Fermion Systems. Nondiagonal Matrix Elements and Perturbation Formulas

9.1. GENERATING FUNCTIONS*

The problem of evaluating nondiagonal matrix elements of the identity and the Hamiltonian can be solved in two steps: (1) Construct a suitable diagonal element to serve as a generating function for the desired nondiagonal element, and (2) apply the methods developed in Chapter 8 to compute the diagonal element.

Step 1 begins with the arbitrary model function $\Phi(|\hat{n})$ constructed from the orbitals

$$u(|\hat{l}) = a_l u(|l) + b_l u(|l'), \qquad l' \neq 1, 2, \ldots, N \qquad \text{if} \quad b_l \neq 0 \tag{9.1}$$

A proliferation of multiple indices is avoided by writing $n = 1, 2, \ldots, N$ and $n' = 1', 2', \ldots, N'$, without implying that either set defines the ground-state configuration. The use of linear combinations of single-particle orbitals l and l' in the lth column of the model function gives the formalism for computing diagonal matrix elements the ability to generate and evaluate nondiagonal elements as well.

In the application to a uniform system ($N \to \infty$, $\Omega \to \infty$, $\rho = N/\Omega = \text{const}$) the single-particle orbitals are products of plane waves and spin functions:

$$(\exp i\mathbf{k} \cdot \mathbf{r})\, \delta(\tfrac{1}{2}, m_s) \qquad \text{or} \qquad (\exp i\mathbf{k} \cdot \mathbf{r})\, \delta(-\tfrac{1}{2}, m_s) \tag{9.2}$$

* See Feenberg and Wu [1]; also Clark and Westhaus [2].

or the appropriate generalization with spin and isospin functions in the problem of nuclear matter. A discrete set of wave vectors is determined by the usual periodic boundary condition in a cube of volume Ω. The choice of orbitals implies a momentum conservation theorem $(\mathbf{n}'|A|\mathbf{n}) = 0$ unless $\sum \mathbf{k}_n = \sum \mathbf{k}_{n'}$ (A = 1 or H).

In general, $u(1|l)$ and $u(1|l')$ may differ in both wave vectors and spin states (as in the theory of static spin density waves [3]).

The following equations illustrate the way in which $(\hat{\mathbf{n}}|A|\hat{\mathbf{n}})$ serves as a generating function ($A = 1$ or H):

(a) *One orbital different* ($a_l = 1$, $b_l = 0$, $l \neq 1$):

$$(\hat{1}2\cdots N|A|\hat{1}2\cdots N) = |a_1|^2(12\cdots N|A|12\cdots N) + |b_1|^2(1'2\cdots N|A|1'2\cdots N) \tag{9.3}$$

(b) *Two orbitals different* ($a_l = 1$, $b_l = 0$, $l \neq 1, 2$):

$$\begin{aligned}(\hat{1}\hat{2}3 \cdots N|\hat{1}\hat{2}3 \cdots N) &= |a_1|^2|b_1|^2(123 \cdots N|A|123 \cdots N)\\ &+ \cdots + |b_1|^2|b_2|^2(1'2'3 \cdots N|A|1'2'3 \cdots N)\\ &+ a_1{}^*a_2{}^*b_1b_2(123 \cdots N|A|1'2'3 \cdots N) + \cdots\end{aligned} \tag{9.4}$$

(c) *Three orbitals different* ($a_l = 1$, $b_l = 0$, $l \neq 1, 2, 3$):

$$\begin{aligned}(\hat{1}\hat{2}\hat{3}4 \cdots N|A|\hat{1}\hat{2}\hat{3}4 \cdots N) &= |a_1|^2|a_2|^2|a_3|^2(1234 \cdots N|A|1234 \cdots N)\\ &+ \cdots + |b_1|^2|b_2|^2|b_3|^2(1'2'3'4 \cdots N|A|\\ &\times 1'2'3'4 \cdots N)\\ &+ |a_1|^2a_2{}^*a_3{}^*b_2b_3(1234 \cdots N|A|\\ &\times 12'3'4\cdots N) + \cdots\\ &+ a_1{}^*a_2{}^*a_3{}^*b_1b_2b_3(1234 \cdots N|A|\\ &\times 1'2'3'4\cdots N) + \cdots\end{aligned} \tag{9.5}$$

9.2. NONDIAGONAL CLUSTER INTEGRALS

Equation (8.11) defining the additive approximants and cluster integrals can be adopted to the present context simply by the replacement of orbital states $m, n, p, \ldots$ by the linear combinations $\hat{m}, \hat{n}, \hat{p}, \ldots$. Thus

$$X_{\hat{m}}(\beta) = |a_m|^2 \exp(\beta\mathbf{k}_m{}^2) + |b_m|^2 \exp(\beta\mathbf{k}_{m'}^2) \tag{9.6}$$

The coefficient of $a_m{}^*b_m$, which would be written $X_{m;m'}$, vanishes because either $\mathbf{k}_{m'} \neq \mathbf{k}_m$ or $\langle m \mid m' \rangle = 0$ or both. Similarly,

$$X_{\hat{m}\hat{n}}(\beta) = |a_m|^2|a_n|^2 X_{mn}(\beta) + \cdots + |b_m|^2|b_n|^2 X_{m'n'}(\beta)$$
$$+ a_m{}^*a_n{}^*b_m b_n X_{mn;\,m'n'}(\beta) + \cdots \tag{9.7}$$

The new nondiagonal cluster integral is defined by

$$X_{mn;\,m'n'}(\beta) = \int \psi_0^{B2} | e^{\beta K(1,\,2)} u(1|m)u(2|n)[(1 - P_{21}^{12})]$$
$$\times u^*(1|m')u^*(2|n')\, dv_{12}\, d\mathbf{r}_{3,\ldots,N} \tag{9.8}$$

yielding the exact explicit forms

$$X_{mn;\,m'n'}(0) = \delta(\mathbf{k}_m + \mathbf{k}_n - \mathbf{k}_{m'} - \mathbf{k}_{n'})[1/(N-1)]$$
$$\times \{[S(\mathbf{k}_m - \mathbf{k}_{m'}) - 1]\langle mn \mid m'n' \rangle$$
$$- [S(\mathbf{k}_m - \mathbf{k}_{n'}) - 1]\langle mn \mid n'm' \rangle\} \tag{9.9}$$

$$X'_{mn;\,m'n'}(0) = \delta(\mathbf{k}_m + \mathbf{k}_n - \mathbf{k}_{m'} - \mathbf{k}_{n'})[-1/(N-1)]$$
$$\times \{(\mathbf{k}_m - \mathbf{k}_{m'})^2[S(\mathbf{k}_m - \mathbf{k}_{m'}) - 1]\langle mn \mid m'n' \rangle$$
$$-(\mathbf{k}_m - \mathbf{k}_{n'})^2[S(\mathbf{k}_m - \mathbf{k}_{n'}) - 1]\langle mn \mid n'm' \rangle\}$$
$$+ \tfrac{1}{2}(k_m{}^2 + k_n{}^2 + k_{m'}^2 + k_{n'}^2)X_{mn;\,m'n'}(0) \tag{9.10}$$

In the applications the nondiagonal element always occurs in the normalized combination

$$x_{mn;\,m'n'}(\beta) = X_{mn;\,m'n'}(\beta)/X_{\hat{m}}(\beta)X_{\hat{n}}(\beta) \tag{9.11}$$

To avoid nonphysical complications, the analysis is continued under the symmetrical condition $|a_m|^2 = |b_m|^2 = a_n|^2 = |b_n|^2 = \frac{1}{2}$. The orbitrary phases of a_m, b_m, a_n, and b_n are still available to identify components of nondiagonal elements. Equations (9.9) and (9.10) lead to

$$x_{mn;\,m'n'}(0) = X_{mn;\,m'n'}(0)$$
$$x'_{mn;\,m'n'}(0) = \delta(\mathbf{k}_m + \mathbf{k}_n - \mathbf{k}_{m'} - \mathbf{k}_{n'})[-1/(N-1)]$$
$$\times \{k_{mm'}^2[S(k_{mm'}) - 1]\langle mn \mid m'n' \rangle - k_{mn'}^2[S(k_{mn'}) - 1]\langle mn \mid n'm' \rangle\} \tag{9.12}$$

The nondiagonal three-index cluster integrals all involve Fourier transforms of the three-particle distribution function:

$$S^{(3)}(\mathbf{k}, \mathbf{h}, \boldsymbol{l}) = (1/N) \int p^{(3)}(1, 2, 3) \exp i(\mathbf{k} \cdot \mathbf{r}_1 + \mathbf{h} \cdot \mathbf{r}_2 + \boldsymbol{l} \cdot \mathbf{r}_3)\, d\mathbf{r}_{1,2,3} \tag{9.13}$$

with $\mathbf{k} + \mathbf{h} + \boldsymbol{l} = 0$. The convolution approximation for $p^{(3)}$ serves to generate the explicit form

$$\begin{aligned} S^{(3)}(\mathbf{k}, \mathbf{h}, \boldsymbol{l}) = {} & [S(k) - 1][S(h) - 1] + [S(h) - 1][S(l) - 1] \\ & + [S(l) - 1][S(k) - 1] + [S(k) - 1][S(h) - 1][S(l) - 1] \end{aligned} \tag{9.14}$$

for $khl \neq 0$.

Two types of nondiagonal three-index cluster integrals occur in the theory. The first type is diagonal in one index and nondiagonal in the other two. By Eq. (8.11) the coefficient of $|a_m|^2 a_n{}^* a_p{}^* b_n{}' b_p{}'$ in the expanded formula for $I_{m\hat{n}\hat{p}}(\beta)$ is

$$\begin{aligned} & X_{mnp;\, mn'p'}(\beta) + X_m(\beta) X_{np;\, n'p'} \\ & = \frac{1}{N(N-1)(N-2)} \int p^{(3)}(1, 2, 3) e^{\beta K(1,2,3)} u(1|m) u(2|n) u(3|p) \\ & \quad \times (1 - P_{21}^{12} - P_{32}^{23} - P_{13}^{31} + P_{312}^{123} + P_{231}^{123}) \\ & \quad \times u^*(1|m) u^*(2|n') u^*(3|p')\, dv_{1,2,3} \end{aligned} \tag{9.15}$$

Equations (9.8) and (9.13) reduce Eq. (9.15) to

$$\begin{aligned} X_{mnp;\, mn'p'}(\beta) = {} & \delta(\mathbf{k}_n + \mathbf{k}_p - k_{n'} - \mathbf{k}_{p'})[1/(N-1)(N-2)] \\ & \times [\exp -\tfrac{1}{2}\beta\{2k_m{}^2 + k_n{}^2 + k_{n'}^2 + k_p{}^2 + k_{p'}^2\}] \\ & \times \{-\langle mnp|n'mp'\rangle S^{(3)}(\mathbf{k}_{mn'}, \mathbf{k}_{nm}, \mathbf{k}_{pp'})[\exp -\tfrac{1}{2}\beta(k_{mn'}^2 + k_{nm}^2 + k_{pp'}^2)] \\ & - \langle mnp|p'n'm\rangle S^{(3)}(\mathbf{k}_{mp'}, \mathbf{k}_{nn'}, \mathbf{k}_{pm})[\exp -\tfrac{1}{2}\beta(k_{mp'}^2 + k_{nn'}^2 + k_{pm}^2)] \\ & + \langle mnp|n'p'm\rangle S^{(3)}(\mathbf{k}_{mn'}, \mathbf{k}_{np'}, k_{pm})[\exp -\tfrac{1}{2}\beta(k_{mn'}^2 + k_{np'}^2 + k_{pm}^2)] \\ & + \langle mnp|p'mn'\rangle S^{(3)}(k_{mp'}, k_{nm}, k_{pn'})[\exp -\tfrac{1}{2}\beta(k_{mp'}^2 + k_{nm}^2 + k_{pn'}^2)]\} \end{aligned} \tag{9.16}$$

The normalized coefficient

$$x_{mnp;\,mn'p'}(\beta) = X_{mnp;\,mn'p'}(\beta)/X_m(\beta)X_{\hat{n}}(\beta)X_{\hat{p}}(\beta) \tag{9.17}$$

is evaluated under the symmetrical condition $|a_n|^2 = |a_p|^2 = |b_n|^2 = |b_p|^2 = \frac{1}{2}$, with the result that

$$x_{mnp;\,mn'p'}(\beta) = X_{mnp;\,mn'p'}(\beta) \exp -\tfrac{1}{2}\beta(2k_m{}^2 + k_n{}^2 + k_{n'}^2 + k_p{}^2 + k_{p'}^2) \tag{9.18}$$

Thus the normalized coefficient is given by Eq. (9.16) with the common exponential factor deleted. Consequently,

$$\begin{aligned} x'_{mnp;\,mn'p'}(0) = {} & \delta(\mathbf{k}_n + \mathbf{k}_p - \mathbf{k}_{n'} - \mathbf{k}_{p'})[1/2(N-1)(N-2)] \\ & \times [\langle mnp|n'mp'\rangle S^{(3)}(\mathbf{k}_{mn'}, \mathbf{k}_{nm}, k_{pp'})(k_{mn'}^2 + k_{nm}^2 + k_{pp'}^2) \\ & + \langle mnp|p'n'm\rangle S^{(3)}(\mathbf{k}_{mp'}, \mathbf{k}_{nn'}, \mathbf{k}_{pm})(k_{mp'}^2 + k_{nn'}^2 + k_{pm}^2) \\ & - \langle mnp|n'p'm\rangle S^{(3)}(\mathbf{k}_{mn'}, \mathbf{k}_{np'}, k_{pm})(k_{mn'}^2 + k_{np'}^2 + k_{pm}^2) \\ & - \langle mnp|p'mn'\rangle S^{(3)}(\mathbf{k}_{mp'}, \mathbf{k}_{nm}, \mathbf{k}_{pn'})(k_{mp'}^2 + k_{nm}^2 + k_{pn'}^2)] \end{aligned} \tag{9.19}$$

A slight generalization of Eq. (8.11) (substitution of $\hat{m}$, $\hat{n}$, $\hat{p}$ for m, n, and p) enables it to generate the coefficient of $a_m{}^*a_n{}^*a_p{}^*b_m b_n b_p$ in the expanded formula for $I_{mnp}(\beta)$:

$$\begin{aligned} X_{mnp;\,m'n'p'}(\beta) = {} & [1/N(N-1)(N-2)] \int p^{(3)}(1, 2, 3)[\exp \beta K(1, 2, 3)] \\ & \times u(1|m)u(2|m)u(3|p)(1 - p_{21}^{12} - p_{32}^{23} - p_{13}^{31} + p_{312}^{123} + p_{231}^{123}) \\ & \times u^*(1|m')u^*(2|n')u^*(3|p')\, dv_{1,2,3} \\ = {} & \delta(\mathbf{k}_m + \mathbf{k}_n + \mathbf{k}_p - \mathbf{k}_{m'} - \mathbf{k}_{n'} - \mathbf{k}_{p'})[1/(N-1)(N-2)] \\ & \times [\exp \tfrac{1}{2}\beta(k_m{}^2 + k_n{}^2 + k_p{}^2 + k_{m'}^2 + k_{n'}^2 + k_{p'}^2)] \\ & \{\langle mnp|m'n'p'\rangle S^{(3)}(\mathbf{k}_{mm'}, \mathbf{k}_{nn'}, \mathbf{k}_{pp'})[\exp -\tfrac{1}{2}\beta(k_{mm'}^2 + k_{nn'}^2 + k_{pp'}^2)] \\ & - \langle mnp|n'm'p'\rangle S^{(3)}(\mathbf{k}_{mn'}, \mathbf{k}_{nm'}, \mathbf{k}_{pp'})[\exp -\tfrac{1}{2}\beta(k_{mn'}^2 + k_{mn'}^2 + k_{pp'}^2)] \\ & - \langle mnp|m'p'n'\rangle S^{(3)}(\mathbf{k}_{mm'}, \mathbf{k}_{np'}, \mathbf{k}_{pn'})[\exp -\tfrac{1}{2}\beta(k_{mm'}^2 + k_{np'}^2 + k_{pn'}^2)] \\ & - \langle mnp|p'n'm'\rangle S^{(3)}(k_{mp'}, k_{nn'}, k_{pm'})[\exp -\tfrac{1}{2}\beta(k_{mp'}^2 + k_{nn'}^2 + k_{pm'}^2)] \\ & + \langle mnp|p'm'n'\rangle S^{(3)}(k_{mp'}, k_{nm'}, k_{pn'})[\exp -\tfrac{1}{2}\beta(k_{mp'}^2 + k_{nm'}^2 + k_{pn'}^2)] \\ & + \langle mnp|n'p'm'\rangle S^{(3)}(k_{mn'}, k_{np'}, k_{pm'})[\exp -\tfrac{1}{2}\beta(k_{mn'}^2 + k_{np'}^2 + k_{pm'}^2)]\} \end{aligned} \tag{9.20}$$

The normalized coefficient

$$x_{mnp;\, m'n'p'}(\beta) = X_{mnp;\, m'n'p'}(\beta)/X_{\hat{m}}(\beta)X_{\hat{n}}(\beta)X_{\hat{p}}(\beta) \tag{9.21}$$

is given by the formula of Eq. (9.20) with the common exponential factor deleted. Finally,

$$\begin{aligned} x'_{mnp;\, m'n'p'}(0) = {} & \delta(\mathbf{k}_m + \mathbf{k}_n + \mathbf{k}_p - \mathbf{k}_{m'} - \mathbf{k}_{n'} - \mathbf{k}_{p'})[1/2(N-1)(N-2)] \\ & \times [-\langle mnp|m'n'p'\rangle S^{(3)}(\mathbf{k}_{mm'}, k_{nn'}, \mathbf{k}_{pp'})(k^2_{mm'} + k^2_{nn'} + k^2_{pp'}) \\ & + \langle mnp|n'm'p'\rangle S^{(3)}(\mathbf{k}_{mn'}, \mathbf{k}_{nm'}, \mathbf{k}_{pp'})(k^2_{mn'} + k^2_{n'm} + k^2_{pp'}) \\ & + \langle mnp|m'p'n'\rangle S^{(3)}(\mathbf{k}_{mm'}, \mathbf{k}_{np'}, \mathbf{k}_{pn'})(k^2_{mm'} + k^2_{np'} + k^2_{pn'}) \\ & + \langle mnp|p'n'm'\rangle S^{(3)}(\mathbf{k}_{mp'}, \mathbf{k}_{nn'}, \mathbf{k}_{pm'})(k^2_{mp'} + k^2_{nn'} + k^2_{pm'}) \\ & - \langle mnp|p'm'n'\rangle S^{(3)}(\mathbf{k}_{mp'}, \mathbf{k}_{nm'}, \mathbf{k}_{pn'})(k^2_{mp'} + k^2_{nm'} + k^2_{pn'}) \\ & - \langle mnp|n'p'm'\rangle S^{(3)}(\mathbf{k}_{mn'}, \mathbf{k}_{np'}, \mathbf{k}_{pm'})(k^2_{mn'} + k^2_{np'} + k^2_{pm'})] \end{aligned} \tag{9.22}$$

9.3. MATRIX ELEMENTS OF THE IDENTITY

Equations (9.6)–(9.22) provide everything needed to evaluate matrix elements of the identity and Hamiltonian through three-index terms in the cluster expansions.

(a) *One orbital different:* $|a_1|^2 = |b_1|^2 = \frac{1}{2}$. Equations (8.8) and (9.3) require

$$\exp[G(\hat{1}2\cdots N|0)] = \tfrac{1}{2}\{\exp[G(12\cdots N|0)] + \exp[G(1'2\cdots N|0)]\} \tag{9.23}$$

or, equivalently,

$$\begin{aligned} \exp[G(\hat{1}2\cdots N|0) & - \tfrac{1}{2}G(12\cdots N|0) - \tfrac{1}{2}G(1'2\cdots N|0)] \\ & = \cosh \tfrac{1}{2}[G(12\cdots N|0) - G(1'2\cdots N|0)] \end{aligned} \tag{9.24}$$

The quantities in brackets in Eq. (9.24) can be evaluated with the aid of Eq. (8.15). First some definitions:

$$\begin{aligned} \delta G(1) & = G(12\cdots N|0) - G(23\cdots N|0) \\ & = \sum_{1<n} x_{1n}(0) + \sum_{1<n<p} [x_{1np}(0) - x_{1n}x_{np} - x_{1p}x_{pn} - x_{1n}x_{1p}] \\ & \quad + \cdots \\ \delta G(1) - \delta G(1') & = \sum_{1<n} [x_{1n}(0) - x_{1'n}(0)] + \cdots \end{aligned} \tag{9.25}$$

$$\begin{aligned}\Delta G(1', 1) &\equiv G(\hat{1}2 \cdots N|0) - \tfrac{1}{2}G(12 \cdots N|0) - \tfrac{1}{2}G(1'2 \cdots N|0) \\ &= - \sum_{1<n<p} [x_{n\hat{1}} x_{p\hat{1}} - \tfrac{1}{2}x_{n1} x_{p1} - \tfrac{1}{2}x_{n1'} x_{p1'}] + \cdots \\ &= \tfrac{1}{8} \Big| \sum_{1<n} \{x_{1n}(0) - x_{1'n}(0)\}\Big|^2 + \cdots \\ &= \tfrac{1}{8} |\delta G(1) - \delta G(1')|^2 + \cdots \end{aligned} \tag{9.26}$$

Notice that the last line of Eq. (9.26) constitutes a check on Eq. (9.24), at least through quadratic terms in $\delta G(1') - \delta G(1)$. Notice also that the leading term for $\Delta G(1', 1)$ given by Eq. (9.26) is generated by the terms with repeated indices in the second addend of Eq. (8.15). The truncated G_{IY} gives consistent results in Eq. (9.24) without invoking contributions from the third and higher addends. With G_{AHT} an equal level of consistency can be attained only by introducing terms from the third addend [Eq. (8.20)]. Thus the truncated IY development (two- and three-index terms in G) meets a test of internal consistency in a satisfactory manner, while the corresponding truncated development of the AHT development fails.

Normalized basis functions are convenient in the following sections. Let

$$\begin{aligned} |12 \cdots N\} &\equiv \Psi(|n)/(\mathbf{n}|1|\mathbf{n})^{1/2} \\ E^{(0)}(\mathbf{n}) &= \{\mathbf{n}|H|\mathbf{n}\} \end{aligned} \tag{9.27}$$

The angular bracket $|\rangle$ is reserved for an orthonormal basis system.

(b) *Two orbtials different:* $(a_1|^2 = |a_2|^2 = |b_1|^2 = |b_2|^2 = \frac{1}{2}$. Equation (9.4) requires

$$\begin{aligned}\exp G(\hat{1}\hat{2}3 \cdots N|0) = \tfrac{1}{4}[&\exp G(123 \cdots N|0) + \exp G(1'23 \cdots N|0) \\ &+ \exp G(12'3 \cdots N|0) + \exp G(1'2'3 \cdots N|0)] \end{aligned} \tag{9.28}$$

except for terms reduced by a factor $1/N$. A common exponential factor multiplying both members of Eq. (9.28) reduces it to

$$\begin{aligned} 4 \exp[&G(\hat{1}\hat{2}3 \cdots N|0) - \tfrac{1}{4}G(123 \cdots N|0) - \tfrac{1}{4}G(1'23 \cdots N|0) \\ &- \tfrac{1}{4}G(12'3 \cdots N|0) - \tfrac{1}{4}G(1'2'3 \cdots N|0)] \\ &= \exp \tfrac{1}{2}[\delta G(1) - \delta G(1') + \delta G(2) - \delta G(2')] \\ &\quad + \exp \tfrac{1}{2}[\delta G(1) - \delta G(1') - \delta G(2) + \delta G(2')] \\ &\quad + \exp \tfrac{1}{2}[-\delta G(1) + \delta G(1') + \delta G(2) - \delta G(2')] \\ &\quad + \exp \tfrac{1}{2}[-\delta G(1) + \delta G(1') - \delta G(2) + \delta G(2')] \\ &= 4 \cosh \tfrac{1}{2}[\delta G(1) - \delta G(1')] \cosh \tfrac{1}{2}[\delta G(2) - \delta G(2')] \end{aligned} \tag{9.29}$$

Equation (8.15) yields

$$G(\hat{1}\hat{2}3 \cdots N|0) - \tfrac{1}{4}[G(123 \cdots N|0) + G(1'23 \cdots N|0) + G(12'3 \cdots N/0) + G(1'2'3 \cdots N|0)] = \Delta G(1, 1') + \Delta G(2, 2') + O(1/N) \tag{9.30}$$

checking the consistency of the truncated IY cluster expansion in the context of Eq. (9.4) and Eqs. (9.24)–(9.28).

To evaluate the nondiagonal matrix element, observe that

$$(123 \cdots N|1|1'2'3 \cdots N) = \text{coefficient of } \; a_1{}^*a_2{}^*b_1b_2 \; \text{ in } \; \exp G(\hat{1}\hat{2} \cdots N|0) = G_{12;1'2'} \exp G(\hat{1}\hat{2}3 \cdots N|0) \tag{9.31}$$

or

$$\{123 \cdots N|1|1'2'3 \cdots N\} = G_{12;1'2'}(0) \times \exp[G(\hat{1}\hat{2}3 \cdots N|0) - \tfrac{1}{2}G(123 \cdots N|0) - \tfrac{1}{2}G(1'2'3 \cdots N|0)] \tag{9.32}$$

$$G_{12;1'2'}(0) = x_{12;1'2'}(0) + \sum_{n<2} \{x_{12n;1'2'n}(0) - \tfrac{1}{2}x_{12;1'2'}(0)[x_{1n}(0) + x_{1'n}(0) + x_{2n}(0) + x_{2'n}(0)] + \cdots\} \tag{9.33}$$

Again applying Eq. (8.15),

$$G(\hat{1}\hat{2}3 \cdots N|0) - \tfrac{1}{2}G(123 \cdots N|0) - \tfrac{1}{2}G(1'2'3 \cdots N|0) = \Delta G(1', 1) + \Delta G(2', 2) + O(1/N) \tag{9.34}$$

and

$$\{123 \cdots N|1|1'2'3 \cdots N\} = G_{12;1'2'}(0) \cosh \tfrac{1}{2}[\delta G(1) - \delta G(1')] \cosh \tfrac{1}{2}[\delta G(2) - \delta G(2')] \tag{9.35}$$

Equation (9.35) is not altogether satisfactory. The function $G_{12;1'2'}$ is antisymmetrical in the final-state indices 1 and 2 and also in the initial state indices $1'$ and $2'$. These properties derive from the antisymmetry of the state functions $\Psi(|\mathbf{n})$ and $\Psi(|\mathbf{n}')$. The remaining factor in the right-hand member of Eq. (9.35) should be a symmetrical function of indices

1 and 2 and also of 1′ and 2′, but obviously it is not. The immediate cause of the discrepancy is surely the association of states 1 and 1′ in $u(|\hat{1})$ and of 2 and 2′ in $u(|\hat{2})$, so that 1 and 2 and also 1′ and 2′ enter the theory in an asymmetrical manner. This association causes no difficulty in the expanded matrix element [Eq. (9.4)] because the linear combination of orbitals leads directly to a linear combination of states determinants, each with unimpaired fermion symmetry properties. On the other hand, the cluster expansion is apparently not sufficiently flexible to reproduce in every detail the properties implied by a linear combination of determinants. This difficulty can be resolved by writing $u(|\hat{1})$ and $u(|\hat{2})$ as two normalized orthogonal linear combinations of all four states 1, 2, $\hat{1}$, and $\hat{2}$ with equal statistical weights. Symmetry can be achieved in working formulas by symmetrizing the coefficient of $G_{12;1'2'}$ in Eq. (9.35) with respect to interchange of 1′ and 2′. We introduce the geometric mean coefficient and write

$$\{123 \cdots N|1|1'2'3 \cdots N\} \approx G_{12;1'2'}(0) \times \left\{ \prod_{i=1}^{2} \prod_{j=1}^{2} \cosh \tfrac{1}{2}[\delta G(i') - \delta G(j)] \right\}^{1/2} \tag{9.36}$$

Actually, the factor multiplying $G_{12;1'2'}$ in Eq. (9.35) is replaced by 1 in the explicit working version of the theory. The theory is useful only when the difference between Eqs. (9.35) and (9.36) is inconsequential. Numerical estimates in the applications verify that this is indeed the actual situation.

(c) *Three orbitals different*: $|a_1|^2 = |a_2|^2 = |a_3|^2 = |b_1|^2 = |b_2|^2 = |b_3|^2 = \frac{1}{2}$. The equation corresponding to Eqs. (9.28) and (9.29) is

$$\begin{aligned} 8 \exp\{G(\hat{1}\hat{2}\hat{3}4 \cdots N|0) - \tfrac{1}{8}[G(1234 \cdots N|0) \\ + G(1'234 \cdots N|0) + \cdots + G(1'2'3'4 \cdots N|0)]\} \\ = \sum \exp \tfrac{1}{2}\{\pm[\delta G(1) - \delta G(1')] \pm [\delta G(2) - \delta G(2')] \\ \pm [\delta G(3) - \delta G(3')]\} \end{aligned} \tag{9.37}$$

the summation ranging over the eight independent choices of $\pm$ signs in the right-hand member. With the help of Eq. (8.15), Eq. (9.37) reduces to

$$\exp[\Delta G(1', 1) + \Delta G(2', 2) + \Delta G(3', 3)] = \prod_{i=1}^{3} \cosh \tfrac{1}{2}[\delta G(i') - \delta G(i)] \tag{9.38}$$

in agreement with Eq. (9.24).

Each of the Eqs. (9.31)–(9.35) has its parallel here:

$$(1234 \cdots N|1|1'2'3'4 \cdots N) = G_{123;1'2'3'}(0) \exp G(\hat{1}\hat{2}\hat{3}4 \cdots N|0) \qquad (9.39)$$

or

$$\begin{aligned}\{1234 \cdots N|1|1'2'3'4 \cdots N\} = G_{123;1'2'3'}(0) \exp[&G(\hat{1}\hat{2}\hat{3}4 \cdots N|0) \\ &-\tfrac{1}{2}G(1234 \cdots N|0) \\ &-\tfrac{1}{2}G(1'2'3'4 \cdots N|0)]\end{aligned} \qquad (9.40)$$

$$G_{123;1'2'3'}(0) = x_{123;1'2'3'}(0) + \cdots \qquad (9.41)$$

Also,

$$\begin{aligned}&G(\hat{1}\hat{2}\hat{3}4 \cdots N|0) - \tfrac{1}{2}G(1234 \cdots N|0) - \tfrac{1}{2}G(1'2'3'4 \cdots N|0) \\ &= \Delta G(1', 1) + \Delta G(2', 2) + \Delta G(3', 3) + O(1/N)\end{aligned} \qquad (9.42)$$

and

$$\{1234 \cdots N|1|1'2'3'4 \cdots N\} = G_{123;1'2'3'} \prod_{i=1}^{3} \cosh \tfrac{1}{2}[\delta G(i') - \delta G(i)] \qquad (9.43)$$

The discrepancy already noted arises again; the matrix element is completely antisymmetrical in the indices 1, 2, and 3 and also in 1′, 2′, and 3′; so also is $G_{123;1'2'3'}$. Consistency requires that the coefficient of $G_{123;1'2'3'}$ should be invariant under permutations of 1, 2, and 3 and also of 1′, 2′, and 3′, but it is not. To secure correct behavior, the coefficient of $G_{123;1'2'3'}$ is replaced by the geometric mean of the nine different coefficients generated by the permutations of 1, 2, and 3:

$$\begin{aligned}&\{1234 \cdots N|1|1'2'3'4 \cdots N\} \\ &= G_{123;1'2'3'}(0)\left\{\prod_{i=1}^{3}\prod_{j=1}^{3} \cosh \tfrac{1}{2}[\delta G(i') - \delta G(j)]\right\}^{1/3}\end{aligned} \qquad (9.44)$$

Again the factor in square brackets is replaced by 1 in the applications with negligible loss of accuracy.

9.4. MATRIX ELEMENTS OF THE HAMILTONIAN

Equations (8.9) and (8.15) generate the basic formula for the matrix elements of the Hamiltonian operator in the form

$$(\hat{\mathbf{n}}|H|\hat{\mathbf{n}}) = \left[E_0{}^{\mathrm{B}} + \frac{\hbar^2}{2m}\sum_n \frac{X_{\hat{n}}'(0)}{X_{\hat{n}}(0)} + \frac{\hbar^2}{2m} G'(\hat{\mathbf{n}}|0)\right](\hat{\mathbf{n}}|1|\hat{\mathbf{n}}) \tag{9.45}$$

Equation (9.6) yields

$$\begin{aligned} X_{\hat{n}}(0) &= 1 \\ X_{\hat{n}}'(0) &= |a_n|^2 k_n{}^2 + |b_n|^2 k_{n'}^2 \\ &\equiv k_{\hat{n}}{}^2 \end{aligned} \tag{9.46}$$

Explicit formulas for nondiagonal matrix elements are derived below.

(a) *One orbital different*: $|a_1|^2 = |b_1|^2 = \frac{1}{2}$. Equation (9.45) reduces to

$$\begin{aligned} &\{\exp \tfrac{1}{2}[\delta G(1) - \delta G(1')]\} E^{(0)}(12 \cdots N) + \{\exp -\tfrac{1}{2}[\delta G(1) - \delta G(1')]\} \\ &\quad \times E^{(0)}(1'2 \cdots N) = 2 \cosh \tfrac{1}{2}[\delta G(1) - \delta G(1')] E^{(0)}(\hat{1}2 \cdots N) \\ &= 2 \cosh \tfrac{1}{2}[\delta G(1) - \delta G(1')][\tfrac{1}{2}E^{(0)}(12 \cdots N) + \tfrac{1}{2}E^{(0)}(1'2 \cdots N) \\ &\quad + \delta E(1', 1)] \end{aligned} \tag{9.47}$$

with the help of Eq. (9.24). The small cross term $\delta E(1', 1)$ is evaluated in reference [1]. Terms proportional to N in Eq. (9.47) balance exactly. There are left on either side small terms independent of N. These may not balance accurately for the reason that terms of order $O(N^0)$ are neglected in the derivation of Eq. (8.15) for G.

(b) *Two orbitals different*: $|a_2|^2 = |b_1|^2 = |a_2|^2 = |b_2|^2 = \frac{1}{2}$.

$$\begin{aligned} &(\hat{1}\hat{2} \cdots N|H - E_0{}^{\mathrm{B}}|\hat{1}\hat{2} \cdots N) \\ &= \frac{1}{4}[(123 \cdots N|H - E_0{}^{\mathrm{B}}|123 \cdots N) \\ &\quad + \cdots + (1'2'3 \cdots N|H - E_0{}^{\mathrm{B}}|1'2'3 \cdots N)] \\ &\quad + a_1{}^* a_2{}^* b_1 b_2 (123 \cdots N|H - E_0{}^{\mathrm{B}}|1'2'3 \cdots N) + \cdots \\ &= \frac{\hbar^2}{2m}\left[\frac{1}{2}(k_1{}^2 + k_{1'}^2 + k_2{}^2 + k_{2'}^2) + \sum_{n>2} k_n{}^2\right](\hat{1}\hat{2}3 \cdots N|1|\hat{1}\hat{2}3 \cdots N) \\ &\quad + \frac{\hbar^2}{2m} G'(\hat{1}\hat{2} \cdots N|0)(\hat{1}\hat{2}3 \cdots |1|\hat{1}\hat{2}3 \cdots N) \end{aligned} \tag{9.48}$$

Again, as in Eq. (9.45), linear terms in N balance exactly. The coefficient of $a_1{}^* a_2{}^* b_1 b_2$ is subject to the relation

$$
\begin{aligned}
&(123 \cdots N|H|1'2'3 \cdots N) \\
&\quad = \frac{1}{4}[E^{(0)}(123 \cdots N) + E^{(0)}(1'23 \cdots N) \\
&\quad + E^{(0)}(12'3 \cdots N) + E^{(0)}(1'2'3 \cdots N)] \\
&\quad \times (123 \cdots N|1|1'2'3 \cdots N) \\
&\quad + \frac{\hbar^2}{8m} G'_{12;1'2'}(0)[(123 \cdots N|1|123 \cdots N) \\
&\quad + (1'23 \cdots N|1|1'23 \cdots N) \\
&\quad + (12'3 \cdots N|1|12'3 \cdots N) + (1'2'3 \cdots N|1|1'2'3 \cdots N)]
\end{aligned} \tag{9.49}
$$

or, equivalently,

$$
\begin{aligned}
&\{123 \cdots N|H|1'2'3 \cdots N\} \\
&\quad \approx [\tfrac{1}{2}E^{(0)}(123 \cdots N) + \tfrac{1}{2}E^{(0)}(1'2'3 \cdots N) \\
&\quad + \delta E(1', 1) + \delta E(2', 2)]\{123 \cdots N|1|1'2'3 \cdots N\} \\
&\quad + (\hbar^2/2m)G'_{12;1'2'}(0) \cosh \tfrac{1}{2}[\delta G(1') - \delta G(1)] \cosh \tfrac{1}{2}[\delta G(2') - \delta G(2)]
\end{aligned} \tag{9.50}
$$

As in Eq. (9.35), the right-hand member of Eq. (9.50) is not exactly antisymmetrical in the indices 1,2 or in 1′, 2′. The precedent set in writing Eq. (9.36) is followed and Eq. (9.50) replaced by the simplest possible antisymmetrical modification:

$$
\begin{aligned}
&\{123 \cdots N|H|1'2'3 \cdots N\} \\
&\quad = \tfrac{1}{2}[E^{(0)}(123 \cdots N) + E^{(0)}(1'2'3 \cdots N) \\
&\quad + \delta E(1', 1) + \delta E(2', 1) + \delta E(1', 2) \\
&\quad + \delta E(2', 2)]\{123 \cdots N|1|1'2'3 \cdots N\} \\
&\quad + (\hbar^2/2m)G'_{12;1'2'}(0)\left[\prod_{i=1}^{2}\prod_{j=1}^{2} \cosh \tfrac{1}{2}[\delta G(i') - \delta G(j)]\right]^{1/2}
\end{aligned} \tag{9.51}
$$

The actual numerical differences are quite small and cannot modify the physical consequences of the formalism in any serious respect [4].

(c) *Three orbitals different*: $|a_1|^2 = |a_2|^2 = |a_3|^2 = |b_1|^2 = |b_2|^2 = |b_3|^2 = \frac{1}{2}$. The actual form for $(1234 \cdots N|H|1'2'3'4 \cdots N)$ given by Eq. (9.45) fails to meet the test of exact antisymmetry in the indices 1, 2, and 3 or in 1′, 2′, and 3′. I substitute a properly symmetrized form

$$\begin{aligned}\{1234 \cdots N|H|1'2'3'4 \cdots N\} &= [\tfrac{1}{2}E^{(0)}(1234 \cdots N) \\ &+ \tfrac{1}{2}E^{(0)}(1'2'3'4 \cdots N) + \tfrac{1}{3}\sum_{i=1}^{3}\sum_{j=1}^{3} \delta E(i', j)]\{1234 \cdots N|1|1'2'3'4 \cdots N\} \\ &+ (\hbar^2/2m)G'_{123;\,1'2'3'}(0)\left\{\prod_{i=1}^{3}\prod_{j=1}^{3} \cosh \tfrac{1}{2}[\delta G(i') - \delta G(j)]\right\}^{1/3}\end{aligned} \tag{9.52}$$

Again the changes are small in magnitude and have essentially no effect on the consequences of the formalism.

9.5. MATRIX REPRESENTATIONS OF THE IDENTITY AND HAMILTONIAN

The matrices $\mathscr{N}$ and $\mathscr{H}$ constructed from $\{\mathbf{m}|1|\mathbf{n}\}$ and $\{\mathbf{m}|H|\mathbf{n}\}$ are complicated by the presence of amplitude factors $\cosh \frac{1}{2}[\delta G(i) - \delta G(j)]$ and small terms involving $\delta E(i, j)$ in the matrix elements. The amplitude factors are replaced by unity and terms in $\delta E(i, j)$ omitted in the working version of the theory. These simplifications are incorporated in the following statements:

$$\begin{aligned}\mathscr{N} &= I + J, \qquad I = (\delta_{\mathbf{m},\,\mathbf{n}}) \\ J_{\mathbf{m},\,\mathbf{n}} &= G_{\mathbf{m};\,\mathbf{n}}(0), \qquad \mathbf{m} \neq \mathbf{n} \\ &= 0, \qquad \mathbf{m} = \mathbf{n}\end{aligned} \tag{9.53}$$

$$\begin{aligned}\mathscr{H} &= (\{\mathbf{m}|H|\mathbf{n}\}) \\ &= \mathscr{W} + \tfrac{1}{2}(\mathscr{E}\mathscr{N} + \mathscr{N}\mathscr{E}) \\ &= \mathscr{E} + \mathscr{W} + \tfrac{1}{2}(\mathscr{E}J + J\mathscr{E}) \\ \mathscr{E} &= (E^{(0)}_{\mathbf{m}}\delta_{\mathbf{m},\,\mathbf{n}}) \\ \mathscr{W}_{\mathbf{m},\,\mathbf{n}} &= G'_{\mathbf{m},\mathbf{n}}(0), \qquad \mathbf{m} \neq \mathbf{n} \\ &= 0, \qquad \mathbf{m} = \mathbf{n}\end{aligned} \tag{9.54}$$

The diagonal elements of $\mathscr{H}$ have immediate physical content in the sense that they can be correlated sensibly with the true eigenvalues (particularly the ground state and a range of low excited states); however, the nondiagonal elements suggest a strength of coupling between different basis states which is wholly misleading if the nonorthogonality of the basis is overlooked. The source of difficulty is the fact that $\frac{1}{2}(E_{\mathbf{m}}^{(0)} + E_{\mathbf{n}}^{(0)})J_{\mathbf{mn}}$ is one whole power of N larger than $\mathscr{W}_{\mathbf{mn}}$. In all calculations involving nondiagonal matrix elements of $\mathscr{H}$ an adjustment or adaptation of the interaction operator is essential before the calculation can proceed as if the states were orthogonal. What is needed is an effective Hamiltonian matrix $\mathscr{H}_{\text{eff}}$ with which calculations can be made as if the state indices (**m** and **n**) represented orthonormal basis states. The meaning of this statement is clarified in the following sections by the construction of $\mathscr{H}_{\text{eff}}$ suitable for treating problems involving the ground state and a range of low excited states.

9.6. EVALUATION OF THE GROUND-STATE ENERGY

An elementary derivation of a working formula for the ground-state energy is given here to provide a model and goal for the more general derivations to follow. Let the index 0 represent the basis function generated by the ground-state configuration, and n all other basis states. The modified basis functions

$$|n\}' = \frac{|n\} - |0\}J_{0n}}{(1 - J_{0n}^2)^{1/2}} \tag{9.55}$$

span the complete function space orthogonal to $|0\}$. The fact that these functions are not mutally orthogonal will be neglected in the evaluation of the ground-state energy. The calculation begins with

$$\begin{aligned}\{0|H|n\}' &\approx \mathscr{H}_{0n} - J_{0n}E_0^{(0)} \\ &= \mathscr{W}_{0n} + \tfrac{1}{2}(E_0^{(0)} + E_n^{(0)})J_{0n} - J_{0n}E_0^{(0)} \\ &= \mathscr{W}_{0n} - \tfrac{1}{2}(E_0^{(0)} - E_n^{(0)})J_{0n}\end{aligned} \tag{9.56}$$

This result enables us to compute the ground-state energy through the second order of the Schrödinger perturbation formalism [4]:

$$
\begin{aligned}
E_0 &= E_0^{(0)} + \delta E_0^{(2)} \\
\delta E_0^{(2)} &= \sum_{m\neq 0} \frac{|\{0|H|m\}'|^2}{E_0^{(0)} - E_m^{(0)}} \\
&= \sum_{m\neq 0} \frac{\mathscr{W}_{0m}^2}{E_0^{(0)} - E_m^{(0)}} - \sum_m \mathscr{W}_{0m} J_{m0} + \frac{1}{4}\sum_m (E_0^{(0)} - E_m^{(0)}) J_{0m}^2
\end{aligned} \tag{9.57}
$$

The weakness in this derivation is neglect of the fact that the $|m\}'$ states are strongly coupled through the terms $\frac{1}{2}(E_m^{(0)} + E_n^{(0)}) J_{nm} \sim O(N^0)$ in the matrix representation of the Hamiltonian operator It is conceivable that this coupling might strongly influence the ground state energy. Alternative derivations are needed to justify Eq. (9.57) or to replace it by a more accurate formula. Two alternative derivations are discussed in the following sections, one confirming Eq. (9.57) in a general, but nonrigorous context, and the other indicating the possibility that the matrix elements making up the second-order energy are renormalized by the strong coupling among the $|m\}'$ states.

9.7. FORMAL TRANSFORMATION TO AN ORTHONORMAL BASIS SYSTEM

The matrix elements of $\mathscr{N}^{-1}$ and $\mathscr{N}^{\pm 1/2}$ are defined by the equations

$$
\begin{aligned}
&\sum_m (\mathscr{N}^{-1})_{nm} \mathscr{N}_{mp} = \delta_{np} \\
&\sum_m (\mathscr{N}^{\pm 1/2})_{nm} (\mathscr{N}^{\pm 1/2})_{mp} = (\mathscr{N}^{\pm 1})_{np} \\
&\sum_m (\mathscr{N}^{\pm 1/2})_{nm} (\mathscr{N}^{\mp 1/2})_{mp} = \delta_{np}
\end{aligned} \tag{9.58}
$$

A new basis system

$$
|n\}' = \sum_m |m\} (\mathscr{N}^{-1/2})_{mn} \tag{9.59}
$$

has the desired orthonormal property. We verify that

$$
\begin{aligned}
{}'\{m|1|n\}' &= \sum_{p,\, q} (\mathscr{N}^{-1/2})_{mp} \mathscr{N}_{pq} (\mathscr{N}^{-1/2})_{qn} \\
&= \delta_{mn}
\end{aligned} \tag{9.60}
$$

This is the Löwdin [5] transformation to an orthonormal basis system. The matrix $\mathscr{H}$ is transformed into

$$\begin{aligned}\mathscr{H}^{\mathrm{L}} &= \mathscr{N}^{-1/2}\mathscr{H}\mathscr{N}^{-1/2} \\ &= \mathscr{N}^{-1/2}\mathscr{W}\mathscr{N}^{-1/2} + \tfrac{1}{2}(\mathscr{N}^{1/2}\mathscr{E}\mathscr{N}^{-1/2} + \mathscr{N}^{-1/2}\mathscr{E}\mathscr{N}^{1/2}) \end{aligned} \tag{9.61}$$

Next the formal binomial expansions

$$\mathscr{N}^{-1/2} = I - \tfrac{1}{2}J + \tfrac{3}{8}J^2 - \cdots, \qquad \mathscr{N}^{1/2} = I + \tfrac{1}{2}J - \tfrac{1}{8}J^2 - \cdots \tag{9.62}$$

are used to reduce Eq. (9.61) to the explicit form

$$\mathscr{H}^{\mathrm{L}} = \mathscr{E} + \mathscr{W} - \tfrac{1}{2}(J\mathscr{W} + \mathscr{W}J) + \tfrac{1}{8}[J,[J,\mathscr{E}]] + \cdots \tag{9.63}$$

with matrix elements

$$\begin{aligned}\mathscr{H}^{\mathrm{L}}_{mn} &= E_n^{(0)}\delta_{mn} + \mathscr{W}_{mn} - \tfrac{1}{2}\sum_p (\mathscr{W}_{mp}J_{pn} + J_{mp}\mathscr{W}_{pn}) \\ &\quad + \tfrac{1}{8}\sum_p (E_m^{(0)} + E_n^{(0)} - 2E_p^{(0)})J_{mp}J_{pn} + \cdots \end{aligned} \tag{9.64}$$

For the ground state ($m = n = 0$) a second order energy

$$\Delta E_0^{(2)} = \sum_m{}' \,[\mathscr{W}^2_{0m}/(E_0^{(0)} - E_m^{(0)})] \tag{9.65}$$

can be added to $\mathscr{H}^{\mathrm{L}}_{00}$ to give an approximate evaluation of the ground-state energy in exact agreement with Eq. (9.57). The substitution of a for 0 in Eqs. (9.65) and (9.57) yields a general explicit and approximate formula for the low eigenvalues of the system.

This derivation of Eq. (9.57) employs a two-step procedure, first, the generation of a diagonal representation of the identity, followed by the transformation of the Hamiltonian to a (nearly) diagonal form. Woo [4] observes that each step alone produces a large shift in the diagonal matrix elements of H, while the total displacements are small. The total energy shift $\delta E^{(2)}$ is negative and an order of magnitude smaller than either $\mathscr{H}^{\mathrm{L}}_{00} - E_0^{(0)} > 0$ or $\Delta E_0^{(2)} < 0$. It appears that the Löwdin transformation actually produces a strong displacement of the ground-state representative away from the true ground state. A single-step procedure, as in the direct adaptation of the Raleigh–Schrödinger formalism to a nonorthogonal basis [6] avoids the artificial convergence problems of the two-step procedure, but has not yet been justified for large systems ($N > \cdots > 1$).

Another aspect of the theory is the general structure of the series for $\mathscr{H}^{\mathrm{L}}$ and the dependence of the matrix elements on N. If the nondiagonal part of $\mathscr{H}^{\mathrm{L}}$ is to be considered as a perturbation, its elements must have the correct dependence of N. For example, when $|m\}$ differs in two orbitals from $|0\}$, the element $\mathscr{H}_{0m}$ must be proportional to N^{-1}, so that the second-order correction to the energy is proportional to N. The general problem raised by this statement was investigated by C. W. Woo, who found that the series for $\mathscr{H}^{\mathrm{L}}$ contains terms which contribute anomalously high N-dependences coming from two sources: (1) terms with reducible vertices in J or $\mathscr{W}$, and (2) terms with unlinked parts.

To illustrate the first type, suppose $|p\}$ differs from $|m\}$ in four orbitals and from $|0\}$ in two. The summand $\sum_p \mathscr{W}_{0p} J_{pm}$ is represented by the diagram in Fig. 9-1. The integer and letter symbols denote particular orbitals,

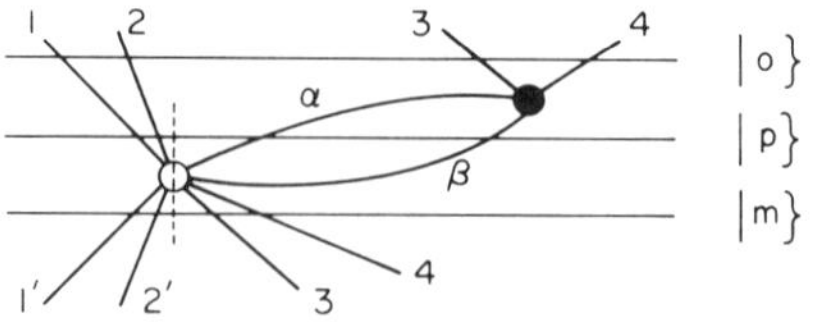

FIG. 9-1. Reducible Vertex in $\mathscr{H}^{\mathrm{L}}_{0m}$.

1234 in $|0\}$, $12\alpha\beta$ in $|p\}$, and $1'2'34$ in $|m\}$. All other orbitals are the same in the three states. Part of the four-orbital-different J vertex, $\{p|J|m\} \equiv \{12\alpha\beta|J|1'2'34\}$, is reducible to a sum of products of two two-orbital-different J vertices. One of these, $\{12|J|1'2'\}\{\alpha\beta|J|34\}$, is indicated by the vertical dashed line splitting the J vertex in Fig. 9-1. The associated contribution to $\mathscr{H}^{\mathrm{L}}_{0m}$, given by

$$\sum_{34\alpha\beta} \{12|J|1'2'\}\{\alpha\beta|J|34\}\{\alpha\beta|\mathscr{W}|34\}$$

has the order of magnitude $(N^{-1})^3 N^3 = N^0$, since the variable indices are subject to one constraint $\mathbf{k}_\alpha + \mathbf{k}_\beta = \mathbf{k}_3 + \mathbf{k}_4$. The admissible dependence on N is N^{-1}.

Figure 9-2 exhibits an example of the second type, two unlinked diagrams generated by the summand $\sum_{p,q} \mathscr{W}_{0p} J_{pq} J_{qm}$, which occurs among the third-order terms in $\mathscr{H}^{\mathrm{L}}_{0m}$. Again the associated contribution to $\mathscr{H}^{\mathrm{L}}_{0m}$ has the wrong order of magnitude N^0.

Using a cluster-ordering scheme devised by Clark and Westhaus [2], Woo [4] succeeded in verifying in several low orders that these anomalous N-dependent terms cancel exactly, terms of type 1 canceling those of type 2. A general proof is not yet available. It is immediately apparent that the anomaly here bears a close resemblance to that discovered by Brueckner [7] in the Raleigh–Schrödinger perturbation theory. As in the latter case, the apparent anomalous N-dependences must be spurious (complete internal cancellation of anomalous terms). The analogy suggests the possibility of radical transformations in the convergence properties of $\mathscr{H}^{\mathrm{L}}$ after all anomalous terms are stripped off.

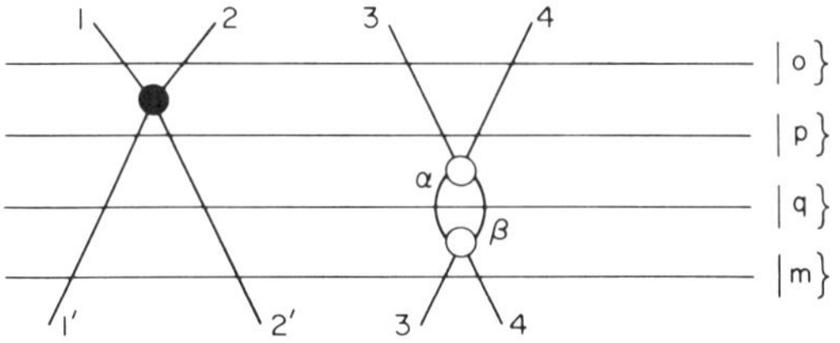

FIG. 9-2. Unlinked diagrams in $\mathscr{H}^{\mathrm{L}}_{0m}$.

9.8. METHOD OF LIMITED ORTHOGONALIZATION

How good is Eq. (9.57) and the corresponding formula for low excited states? To answer this question, we turn now to the second procedure mentioned in the introduction.

The condition

$$E_a^{(0)} - E_0^{(0)} \leq \theta K T_{\mathrm{M}}\, \delta N_{a,0} \tag{9.66}$$

is introduced to define a subspace of the complete Hilbert space generated by the set $|x\}$. Here $\delta N_{a,0}$ is the number of excited orbitals and holes in state a and θ is a positive constant large enough so that the subspace is adequate to describe thermal equilibrium below a maximum temperature T_{M}. The subspace defined by Eq. (9.66) is denoted by A, the total space by M, and the subspace of N states not in A by $M-A$. Since the subspaces A and $M-A$ are defined in terms of a nonorthogonal basis, they are not mutually orthogonal.

The physical meaning of Eq. (9.66) emerges clearly if $E_a^{(0)} - E_0^{(0)}$ and $\delta N_{a,0}$ are replaced by the corresponding expectation values for thermal equilibrium at the temperature T. For a nearly degenerate system of non-interacting particle the result is

$$N\frac{\pi^2}{4}\frac{(KT)^2}{e_{\mathrm{F}}} \leq \theta K T_{\mathrm{M}} N 3 \ln 2 \frac{KT}{e_{\mathrm{F}}} \tag{9.67}$$

or

$$T \leq \theta(12 \ln 2/\pi^2) T_{\mathrm{M}} \tag{9.68}$$

Consistency requires $\theta > 1.2$. These formulas should be valid for a system of interacting particles at sufficiently small T_{M}.

Reduced matrices

$$\bar{\mathscr{N}} = I + \bar{J} \tag{9.69}$$

are defined by stripping J of all elements with one or both indices in $M - A$:

$$\begin{aligned} \bar{J}_{ab} &= J_{ab}, \qquad a \text{ and } b \text{ in } A \\ \bar{J}_{am} &= \bar{J}_{ma} = 0, \qquad m \text{ not in } A \\ \bar{J}_{mn} &= \bar{J}_{nm} = 0, \qquad m \text{ and } n \text{ not in } A \end{aligned} \tag{9.70}$$

A set of normalized orthogonal functions spanning the subspace A is defined by the reduced Löwdin transformation

$$\begin{aligned} |a] &= \sum_b |b\}(\bar{\mathscr{N}}^{-1/2})_{ba} \\ &= |a\} - \sum_b |b\}[\tfrac{1}{2}\bar{J}_{ba} - \tfrac{3}{8}(\bar{J}^2)_{ba} + \cdots] \end{aligned} \tag{9.71}$$

The corresponding transform of $\mathscr{H}$ is

$$\begin{aligned} \bar{\mathscr{H}} &= \bar{\mathscr{N}}^{-1/2} \mathscr{H} \bar{\mathscr{N}}^{-1/2} \\ &= \mathscr{E} + \mathscr{W} - \tfrac{1}{2}(\bar{J}\mathscr{W} + \mathscr{W}\bar{J}) + \tfrac{1}{8}[\bar{J},[\bar{J}\,\mathscr{E}]] + \tfrac{1}{2}\{(J-\bar{J})\mathscr{E} + \mathscr{E}(J-\bar{J})\} \\ &\quad - \tfrac{1}{4}\{\bar{J}(J-\bar{J})\mathscr{E} + (J-\bar{J})\mathscr{E}\bar{J} + \bar{J}\mathscr{E}(J-\bar{J}) + \mathscr{E}(J-\bar{J})\bar{J}\} + \cdots \end{aligned} \tag{9.72}$$

with diagonal matrix elements

$$\bar{\mathscr{H}}_{aa} = E_a^{(0)} - \sum_b J_{ab}\mathscr{W}_{ba} + \tfrac{1}{4}\sum_b (E_a^{(0)} - E_b^{(0)}) J_{ab}^2 + \cdots \tag{9.73}$$

for a in A and

$$\bar{\mathscr{H}}_{nn} = E_n^{(0)}, \qquad n \text{ not in } A \tag{9.74}$$

The transformed nondiagonal elements are

$$\mathscr{H}_{ab} = \mathscr{W}_{ab} - \tfrac{1}{2}\sum_{c}(J_{ac}\mathscr{W}_{cb} + \mathscr{W}_{ac}J_{cb})$$
$$+ \tfrac{1}{8}\sum_{c}(E_a^{(0)} + E_b^{(0)} - 2E_c^{(0)}J_{ac}J_{cb} + \cdots \qquad (9.75)$$

for a and b in A (c ranges over A),

$$\mathscr{H}_{an} = \mathscr{W}_{an} - \tfrac{1}{2}\sum_{c}J_{ac}\mathscr{W}_{cn}$$
$$+ \tfrac{1}{2}(E_a^{(0)} + E_n^{(0)})J_{an} - \tfrac{1}{4}\sum_{c}(E_c^{(0)} + E_n^{(0)})J_{ac}J_{cn} + \cdots \qquad (9.76)$$

for n not in A, and

$$\mathscr{H}_{mn} = \mathscr{W}_{mn} + \tfrac{1}{2}J_{mn}(E_m^{(0)} + E_n^{(0)}) \qquad (9.77)$$

for m, n not in A.

In Eqs. (9.73) and (9.75) terms involving sums over the A function space are negligible. To see this, we note the order of magnitude relations

$$|\mathscr{W}_{xy}| \sim e_F O(J_{xy}), \qquad |J_{xy}| \sim O(1/N)$$
$$\underbrace{\mathbf{k} + \boldsymbol{l}}_{x} = \underbrace{\mathbf{k}' + \boldsymbol{l}'}_{y} \qquad (9.78)$$

In Eq. (9.78) $e_F = \hbar^2 k_F{}^2/2m$; the x and y states differ in two orbitals. Equation (2.78) yields the estimates

$$|(\bar{J}^2)_{ab}| = \left|\sum_{c} J_{ac}J_{ab}\right| \sim O\left(\frac{1}{N^2}\right)N\frac{KT_M}{e_F} \sim O(J_{ab})\frac{KT_M}{e_F}$$
$$\left|\sum_{c} J_{ac}\mathscr{W}_{cb}\right| \sim e_F O\left(\frac{1}{N^2}\right)N\frac{KT_M}{e_F} \sim O(\mathscr{W}_{ab})\frac{KT_M}{e_F} \qquad (9.79)$$

The factor KT_M/e_F occurs to the first power because conservation of linear momentum limits the intermediate states to one degree of freedom (assuming always that c states differing from both a and b states in only two orbitals make the major contributions to the sums).

If a and b differ in three orbitals, the corresponding relations are

$$|(\bar{J}^2)_{ab}| \sim (KT_M/e_F)^2 O(J_{ab}), \qquad |(\bar{J}\mathscr{W})_{ab}| \sim (KT_M/e_F)^2 O(\mathscr{W}_{ab}) \qquad (9.80)$$

The analysis is continued under the explicit restriction to a nearly degenerate system ($KT_M \ll e_F$); consequently, the following simplified formulas represent adequate approximations:

$$\mathscr{H}_{aa} \approx E_a^{(0)} + KT_\mathrm{M} O(N^{-1}), \qquad \mathscr{H}_{ab} \approx \mathscr{W}_{ab} + (KT_\mathrm{M}/e_\mathrm{F})O(\mathscr{W}_{ab}) \tag{9.81}$$

The space $\overline{M-A}$ orthogonal to A is spanned by the functions

$$|n] = \frac{|n\} - \sum_b |b][b|1|n\}}{(1 - \sum_b |[b|1|n\}|^2)^{1/2}} \tag{9.82}$$

for n not in A. Equation (9.71) can be used to evaluate the overlap coefficient occurring in Eq. (9.82):

$$\begin{aligned} \{n|1|b] &= J_{nb} - \sum_c J_{nc}[\tfrac{1}{2}J_{cb} - \tfrac{3}{8}(\bar{J}^2)_{cb} + \cdots] \\ &= J_{nb} - \tfrac{1}{2}(J\bar{J})_{nb} + \tfrac{3}{8}(J\bar{J}^2)_{nb} + \cdots \\ &\approx J_{nb} + (KT_\mathrm{M}/e_\mathrm{F})O(J_{nb}) \end{aligned} \tag{9.83}$$

$$\begin{aligned} \sum_b |\{n|1|b]|^2 &\approx \sum_b J_{nb}^2 \\ &\sim (KT_\mathrm{M}/e_\mathrm{F})O(1/N) \end{aligned} \tag{9.84}$$

The order-of-magnitude estimate of the remainder terms in Eq. (9.83) is appropriate to the special case of n and b differing in just two orbitals. Conservation of momentum limits the leading intermediate c states to one degree of freedom, resulting in a single $KT_\mathrm{M}/e_\mathrm{F}$ factor. In Eq. (9.84) the same argument multiplies the average J_{nb}^2 element by $NKT_\mathrm{M}/e_\mathrm{F}$.

Nondiagonal matrix elements of H connecting the A and $\overline{M-A}$ subspaces reduce to the simple form

$$\begin{aligned} [n|H|a] &= [a|H|n] \\ &= \mathscr{W}_{an} - \tfrac{1}{2}(E_a^{(0)} - E_n^{(0)})J_{an} \end{aligned} \tag{9.85}$$

neglecting terms smaller than those given in Eq. (9.85) by a factor of order $KT_\mathrm{M}/e_\mathrm{F}$. Diagonal matrix elements in the $\overline{M-A}$ subspace are also simple:

$$\begin{aligned} [n|H|n] &\approx \frac{E_n^{(0)} - 2\sum_b \mathscr{H}_{nb} J_{bn} + \sum_b E_b^{(0)} J_{bn}^2}{1 - \sum_b J_{nb}^2} \\ &\approx E_n^{(0)} - 2\sum_b \mathscr{W}_{nb} J_{bn} \\ &\approx E_n^{(0)} + KT_\mathrm{M} O(N^{-1}) \end{aligned} \tag{9.86}$$

Equation (9.85) should be compared with Eq. (9.76). The transformation from $|x\}$ to $|x]$ states results in the replacement of $\frac{1}{2}(E_a^{(0)}+E_n^{(0)})J_{an} \sim e_F\, O(N^{(0)})$ by $-\frac{1}{2}(E_a^{(0)}-E_n^{(0)})J_{an} \sim e_F\, O(1/N)$ in the matrix element coupling the n and a states. Other changes are negligible.

Our objective now is the construction of an effective interaction operator within the A subspace. This requires that the coupling between A and $\overline{M-A}$ states be converted into an interaction between A-type states. We are not able to present a complete derivation explicitly taking into account the large nondiagonal matrix elements of the Hamiltonian still remaining in the $|n]$ function space (n not in A). In fact, a clean approach to the physical problem is possible only after these elements are transformed away. We begin by introducing a linear transformation S on the functions $|x]$ with the properties

$$S_{an}=S_{na}=0, \qquad a \text{ in } A; \; n \text{ in } \overline{M-A} \tag{9.87a}$$

$$|y\rangle=\sum_x S_{yx}|x] \qquad \langle z|1|y\rangle=\delta_{zy}$$

$$\langle a|H|b\rangle=\langle a|H|a\rangle\delta_{ab}, \qquad a \text{ and } b \text{ in } A \tag{9.87b}$$

$$\langle m|H|n\rangle=\langle m|H|m\rangle\delta_{mn}, \qquad m \text{ and } n \text{ in } \overline{M-A}$$

The transformation produces an orthonormal basis and brings H to diagonal form in the complementary subspaces A and $\overline{M-A}$. An eigenstate ψ is represented as a linear combination of $|x\rangle$ states:

$$\psi=\sum_x C_x|x\rangle \tag{9.88}$$

with coefficients C_x which are solutions of the homogeneous linear system

$$\{E-\langle y|H|y\rangle\}C_y=\sum_{x\neq y}\langle y|H|x\rangle C_x \tag{9.89}$$

A more explicit statement

$$\begin{aligned}\{E-\langle a|H|a\rangle\}C_a&=\sum_m \langle a|H|m\rangle C_m\\ \{E-\langle m|H|m\rangle\}C_m&=\sum_b \langle m|H|b\rangle C_b\end{aligned} \tag{9.90}$$

shows how the A and $\overline{M-A}$ subspaces are coupled by the residual nondiagonal elements of H. Equations (9.90) imply

$$\{E-\langle a|H|a\rangle\}C_a=\sum_b C_b\sum_m \frac{\langle a|H|m\rangle\langle m|H|a\rangle}{E-\langle m|H|m\rangle} \tag{9.91}$$

Consider now a low eigenvalue, i.e., one for which $E = E_a < \langle m|H|m\rangle$ for all m states which couple to the a state ($\langle a|H|m\rangle \neq 0$). We introduce the working hypotheses

$$E_a - \langle m|H|m\rangle \approx Y[E_a^{(0)} - E_m^{(0)}] \tag{9.91a}$$

$$\langle a|H|m\rangle \approx X[a|H|m] \tag{9.91b}$$

in which X and Y are treated as constants. These working hypotheses are introduced to bypass the problem of actually constructing the transformation S. We want to draw physical conclusions from the existence of S without actually constructing it. The meaning of Eq. (9.91a) is simply that the energy spacing of connecting a and m states is simply compressed or stretched out by a nearly constant scaling factor when the coupling within the $\overline{M - A}$ space is taken into account. It is important that the eigenvalue E_a appears in the left-hand member of Eq. (9.91a) rather than the diagonal element $\langle a|H|a\rangle$ (since E_a may differ from $\langle a|H|a\rangle$ by an amount proportional to N). For the low connecting m states, $E_a - \langle m|H|m\rangle$ is a small quantity of order $KT_{\mathrm{M}}\,\delta N_{m,a}$. Equation (9.91b) represents the change in the coupling between a and m states produced by the S transformation as simply a uniform change in the strength of the coupling (a renormalization).

The definition of an effective interaction matrix

$$\begin{aligned} V_{ab} &= \sum_m \frac{\langle a|H|m\rangle\langle m|H|b\rangle}{E_a - \langle m|H|m\rangle} \\ &\approx \frac{X^2}{Y} \sum_m \frac{[a|H|m][m|H|b]}{\frac{1}{2}(E_a^{(0)} + E_b^{(0)}) - E_m^{(0)}} \end{aligned} \tag{9.92}$$

allows Eq. (9.91) to be written in the nearly diagonal form

$$\begin{aligned} [E_a - E_a^{(0)} - V_{aa}]C_a &= \sum_{a \neq b} V_{ab} C_b \\ [E_a - E_a^{(0)} - V_{bb}]C_b &= V_{ba} C_a + \sum_{c \neq a,\, b} V_{ba} C_c \end{aligned} \tag{9.93}$$

If nondiagonal elements V_{ba}, V_{ob} are neglected, the solution is $C_b = 0$, $b \neq a$, and

$$\begin{aligned} E_a &= E_a^{(0)} + V_{aa} \\ &= E_a^{(0)} + \frac{X^2}{Y} \sum_m \frac{|\mathscr{W}_{am} - \frac{1}{2}(E_a^{(0)} - E_m^{(0)})J_{am}|^2}{E_a^{(0)} - E_a^{(0)}} \end{aligned} \tag{9.94}$$

The neglected terms are certainly negligible if the dimensionality of the subspace A is sufficiently small. Equation (9.93) suggests the estimate

$$\left|\frac{1}{C_a}\sum_{a\neq b} V_{ab}\, C_b\right| \sim \left|\sum_{b\neq a}\frac{V_{ab}^2}{E_a - E_b^{(0)} - V_{bb}}\right| \tag{9.95}$$

A rough estimate of the right-hand sum is found in the following manner. Terms on opposite sides of the singularity are paired off, leaving only contributions from regions in which $E_a - E_a^{(0)} - V_{bb} \sim +KT_{\mathrm{M}}$. The V_{ab} elements are replaced by e_{F}/N; the number of b states is fixed first by the number of pairs of orbitals in the a state sufficiently close to the Fermi surface $[(NKT_{\mathrm{M}}/e_{\mathrm{F}})^2]$ and the range of orbitals outside the Fermi surface available for b states (another factor $NKT_{\mathrm{M}}/e_{\mathrm{F}}$.) Altogether this gives

$$\begin{aligned}\frac{1}{C_a}\left|\sum_{b\neq a} C_b\, V_{ba}\right| &\lesssim \frac{1}{KT_{\mathrm{M}}}\left(\frac{e_{\mathrm{F}}}{N}^2\right)\left(N\frac{KT_{\mathrm{M}}}{e_{\mathrm{F}}}^3\right)\\ &\sim \frac{(KT_m)^2}{e_{\mathrm{F}}}\end{aligned} \tag{9.96}$$

The approximate eigenvalue given by Eq. (9.94) differs from Eq. (9.57) (with a substituted for 0) in two respects, the presence of the renormalization factor X^2/Y in Eq. (9.94) and the constraint on m implied by the statement "m not in A." This last difference eliminates an unimportant and nonphysical singularity; the first introduces an unwanted degree of flexibility in the correlation of theory with experiment. Apparently, the flexibility is not needed; the theory with $X^2/Y=1$ is able to give a good account of the experimental behavior. The possibility that X^2 and Y are nearly equal, but differ substantially from 1 cannot be excluded.

References

1. E. Feenberg and C. W. Woo, *Phys. Rev.* **137**, A391 (1965).
2. J. W. Clark and P. Westhaus, *Phys. Rev.* **141**, 833 (1966).
3. A. W. Overhauser, *Phys. Rev.* **128**. 1437 (1962).
4. C. W. Woo, unpublished doctorial dissertation, Washington University, 1966; *Phys. Rev.* **151**, 138 (1966).
5. P. O. Löwdin, *J. Chem. Phys.* **18**, 365 (1950).
6. J. W. Clark and E. Feenberg, *Phys. Rev.* **113**, 388 (1959).
7. K. A. Brueckner, *Phys. Rev.* **100**, 36 (1955).

CHAPTER 10

Low Excited States and Statistical and Transport Properties of Liquid ^{3}He

10.1. QUASIPARTICLE FORMULATION

Landau [1]–[3] recognized the possibility of treating the nearly degenerate system of interacting fermions as a distribution of weakly interacting quasiparticles occupying a thin shell in wave-vector space centered about the Fermi surface. A quasiparticle carries momentum $\hbar\mathbf{k}$, spin orientation $\uparrow\downarrow$, and energy $e_\sigma(\mathbf{k})$; pairs of quasiparticles interact, and the system of quasi particles obeys the exclusion principle. The general theoretical framework embodying these ideas can be developed from the basic relations of the grand canonical formulation of statistical mechanics:

$$F = \sum_{N'q'} \exp -\beta(E_{N'q'} - \mu N') \qquad N = \frac{1}{\beta}\frac{\partial}{\partial\mu}\ln F$$
$$U = -\frac{\partial}{\partial\beta}\ln F + \mu N, \qquad \frac{1}{K}S = \beta(U - \mu N) + \ln F \tag{10.1}$$

The index q' represents the set of hole and particle occupation numbers

$$\nu_1\nu_2 \cdots \nu_i \cdots \nu_{N'}|\nu_{N'+1} \cdots \nu_j \cdots$$

defined by the statement

$k \le k_F'(i \le N')$

$\nu_i = -1$	Vacant orbital below the Fermi surface (hole)
$= 0$	Occupied orbital below the Fermi surface

$k > k_F'(j > N')$
$\nu_j = 1$ Occupied orbital above the Fermi surface (particle)
$= 0$ Vacant orbital above the Fermi surface

A Slater determinant of single-particle orbitals is completely characterized by the index $N'; \nu_1 \nu_2 \cdots$. It is assumed that the physical eigenstates can be generated from the Slater determinants by an adiabatic algorithm which bridges the gap between the energy eigenstates of the noninteracting system and the corresponding eigenstates of the actual physical system of interacting particles and thus associates the index $N'; \nu_1 v_2 \cdots$ in a meaningful way with the physical eigenstates. Alternatively, one may start from correlated basis functions and develop the true energy eigenvalues by introducing the nondiagonal matrix elements of the identity and Hamiltonian into a suitable perturbation algorithm.

The first step in the extraction of a quasiparticle formalism from the exact theory is the introduction of quasiparticle energies e_i and quasiparticle interaction energies f_{ij} by means of the approximate relations

$$[E_{N'; \nu_1 \nu_2 \cdots \nu_{i-1} \nu_i \nu_{i+1} \cdots} - N'\mu]$$
$$\approx [E_{N'-\nu_i; \nu_1 \nu_2 \cdots \nu_{i-1} 0 \nu_{i+1} \cdots} - (N' - \nu_i)\mu] + \nu_i(e_i - \mu) \quad (10.2)$$

$$e_i = e_i^{(0)} + \sum f_{ij} \langle \nu_j \rangle_T \quad (10.3)$$

The defining statement of Eq. (10.2) is trivially exact for $\nu_i = 0$; for a hole below the Fermi surface $\nu_i(e_i - \mu) = -(e_i - \mu)$, and for an occupied orbital above the Fermi surface $\nu_i(e_i - \mu) = e_i - \mu$. The essential approximation is that e_i does not depend on the precise numbers $\nu_1 \nu_2 \cdots \nu_{i-1} \nu_{i+1} \cdots$; it does depend on the statistical mean values $\langle \nu_1 \rangle_T, \langle \nu_2 \rangle_T, \ldots$, with the consequence that the modification of the single-particle energies produced by interactions among the quasiparticles becomes a significant element in the theory. The interaction element f_{ij} is symmetrical in the indices ($f_{ij} = f_{ji}$); this property will emerge as necessary for a consistent formalism.

Equations (10.1) and (10.2) together yield

$$F \approx \sum_{N'q'\nu_i=0} \exp -\beta(E_{N'q'\nu_i=0} - \mu N')$$
$$+ (\exp -\beta|e_i - \mu|) \sum_{N'q'\nu_i=0} \exp -\beta[E_{N'\pm 1; q'\nu_i=0} - \mu(N' \pm 1)]$$
$$= (1 + \exp -\beta|e_i - \mu|) F_{\nu_i=0} \quad (10.4)$$

interpreting $\pm$ as $+$ for $i \leq N'$ and $-$ for $i > N'$. The last line of Eq. (10.4) follows because the index $N' \pm 1$ is summed over the same range as the index N'.

The process of extracting single-particle energies begun in Eq. (10.4) can be continued with the result

$$F \approx \prod_{(i)} (1 + \exp -\beta|e_i - \mu|) F_{(\nu_i = 0)} \tag{10.5}$$

Here (i) denotes a relatively small number of orbitals just below and just above the Fermi surface. The restriction to a small number is necessary to avoid a noticeable accumulation of error generated by the double counting of the interaction energies f_{lk} for values of l and k both included in the limited range defined by (i).

The canonical forms of the distribution functions,

$$\begin{aligned} \langle \nu_i \rangle &= \frac{1}{\exp \beta|e_i - \mu| + 1} \frac{e_i - \mu}{|e_i - \mu|} \\ n_i &= \frac{1}{\exp \beta(e_i - \mu) + 1} \end{aligned} \tag{10.6}$$

are immediate consequences of Eqs. (10.4) or (10.5). The restriction to a small number of factors in Eq. (10.5) can be expressed as an upper limit on the half-thickness of the shell in wave-vector space in which the quasi-particles are well defined. From

$$N = \frac{8\pi}{3} \frac{\Omega k_{\mathrm{F}}^3}{(2\pi)^3}, \qquad \delta N = \frac{\Omega k_{\mathrm{F}}^2}{\pi^2} \delta k_{\mathrm{F}} \tag{10.7}$$

the necessary condition $|\delta N| \ll N$ implies $3|\delta k_{\mathrm{F}}|/k_{\mathrm{F}} \ll 1$. A second inequality is required to ensure that the limited product factor in Eq. (10.5) does not depend appreciably on the thickness of the shell defined by $k_{\mathrm{F}} \pm \delta k_{\mathrm{F}}$. This means

$$\beta|e_i - \mu|_{\max} \approx \beta(\partial e/\partial k)_{\mathrm{F}} |\delta k_{\mathrm{F}}| \gg 1 \tag{10.8}$$

or $|\delta k_{\mathrm{F}}| \gg KT(\partial k/\partial e)_{\mathrm{F}}$. The two inequalities are combined in the single statement

$$\frac{3KT}{(\partial e/\partial k)_{\mathrm{F}} k_{\mathrm{F}}} \ll \frac{3|\delta k|}{k_{\mathrm{F}}} \ll 1 \tag{10.9}$$

The upper limit on temperature implied by Eq. (10.9) can be expressed in terms of the density and an effective mass m^* through the defining equation

$$(\partial e^{(0)}/\partial k)_{\mathrm{F}} = \hbar^2 k_{\mathrm{F}}/m^* \tag{10.10}$$

For liquid ^{3}He at the equilibrium density (0.0164 Å^{-3}), $m^* \approx 2.5 m_3$; consequently,

$$\frac{1}{K}\left(\frac{\partial e^{(0)}}{\partial k}\right)_{\mathrm{F}} k_{\mathrm{F}} = \frac{\hbar^2 k_{\mathrm{F}}^{\,2}}{2mK}\frac{2m}{m^*} \approx 4 \quad {}^\circ\mathrm{K}$$

and, allowing a factor of 20 between extreme terms of Eq. (10.9), the inequality requires

$$T \lesssim \tfrac{1}{20}\,\tfrac{4}{3} \approx 0.07 \quad {}^\circ\mathrm{K}$$

Thus $T_{\mathrm{M}} \approx 0.05$–$0.10$°K represents a reasonable estimate for liquid ^{3}He of the temperature at which the quasiparticle formalism may be expected to break down.

The inequalities of Eq. (10.9) are necessary conditions for the accuracy of Eq. (10.6) in the shell defined by $k_{\mathrm{F}} \pm dk$ where $\langle \nu_i \rangle$ and n_i are changing rapidly. Everywhere else the physical requirement $|\langle \nu_i \rangle| \ll 1$ is satisfied by Eq. (10.6) even though the meaning of the quasiparticle energy becomes somewhat ambiguous and uncertain. Keeping this in mind, the physical quantities of Eq. (10.1) can be expressed adequately as

$$\begin{aligned} F &\approx \prod_i (1 + \exp - \beta\,|e_i - \mu|) \\ N &= \sum_i n_i = \sum_i \frac{1}{\exp[\beta(e_i - \mu)] + 1} \\ U &= \sum_i e_i n_i = \sum_i (e_i - \mu) n_i + \mu N \\ (1/K)S &= \beta(U - \mu N) + \ln F \end{aligned} \tag{10.11}$$

The differential form

$$đQ = T\,dS = \sum_i (e_i - \mu)\,\delta n_i \tag{10.12}$$

for an element of heat transferred to the system provides an alternative starting point for a quasiparticle description.

Equation (10.12) exhibits the interaction function as a second derivative of the entropy with respect to n_i and n_j. The symmetry of the cross derivatives requires $f_{ij} = f_{ji}$, as mentioned earlier.

10.2. QUASIPARTICLE ENERGY SPECTRUM*

The results of Chapters 8 and 9 can be used to generate an explicit realization of the quasiparticle formalism including theoretical formulas and numerical values for the interaction function f_{ij}. Equations (9.66)–(9.68) introduce a temperature T_M which should not be exceeded in applications of the approximate formula for the energy eigenvalues. The perturbation formula and the quasiparticle formalism are brought into approximate coincidence by identifying T_M with the upper limit on T defined by Eq. (10.9).

The derivation of the quasiparticle energy and interaction functions is facilitated by expressing $E_a^{(0)}$ and V_{aa} as explicit functions of the equilibrium occupation number functions $n_\sigma(\mathbf{k})$ with $\sigma = \uparrow$ or $\downarrow$. The physical quantities are then well-defined partial derivatives of $U = \langle E_a \rangle_T$ with respect to the variables $n_\sigma(\mathbf{k})$. Nonphysical complications in these calculations are avoided by treating $E_0{}^B/N$, $S(k)$, and the interaction matrix elements as independent of the varying number of fermions involved in the evaluation of the grand canonical mean values. Derivatives with respect to N (the mean number of particles) occur only in connection with the evaluation of the chemical constant $\mu(\rho)$ and the isothermal compressibility K_T at $T = 0$. For these the equilibrium formalism is unnecessary, since only $E_0(\rho)$ is involved.

Equation (8.48) is readily adapted to represent the expectation value of H generated by the correlated basis function as first derived by Wu[5]:

$$E_x^{(0)} = E_0{}^B + E_{x1}^F + E_{x2}^F + E_{x3}^F + \cdots$$

$$E_{x1}^F = \sum_{\mathbf{k}} \frac{\hbar^2 k^2}{2m} [n_\uparrow{}^x(\mathbf{k}) + n_\downarrow{}^x(\mathbf{k})]$$

$$E_{x2}^F = \sum_{\mathbf{k},\boldsymbol{l}} \frac{\hbar^2(\mathbf{k}-\boldsymbol{l})^2}{4mN} [S(|\mathbf{k}-\boldsymbol{l}|) - 1][n_\uparrow{}^x(\mathbf{k}) n_\uparrow{}^x(\boldsymbol{l}) + n_\downarrow{}^x(\mathbf{k}) n_\downarrow{}^x(\boldsymbol{l})]$$

$$E_{x3}^F = -\sum_{\mathbf{k},\boldsymbol{l},\mathbf{h}} \frac{\hbar^2(\mathbf{k}-\boldsymbol{l})^2}{4mN^2} S(|\mathbf{k}-\boldsymbol{l}|)[S(|\boldsymbol{l}-\mathbf{h}|) - 1][S(\mathbf{k}-\mathbf{h}|) - 1]$$
$$\times [n_\uparrow{}^x(\mathbf{k}) n_\uparrow{}^x(\boldsymbol{l}) n_\uparrow{}^x(\mathbf{h}) + n_\downarrow{}^x(\mathbf{k}) n_\downarrow{}^x(\boldsymbol{l}) n_\downarrow{}^x(\mathbf{h})]$$

* See Tan [4].

$$
\begin{aligned}
n_\sigma{}^x(\mathbf{k}) &= 1 \qquad \text{if the } \mathbf{k}, \sigma \text{ orbital occurs in } |x\} \\
&= 0 \qquad \text{if the } \mathbf{k}, \sigma \text{ orbital is absent from } |x\}
\end{aligned} \tag{10.13}
$$

In the evaluation of V_{aa} two systematic approximations are made necessary by the prohibitive magnitude and cost of a complete calculation using all the available matrix elements. The approximations are (1) retaining only J_{am} and $\mathscr{W}_{am}$ for m and a states differing in just two orbitals, and (2) retaining just the leading terms in the formulas for J_{am}, $\mathscr{W}_{am}$, and $E_a^{(0)} - E_m^{(0)}$ It appears that a more complete evaluation must wait on a substantial increase in the speed and capacity of available computers. Equations (9.9)–(9.10), (9.32)–(9.33) provide the working formulas

$$
\begin{aligned}
J_{am} &= \frac{1}{N}\delta(\mathbf{k}+\boldsymbol{l}-\mathbf{p}-\mathbf{q})\{[S(|\mathbf{k}-\mathbf{p}|)-1]\langle \mathbf{k}\boldsymbol{l}\,|\,\mathbf{pq}\rangle \\
&\qquad -[S(|\mathbf{k}-\mathbf{q}|)-1]\langle \mathbf{k}\boldsymbol{l}\,|\,\mathbf{qp}\rangle\} + \cdots \\
\mathscr{W}_{am} &= -\frac{1}{N}\delta(\mathbf{k}+\boldsymbol{l}-\mathbf{p}-\mathbf{q})\left\{\frac{\hbar^2(\mathbf{k}-\mathbf{p})^2}{2m}[S(|\mathbf{k}-\mathbf{p}|)-1]\langle \mathbf{k}\boldsymbol{l}\,|\,\mathbf{pq}\rangle\right. \\
&\qquad \left. -\frac{\hbar^2(\mathbf{k}-\mathbf{q})^2}{2m}[S(|k-q|)-1]\langle \mathbf{kl}|\mathbf{qp}\rangle\right\} + \cdots
\end{aligned} \tag{10.14}
$$

in which $\mathbf{k}$ and $\boldsymbol{l}$ are wave vectors in the a configuration and $\mathbf{p}$ and $\mathbf{q}$ are the corresponding replacements in the m configuration (a and m differ in two orbitals). The element $\langle \mathbf{k}\boldsymbol{l}|\,\mathbf{pq}\rangle$ is a matrix element of the identity for the spin states associated with the wave vectors $\mathbf{k}$, $\boldsymbol{l}$, $\mathbf{p}$, and $\mathbf{q}$.

The equilibrium occupation numbers $n_0(\mathbf{k})$ appear in the formula for U through the mean values of the spin matrix elements summed over all spin orientations:

$$
\begin{aligned}
\left\langle \sum_{\text{spin}} \langle \mathbf{k}\boldsymbol{l}\,|\,\mathbf{pq}\rangle^2 \right\rangle_{\mathrm{T}} &= \left\langle \sum_{\text{spin}} \langle \mathbf{k}\boldsymbol{l}\,|\,\mathbf{pq}\rangle \right\rangle_{\mathrm{T}} \\
&= \{n_\uparrow(\mathbf{k})[1-n_\uparrow(\mathbf{p})] + n_\downarrow(\mathbf{k})[1-n_\downarrow(\mathbf{p})]\} \\
&\quad \times \{n_\uparrow(\boldsymbol{l})[1-n_\uparrow(\mathbf{q})] + n_\downarrow(\boldsymbol{l})[1-n_\downarrow(\mathbf{q})\}
\end{aligned} \tag{10.15}
$$

$$
\begin{aligned}
\left\langle \sum_{\text{spin}} \langle \mathbf{k}\boldsymbol{l}\,|\,\mathbf{pq}\rangle\langle \mathbf{qp}\,|\,\mathbf{k}\boldsymbol{l}\rangle \right\rangle_{\mathrm{T}} &= n_\uparrow(\mathbf{k})n_\uparrow(\boldsymbol{l})[1-n_\uparrow(\mathbf{p})][1-n_\uparrow(\mathbf{q})] \\
&\quad + n_\downarrow(\mathbf{k})n_\downarrow(\boldsymbol{l})[1-n_\downarrow(\mathbf{p})][1-n_\downarrow(\mathbf{q})]
\end{aligned}
$$

To illustrate the derivation of Eq. (10.15), consider the element $\langle k|p\rangle = \delta_{\sigma(\mathbf{k}),\,\sigma(\mathbf{p})}$. Now

$$\left\langle \sum_{\text{spin}} \delta_{\sigma(\mathbf{k}),\,\sigma(\mathbf{p})} \right\rangle_{\mathrm{T}} = n_{\uparrow}(\mathbf{k})[\text{probability that } \mathbf{p}\uparrow \text{ is empty} \\ + n_{\downarrow}(\mathbf{k})[\text{probability that } \mathbf{p}\downarrow \text{ is empty}] \\ = n_{\uparrow}(\mathbf{k})[1 - n_{\uparrow}(\mathbf{p})] + n_{\downarrow}(\mathbf{k})[1 - n_{\downarrow}(\mathbf{p})]$$

In Eq. (10.15) the sum over spin orientations ranges over all spin states associated with the wave vectors **k**, ***l***, **p**, and **q**. Ultimately, in the actual numerical evaluation the vectors **k** and ***l*** range over the Fermi spheres, while **p** and **q** range over the space outside of the Fermi spheres.

In Eq. (10.13) the statistical average $\langle E_x{}^{\mathrm{F}}\rangle_{\mathrm{T}}$ is formed by omitting the superscript x on the occupation number functions $[n_\sigma{}^x(\mathbf{k}) \rightarrow n_\sigma(\mathbf{k})]$. A first-order component in the quasiparticle energy is generated by the formula

$$\begin{aligned} e_\sigma^{(1)}(k) &= \left[\frac{\partial}{\partial n_\sigma(\mathbf{k})} \langle E_x{}^{\mathrm{F}}\rangle_{\mathrm{T}}\right]_{\mathrm{T}=0} \\ &= \frac{\hbar^2 k^2}{2m} + \frac{1}{N} \sum_{l \le k_{\mathrm{F}\sigma}} \frac{\hbar^2(\mathbf{k}-\boldsymbol{l})^2}{2m} [S(|\mathbf{k}-\boldsymbol{l}|) - 1] \\ &\quad - \frac{1}{N^2} \sum_{l,\,h \le k_{\mathrm{F}\sigma}} \left\{ \frac{\hbar^2(\mathbf{k}-\boldsymbol{l})^2}{2m} S(|\mathbf{k}-\boldsymbol{l}|)[S(|\boldsymbol{l}-\mathbf{h}|) - 1][S(|\mathbf{h}-\mathbf{k}) - 1] \right. \\ &\quad \left. + \frac{\hbar^2(\boldsymbol{l}-\mathbf{h})^2}{4m} S(|\boldsymbol{l}-\mathbf{h}|)[S|\mathbf{k}-\mathbf{h}|) - 1][S|\mathbf{k}-\boldsymbol{l}) - 1] \right\} \end{aligned} \tag{10.16}$$

The energy differences appearing in Eq. (9.94) for V_{aa} can now be expressed directly in terms of $e_\sigma^{(1)}(k)$.

Next, with help from Eq. (10.15) the statistical average value of V_{aa} is written as an explicit function of the mean occupation numbers:

$$\begin{aligned} \langle V_{aa}\rangle_{\mathrm{T}} = \tfrac{1}{4} \sum_{\sigma\tau} \left\{ \sum_{\mathbf{k}\boldsymbol{l}\mathbf{pq}} R_{1\sigma\tau}(\mathbf{k}\boldsymbol{l};\, \mathbf{pq}) n_\sigma(\mathbf{k}) n_\tau(\boldsymbol{l})[1 - n_\sigma(\mathbf{p})][1 - n_\tau(\mathbf{q})] \right. \\ \left. + \delta_{\sigma\tau} \sum_{\mathbf{k}\boldsymbol{l}\mathbf{pq}} R_{2\sigma\sigma}(\mathbf{k}\boldsymbol{l};\, \mathbf{pq}) n_\sigma(\mathbf{k}) n_\tau(\boldsymbol{l})[1 - n_\sigma(\mathbf{p})][1 - n_\tau(\mathbf{q})] \right\} \end{aligned} \tag{10.17}$$

The factor $\frac{1}{4}$ compensates for nonphysical duplications in the summation (a particular pair **k**, ***l*** or **p**, **q** also appears as ***l***, **k** or **q**, **p**). Equations (9.94) and (10.14) generate the following explicit formulas for $R_{1\sigma\tau}$ and $R_{2\sigma\sigma}$:

$$R_{1\sigma\tau}(\mathbf{k}\boldsymbol{l};\mathbf{pq}) = \frac{2}{N^2}\,\delta(\mathbf{k}+\boldsymbol{l}-\mathbf{p}-\mathbf{q})[S(|\mathbf{k}-\mathbf{p}|)-1]^2$$
$$\times\frac{\{[\hbar^2(\mathbf{k}-\mathbf{p})^2/2m]+\frac{1}{2}[e_\sigma^{(1)}(k)+e_\tau^{(1)}(l)-e_\sigma^{(1)}(p)-e_\tau^{(1)}(q)]\}^2}{e_\sigma^{(1)}(k)+e_\tau^{(1)}(l)-e_\sigma^{(1)}(p)-e_\tau^{(1)}(q)} \tag{10.18}$$

$$R_{2\sigma\sigma}(\mathbf{k}\boldsymbol{l};\mathbf{pq}) = -\frac{2}{N^2}\,\delta(\mathbf{k}+\boldsymbol{l}-\mathbf{p}-\mathbf{q})[S(|\mathbf{k}-\mathbf{p}|)-1][S(|\mathbf{k}-\mathbf{q}|)-1]$$
$$\times\frac{\{[\hbar^2(\mathbf{k}-\mathbf{p})^2/2m]+\frac{1}{2}[e_\sigma^{(1)}(k)+e_\sigma^{(1)}(l)-e_\sigma^{(1)}(p)-e_\sigma^{(1)}(q)]\}^2}{e_\sigma^{(1)}(k)+e_\sigma^{(1)}(l)-e_\sigma^{(1)}(p)-e_\sigma^{(1)}(q)} \tag{10.19}$$

We are interested in first and second partial derivatives of $\langle V_{aa}\rangle_{\mathrm{T}}$ with respect to $n_\sigma(\mathbf{k})$ and $n_\tau(\mathbf{h})$, evaluated at $T=0$ and $k_{\mathrm{F}\sigma}=k_{\mathrm{F}}$. The last condition permits dropping the spin indices on $e_\sigma^{(1)}(\mathbf{k})$ $[e_\sigma^{(1)}(k)\to e^{(1)}(k)]$ and on $R_{1\sigma\sigma}$ and $R_{2\sigma\sigma}$(write simply R_1 and R_2). A second-order component in the quasiparticle energy is generated by the formula

$$\begin{aligned} e^{(2)}(h) &= \left[\frac{\partial}{\partial n_\sigma(\mathbf{h})}\langle V_{aa}\rangle_{\mathrm{T}}\right]_{T=0} \\ &= \sum_{l\le k_{\mathrm{F}};\; p,\,q>k_{\mathrm{F}}}\left[R_1(\mathbf{h}\boldsymbol{l};\mathbf{pq})+\frac{1}{2}R_2(\mathbf{h}\boldsymbol{l};\mathbf{pq})\right] \\ &\quad -\sum_{k,\,l\le k_{\mathrm{F}};\; p>k_{\mathrm{F}}}\left[R_1(\mathbf{k}\boldsymbol{l};\mathbf{hp})+\frac{1}{2}R_2(\mathbf{k}\boldsymbol{l};\mathbf{hp})\right] \end{aligned} \tag{10.20}$$

The chemical potential $\mu(\rho)$ at $T=0$ is the increment in the ground-state energy when one particle is added to the system; this statement yields the formula

$$\begin{aligned} \mu(\rho) &= \frac{1}{N}\left[E_0(\rho)+\rho\,\frac{\partial E_0}{\partial\rho}\right] \\ &= \frac{1}{N}(E_0+P\Omega) \end{aligned} \tag{10.21}$$

For the total quasiparticle energy at $T=0$ we write

$$e^{(0)}(h) = e^{(1)}(h)+e^{(2)}(h)+[\mu-e^{(1)}(k_{\mathrm{F}})-e^{(2)}(k_{\mathrm{F}})] \tag{10.22}$$

adjusting the zero level so that $e^{(0)}(k_{\mathrm{F}})=\mu$.

Under general small perturbations (associated with $T > 0$, $\delta N \neq 0$, external force fields, nonuniform temperature, and nonuniform particle and spin densities) the occupation number functions are perturbed by amounts $\delta n_\sigma(\mathbf{h})$. In the Landau formalism the quasiparticle energies are modified by the addition of a linear function of δn_σ with coefficients which are interpreted as elements of an interaction energy operator coupling different states of the quasiparticles:

$$e_\sigma(\mathbf{h}) = e_\sigma^{(0)}(h) + \sum_{\boldsymbol{l},\,\tau} f_{\sigma\tau}(\mathbf{h}, \boldsymbol{l})\, \delta n_\tau(\boldsymbol{l}) \tag{10.23}$$

The variation $\delta n_\tau(\boldsymbol{l})$ adapts the quantity $\langle \nu_j \rangle_{\mathrm{T}}$ of Eq. (10.3) to the present more general physical situation. Conditions of symmetry, invariance under time reversal, and invariance under reflection through the origin in **k** space require

$$f_{\sigma\tau}(\mathbf{h}, \boldsymbol{l}) = f_{\tau\sigma}(\boldsymbol{l}, \mathbf{h}) = f_{-\sigma,\,-\tau}(-\mathbf{h}, -\boldsymbol{l}) = f_{\sigma\tau}(-\mathbf{h}, -\boldsymbol{l}) = f_{-\sigma,\,-\tau}(\mathbf{h}, \boldsymbol{l}) \tag{10.24}$$

In the applications $f_{\sigma\tau}(\mathbf{h}, \boldsymbol{l})$ appears only for **h** and $\boldsymbol{l}$ on the Fermi surface ($h = l = k_{\mathrm{F}}$), and $f_{\sigma\tau}$ is then a function of a single variable, $z = \cos(\mathbf{h}, \boldsymbol{l})$. Physical quantities are expressed in terms of the coefficients

$$\begin{aligned} f^{\mathrm{s}}(z) &= \tfrac{1}{2}[f_{\uparrow\uparrow}(\mathbf{h}, \boldsymbol{l}) + f_{\uparrow\downarrow}(\mathbf{h}, \boldsymbol{l})] \\ f^{\mathrm{a}}(z) &= \tfrac{1}{2}[f_{\uparrow\uparrow}(\mathbf{h}, \boldsymbol{l}) - f_{\uparrow\downarrow}(\mathbf{h}, \boldsymbol{l})] \\ [2/(2L+1)]F_L^{\mathrm{s(a)}} &= \nu(0) \int_{-1}^{1} f^{\mathrm{s(a)}}(z) P_L(z)\, dz \end{aligned} \tag{10.25}$$

in which $\nu(0) = \Omega k_{\mathrm{F}} m^*/\pi^2\hbar^2$ is the density of quasiparticle states for both spins per unit energy range at the Fermi surface. Here m^* is the effective mass of a quasiparticle near the Fermi surface; it can be computed from two equivalent formulas

$$\begin{aligned} [\partial e^{(0)}(k)/\partial k]_{k=k_{\mathrm{F}}} &= \hbar^2 k_{\mathrm{F}}/m^* \\ m^*/m &= 1 + \tfrac{1}{3}F_1^{\mathrm{s}} \end{aligned} \tag{10.26}$$

Finally, $P_L(z)$ is the Legendre polynomial of order L.

Our microscopic analysis allows the representation of the function $f_{\sigma\tau}(\mathbf{h}, \mathbf{h}')$ as a sum of three components:

$$f_{\sigma\tau}(\mathbf{h}, \mathbf{h}') = f_{\sigma\tau}^{(1)}(\mathbf{h}, \mathbf{h}') + f_{\sigma\tau}^{(2)}(\mathbf{h}, \mathbf{h}') + (1/N)g(\rho) \tag{10.27}$$

$$\begin{aligned} f_{\sigma\sigma}^{(1)}(\mathbf{h}, \mathbf{h}') &= \left[\frac{\partial}{\partial n_\sigma(\mathbf{h})}\frac{\partial}{\partial n_\sigma(\mathbf{h}')}\langle E_a{}^{\mathrm{F}}\rangle_{\mathrm{T}}\right]_{T=0} \\ &= \frac{1}{N}\frac{\hbar^2(\mathbf{h}-\mathbf{h}')^2}{2m}[S(|\mathbf{h}-\mathbf{h}'|)-1] \\ &\quad - \frac{1}{N^2}\sum_{k\le k_{\mathrm{F}}}\left\{\frac{\hbar^2(\mathbf{h}-\mathbf{h}')^2}{2m}S(|\mathbf{h}-\mathbf{h}'|)[S(|\mathbf{h}-\mathbf{k}|)-1][S(|\mathbf{h}'-\mathbf{k}|)-1]\right. \\ &\quad + \frac{\hbar^2(\mathbf{h}-\mathbf{k})^2}{2m}S(|\mathbf{h}-\mathbf{k}|)[S(|\mathbf{h}-\mathbf{h}'|)-1][S|(\mathbf{h}'-\mathbf{k}|)-1] \\ &\quad \left. + \frac{\hbar^2(\mathbf{h}'-\mathbf{k})^2}{2m}S(|\mathbf{h}'-\mathbf{k}|)[S(|\mathbf{h}-\mathbf{h}'|)-1][S(|\mathbf{h}-\mathbf{k}|)-1]\right\} \end{aligned} \tag{10.28}$$

$$f_{\uparrow\downarrow}^{(1)} = f_{\downarrow\uparrow}^{(1)} = 0$$

$$\begin{aligned} f_{\uparrow\downarrow}^{(2)}(\mathbf{h}, \mathbf{h}') &= \left[\frac{\partial}{\partial n_\downarrow(\mathbf{h}')}\frac{\partial}{\partial n_\uparrow(\mathbf{h})}\langle V_{aa}\rangle_{\mathrm{T}}\right]_{T=0} \\ &= \frac{1}{2}\sum_{p,\,q>k_{\mathrm{F}}} R_1(\mathbf{hh}';\mathbf{pq}) + \frac{1}{2}\sum_{k,\,l\le k_{\mathrm{F}}} R_1(\mathbf{k}\boldsymbol{l};\mathbf{hh}') \\ &\quad - \sum_{l\le k_{\mathrm{F}};\,p>k_{\mathrm{F}}} R_1(\mathbf{h}\boldsymbol{l};\mathbf{ph}') - \sum_{l\le k_{\mathrm{F}};\,p>k_{\mathrm{F}}} R_1(\boldsymbol{l}\mathbf{h}';\mathbf{hp}) \end{aligned} \tag{10.29}$$

$$\begin{aligned} f_{\uparrow\uparrow}^{(2)}(\mathbf{h}, \mathbf{h}') &= \left[\frac{\partial}{\partial n_\uparrow(\mathbf{h}')}\frac{\partial}{\partial n_\uparrow(\mathbf{h})}\langle V_{aa}\rangle_{\mathrm{T}}\right]_{T=0} \\ &= \frac{1}{2}\sum_{p,\,q>k_{\mathrm{F}}}[R_1(\mathbf{hh}';\mathbf{pq}) + R_2(\mathbf{hh}';\mathbf{pq})] \\ &\quad + \frac{1}{2}\sum_{k,\,l\le k_{\mathrm{F}}}[R_1(\mathbf{k}\boldsymbol{l};\mathbf{hh}') + R_2(\mathbf{k}\boldsymbol{l};\mathbf{hh}')] \\ &\quad - \sum_{l\le k_{\mathrm{F}};\,p>k_{\mathrm{F}}}[R_1(\mathbf{h}\boldsymbol{l};\mathbf{ph}') + R_2(\mathbf{h}\boldsymbol{l};\mathbf{ph}')] \\ &\quad - \sum_{l\le k_{\mathrm{F}};\,p>k_{\mathrm{F}}}[R_1(\boldsymbol{l}\mathbf{h}';\mathbf{hp}) + R_2(\boldsymbol{l}\mathbf{h}';\mathbf{hp})] \end{aligned} \tag{10.30}$$

The third component $g(\rho)/N$ appears only in the coefficient $F_0{}^s$. It will be clear presently that the theory is complete without an explicit microscopic formula for $g(\rho)$.

10.3. SUMMARY OF FORMULAS FOR EQUILIBRIUM AND TRANSPORT PROPERTIES

The Landau formalism includes a number of relations expressing equilibrium and transport properties in terms of the $F_L^{s(a)}$ coefficients. Equations (10.26) for m^*/m is one of these. Formulas for the isothermal compressibility, magnetic susceptibility, and specific heat are, respectively,

$$\begin{aligned} \frac{1}{\rho K_T} &= mc^2 = \frac{1}{N}\frac{d\mu}{dN} \\ &= \frac{\hbar^2 k_F{}^2}{3m^*}(1 + F_0{}^s) \\ &= \frac{\hbar^2 k_F{}^2}{3m}\frac{1 + F_0{}^s}{1 + \frac{1}{3}F_1{}^s} \end{aligned} \tag{10.31}$$

$$\begin{aligned} \frac{\chi}{\chi_0} &= \frac{m^*/m}{1 + F_0{}^a} \\ &= \frac{1 + \frac{1}{3}F_1{}^s}{1 + F_0{}^a} \end{aligned} \tag{10.32}$$

$$\begin{aligned} C_\Omega &= (\Omega m^* k_F/3\hbar^2)K^2 T \\ &= NK(\pi^2 KT/2e_F)(1 + \tfrac{1}{3}F_1{}^s) \end{aligned} \tag{10.33}$$

Equation (10.31) displays the connection between the isothermal compressibility and the phase velocity c of density fluctuation waves. References 1–3 contain discussions of the physical limitations on the propagation of density fluctuation waves (ordinary sound) and on the possibility of other types of propagated distortion (c_0, zero sound) in the low-frequency range. Since our analysis yields the chemical potential as a function of density, we compute $d\mu/dN$ directly and use Eq. (10.31) to evaluate $F_0{}^s$.

This procedure allows us to avoid writing an explicit and redundant microformula for $g(\rho)$. Incidentally, $g(\rho)$ can be interpreted as the Fourier transform of a delta-function interaction potential between quasiparticles in coordinate space.

The magnetic susceptibility of the degenerate system without interactions is

$$\chi_0 = k_F m\mu_m{}^2/\pi^2\hbar^2 \tag{10.34}$$

Equation (10.32) shows that the interactions multiply χ_0 by an amplification factor with two components, m^*/m from the density of states and $(1+F_0{}^a)^{-1}$ from the energy change associated with the reversal of a single spin.

The theory of transport processes in the nearly degenerate fermion system is based on the elementary scattering process $p+q \to p'+q'$ (subject to constraints $\mathbf{p}+\mathbf{q}=\mathbf{p}'+\mathbf{q}'$, $\sigma_{\mathbf{p}}+\sigma_{\mathbf{q}}=\sigma_{\mathbf{p}'}+\sigma_{\mathbf{q}'}$, and p, q, p', $q' \approx k_F$). The scattering amplitudes $A^{s(a)}(\theta, \varphi)$ are functions of the angle θ between $\mathbf{p}$ and $\mathbf{q}$ (and also between $\mathbf{p}'$ and $\mathbf{q}'$) and the angle φ between the $\mathbf{p}$, $\mathbf{q}$ and $\mathbf{p}'$, $\mathbf{q}'$ planes. In the Landau formalism the forward scattering amplitudes $A^{s(a)}(\theta, 0)$ are related in a simple manner to the $F^{s(a)}$ functions (forward scattering means $\varphi = 0$, or $\mathbf{p}$, $\mathbf{q}$, $\mathbf{p}'$, and $\mathbf{q}'$ all in the same plane). The connection is

$$A_L^{s(a)} = \frac{F_L^{s(a)}}{1 + F_L^{s(a)}/(2L+1)} \tag{10.35}$$

in the representation of the scattering amplitude as a series in Legendre polynomials:

$$A^{s(a)}(\theta, 0) = \sum_L A_L^{s(a)} P_L(\cos\theta) \tag{10.36}$$

The CBF formalism contains the Landau formalism as a special case and it also contains all the information needed to evaluate $A^{s(a)}(\theta, \varphi)$, $\varphi \neq 0$; however, working formulas are available only for $\varphi = 0$. It must be stressed that errors of unknown magnitude are involved in the formula for the transport coefficients based on the substitution of the known forward scattering amplitudes for the general forms depending on φ.

The physical transition probabilities involve interference between (s) and (a) amplitudes, the sign of the interference term depending on whether the spins are identical or different; i.e.,

$$\omega_{\text{trip}}(\theta, \varphi) = \omega_{\uparrow\uparrow} = \omega_{\downarrow\downarrow} = \frac{2\pi}{\hbar}\left(\frac{\pi^2\hbar^2}{m^*k_{\text{F}}}\right)^2 |A^{\text{s}}(\theta, \varphi) + A^{\text{a}}(\theta, \varphi)|^2$$

$$\omega_{\text{sing}}(\theta, \varphi) = \frac{2\pi}{\hbar}\left(\frac{\pi^2\hbar^2}{m^*k_{\text{F}}}\right)^2 |A^{\text{s}}(\theta, \varphi) - 3A^{\text{a}}(\theta, \varphi)|^2$$

$$\omega_{\uparrow\downarrow}(\theta, \varphi) = \frac{2\pi}{\hbar}\left(\frac{\pi^3\hbar^2}{m^*k_{\text{F}}}\right)^2 |A^{\text{s}}(\theta, \varphi) - A^{\text{a}}(\theta, \varphi)|^2 \tag{10.37}$$

The mean transition probability

$$2\hat{\omega}(\theta, \varphi) = \tfrac{3}{4}\omega_{\text{trip}} + \tfrac{1}{4}\omega_{\text{sing}} \tag{10.38}$$

is needed in the evaluation of the thermal conductivity and viscosity coefficients. The third transition probability occurs in the theory of the spin diffusion coefficient.

It is worthwhile to see that $\hat{\omega}$ can be expressed in terms of $\omega_{\uparrow\uparrow}$ and $\omega_{\uparrow\downarrow}$. First of all, $\omega_{\uparrow\uparrow}$ is just the triplet probability. Second,

$$A^{\text{s}} - A^{\text{a}} = \tfrac{1}{2}[A^{\text{s}} + A^{\text{a}} + A^{\text{s}} - 3A^{\text{a}}]$$
$$\omega_{\uparrow\downarrow} = \tfrac{1}{4}(\omega_{\text{sing}} + \omega_{\text{trip}}) + \tfrac{1}{2}\,\text{Re}(A^{\text{s}} + A^{\text{a}})^*(A^{\text{s}} - 3A^{\text{a}})\frac{2\pi}{\hbar}\left(\frac{\pi^2\hbar^2}{m^*k_{\text{F}}}\right)^2 \tag{10.39}$$

The cross term averages to zero when integrated over the range $0 \leq \varphi \leq \pi$, and consequently makes no contribution in the evaluation of the coefficients of viscosity and thermal conductivity. In detail, the exclusion principle requires that $A^{\text{s}} + A^{\text{a}}$ reverses sign when $\mathbf{p}'$ and $\mathbf{q}'$ are interchanged, and also that $A^{\text{s}} - 3A^{\text{a}}$ is unchanged by the same operation. This interchange is equivalent to replacing φ by $\pi + \varphi$; hence $A^{\text{s}} + A^{\text{a}}$ is an odd function of $\cos\varphi$ and $A^{\text{s}} - 3A^{\text{a}}$ is an even function. Equation (10.38) can be replaced by the equivalent relation

$$2\hat{\omega}(\theta, \varphi) = \tfrac{1}{2}\omega_{\text{trip}} + \tfrac{1}{4}(\omega_{\text{trip}} + \omega_{\text{sing}})$$
$$\rightarrow \tfrac{1}{2}\omega_{\uparrow\uparrow} + \omega_{\uparrow\downarrow} \tag{10.40}$$

employed by Noziere and Pines [3]. Using Eq. (10.38), it is clear that final states labeled $\mathbf{p}'$, $\mathbf{q}'$ and $\mathbf{q}'$, $\mathbf{p}'$ are the same state. Double counting of the same final state is avoided by limiting the variable φ to the range $0 \leq \varphi \leq \pi$.

The symmetry properties of the singlet and triplet amplitudes as expressed by the relations

$$\begin{aligned} A^{s}(\theta, \pi+\varphi)+A^{a}(\theta, \pi+\varphi) &= -A^{s}(\theta, \varphi)-A^{a}(\theta, \varphi) \\ A^{s}(\theta, \pi+\varphi)-3A\,(\theta, \pi+\varphi) &= A^{s}(\theta, \varphi)-3A^{a}(\theta, \varphi) \end{aligned} \tag{10.41}$$

have the consequence that

$$A^{s}(\theta, \pi+\varphi)-A^{a}(\theta, \pi+\varphi)=-2A^{a}(\theta, \varphi) \tag{10.42}$$

and permit writing the equivalence relation of Eq. (10.40) in the form

$$\begin{aligned} \frac{\hbar}{2\pi}\left(\frac{m^{*}k_{F}}{\pi^{2}\hbar^{2}}\right)^{2} 2\hat{\omega}(\theta, \varphi) &\to \frac{1}{2}\,|A^{s}(\theta, \varphi)+A^{a}(\theta, \varphi)|^{2} \\ &\quad +\frac{1}{2}\,|A^{s}(\theta, \varphi)-A^{a}(\theta, \varphi)|^{2}+\frac{1}{2}\,|2A^{a}(\theta, \varphi)|^{2} \\ &= |A^{s}(\theta, \varphi)|^{2}+3|A^{a}(\theta, \varphi)|^{2} \end{aligned} \tag{10.43}$$

Here again φ is confined to the range $0 \leq \varphi \leq \pi$.

Abrikosov and Klalatnikov [2] give the following approximate formulas for the thermal conductivity K_{AK} and the viscosity η_{AK}:

$$\begin{aligned} K_{AK} &= \frac{4\pi^{2}}{3}\,\frac{(\hbar^{2}k_{F})^{3}}{m^{*4}\langle\hat{\omega}\sin\frac{1}{2}\theta\sin\frac{1}{2}\theta\rangle} \\ \eta_{AK}\,T^{2} &= \frac{16}{45}\,\frac{\hbar^{3}(\hbar k_{F})^{5}}{K^{2}\langle\hat{\omega}(\sin\frac{1}{2}\theta)^{3}\tan\frac{1}{2}\theta\,(\sin\varphi)^{2}\rangle} \end{aligned} \tag{10.44}$$

For the spin diffusion coefficient D Hone [6] gives the formula

$$D_{H}T^{2}=\frac{16\pi^{2}}{3}\,\frac{\hbar^{6}(\hbar k_{F})^{2}(1+F_{0}{}^{a})}{m^{*5}K^{2}\langle\omega_{\uparrow\downarrow}\sin\frac{1}{2}\theta\tan\frac{1}{2}\theta\,(1-\cos\varphi)\rangle} \tag{10.45}$$

In Eqs. (10.44) and (10.45) K is the Boltzmann constant and $\langle\ \rangle$ denotes an average over all orientations defined by the polar angle θ and the azimuth φ.

Baym and Ebner [7] obtain lower limits on the transport coefficients from an extremum formulation of the diffusion problem. Brooker and Sykes [8] and, independently, Pethick and Dy [9] and Jensen, Smith, and Wilkins [10] obtain accurate evaluations of the diffusion equations with the results (as stated by Brooker and Sykes [8])

$$\begin{aligned} K_{\text{th.cond.}}\, T &= C_K K_{\text{AK}}, && 0.417 < C_K < 0.561 \\ \eta &= C_\eta \eta_{\text{AK}}, && 0.750 < C_\eta < 0.925 \\ D &= C_{\text{D}} D_{\text{H}}, && 0.750 < C_{\text{D}} < 0.964 \end{aligned} \tag{10.46}$$

in agreement with Baym and Ebner with respect to the lower limits, but yielding the additional information that the accurate solutions are close to the lower limits. The range of values for the correction factors reflects the possible variations allowed by the unspecified dependence of the scattering intensities on θ and φ.

Emery [11] emphasizes the point that the symmetry properties of the amplitudes should not be ignored in estimating the transport coefficients. This remark is particularly appropriate for calculations based on Eqs. (10.40) and (10.43). The primary form, Eq. (10.38), is less sensitive to failure to meet the requirements of the exclusion principle. In fact, two extreme approximations (1) replacement of $A^{\text{s(a)}}(\theta, \varphi)$ by $A^{\text{s(a)}}(\theta, 0)$ and (2) representation of the amplitudes as step functions in φ,

$$\begin{aligned} A^{\text{s}}(\theta, \varphi) + A^{\text{a}}(\theta, \varphi) &= A^{\text{s}}(\theta, 0) + A^{\text{a}}(\theta, 0), && 0 \le \varphi < \pi/2, \\ &= -A^{\text{s}}(\theta, 0) - A^{\text{a}}(\theta, 0), && \pi/2 \le \varphi \le \pi, \\ A^{\text{s}}(\theta, \varphi) - 3A^{\text{a}}(\theta, \varphi) &= A^{\text{s}}(\theta, 0) - 3A^{\text{a}}(\theta, 0), && 0 \le \varphi \le \pi, \end{aligned} \tag{10.47}$$

give exactly the same values for $\hat{\omega}(\theta, \varphi)$ in Eq. (10.38), although the first form ignores the exclusion principle, while the second meets all requirements. A particular consequence of Eq. (10.47) is that Eq. (10.43) with $\varphi = 0$ in the right-hand member is not in conflict with the exclusion principle. The dependence on φ defined by Eq. (10.47) is of course arbitrary, but no more so than any other simple dependence consistent with the exclusion principle [9].

Finally, to facilitate numerical comparisons and estimates, we introduce the dimensionless parameters

$$v_K = (1/\pi) \int_0^\pi \int_0^\pi [\tfrac{3}{4}|A^{\text{s}} + A^{\text{a}}|^2 + \tfrac{1}{4}|A^{\text{s}} - 3A^{\text{a}}|^2](\sin \tfrac{1}{2}\theta)^3 \, d\theta \, d\varphi$$

$$v_\eta = (2/\pi) \int_0^\pi \int_0^\pi [\tfrac{3}{4}|A^{\text{s}} + A^{\text{a}}|^2 + \tfrac{1}{4}|A^{\text{s}} - 3A^{\text{a}}|^2](\sin \tfrac{1}{2}\theta)^5 (\sin \varphi)^2 \, d\theta \, d\varphi$$

$$v_{\text{D}} = (1/\pi) \int_0^\pi \int_0^\pi |A^{\text{s}} - A^{\text{a}}|^2 (\sin \tfrac{1}{2}\theta)^2 (1 - \cos \varphi) \, d\theta \, d\varphi \tag{10.48}$$

and write for the transport coefficients the explicit forms

$$
\begin{aligned}
K_{\text{th.contd.}} T &= C_K 6 \left(\frac{\pi}{3}\right)^{1/3} \frac{\hbar^2 \rho^{5/3}}{m^{*2}} v_K^{-1} \\
&= 6030\, C_K \left(\frac{m}{m^*}\right)^2 \left(\frac{\rho}{\rho_0}\right)^{5/3} v_K^{-1} \quad \frac{\text{ergs}}{\text{cm sec}} \\
\eta T^2 &= C_\eta \frac{32}{5} \left(\frac{3}{\pi}\right)^{1/3} \frac{\hbar^5 \rho^{7/3}}{K^2 m^{*2}} v_\eta^{-1} \\
&= 117.4\, C_\eta \left(\frac{m}{m^*}\right)^2 \left(\frac{\rho}{\rho_0}\right)^{7/3} v_\eta^{-1} \quad 10^{-6} (^\circ\text{K})^2 \text{ poise} \\
D T^2 &= C_\text{D} 8 \left(\frac{3}{\pi}\right)^{1/3} \frac{\hbar^5 \rho^{4/3} (1 + F_0{}^\text{a})}{K^2 m^{*3}} v_D^{-1} \\
&= 1788\, C_\text{D} \left(\frac{m}{m^*}\right)^3 \left(\frac{\rho}{\rho_0}\right)^{4/3} (1 + F_0{}^\text{a}) v_D^{-1} \quad 10^{-6} \frac{\text{cm}^2}{\text{sec}} (^\circ\text{K})^2
\end{aligned}
\tag{10.49}
$$

with $\rho_0 = 0.0164$ Å^{-3}.

10.4. NUMERICAL RESULTS*

The calculations by H. T. Tan [4] are all based on a recent redetermination of $E_0{}^\text{B}(\rho)$, $S(k)$, and $g(r)$ by Massey and Woo [12] using the de Boer–Michels parameters in a 6–12 Lennard-Jones potential. In the tables and diagrams to be presented here the index MW refers to input data taken from Ref. 12. An earlier evaluation of the ground-state properties of liquid ^{3}He by Woo [13] (in the context of the CBF formalism) used input data provided by Massey's first treatment of the boson problem [14] for the mass-3 system. In this case the potential parameters were adjusted slightly to fit the computed equilibrium energy and density of liquid ^{4}He to the experimental values. In a still earlier treatment of the fermion problem under realistic conditions Brueckner and Gammel [15] used the Yntema–Schneider potential as input data in evaluating Brueckner's reaction operator formalism. For comparison the three potentials are plotted in Fig. 10-1.

* See Tan [4]; also Woo [13].

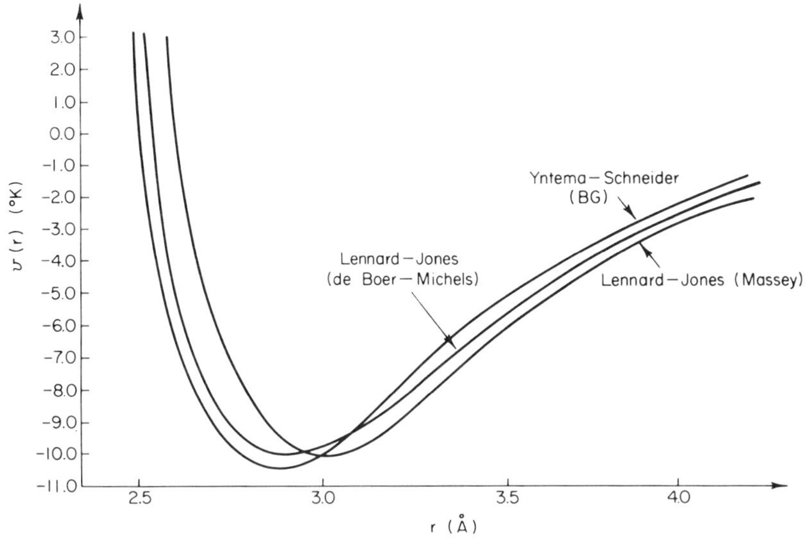

FIG. 10-1. Two-body potentials.

The calculation of ground-state properties is described fully by Woo [13]. Tan [4] used the same formulas and followed the same procedures, except in the evaluation of the magnetic susceptibility, where the Landau formalism provides a convenient intermediate stage. Numerical results are summarized in Table 10-1. The parameter B appears in the approximate form $S(k) \approx B(k/k_F)^2$, which is useful when k is the distance between two points within the Fermi sphere. A procedure for determining B is described in Refs. 5 and 13. The second-order energy including orthogonalization corrections is denoted by $\delta E_0^{(2)}$ [Eq. (9.57)]. Woo [13] gives a numerical example illustrating the strong cancellation between $\mathscr{W}_{0j}$ and $\frac{1}{2}(E_0^{(0)} - E_j^{(0)})J_{0j}$ terms in the evaluation of $\delta E_0^{(2)}$.

Equilibrium density occurs at $\rho = 0.0156$ Å^{-3}, and the corresponding ground-state energy per particle is $E_0/N = -0.49$ °K/atom. The experimental values are 0.0164 Å^{-3} and -2.52 °K/atom. I surmise that the discrepancy in energy comes almost entirely from the evaluation of E_0^{B}. Various approximations and simplifications in the evaluation of the ground-state boson energy which may contribute significantly to the discrepancy are discussed in Chapter 6, Section 6-7 under the headings (A) energy generated by the three-phonon vertex [16], (B) three-particle polarization energy [17]–[19], and (C) progress from the available to the optimum

TABLE 10-1

GROUND-STATE ENERGY (in °K/atom)

$\rho(\text{Å}^{-3})$	$k_F\ (\text{Å}^{-1})$	e_F	B	$E_0{}^B/N$	$E_1{}^F(0)/N$	$E_2{}^F(0)/N$	$E_3{}^F(0)/N$	$\delta E_0^{(2)}/N$	$E_{(0)}^{(0)}/N$	$E(0)/N$
0.0148	0.760	4.639	0.268	−2.097	2.778	−0.752	−0.133	−0.286	−0.200	−0.486
0.0156	0.773	4.804	0.259	−2.106	2.889	−0.802	−0.136	−0.325	−0.163	−0.487
0.0164	0.786	4.967	0.250	−2.093	2.979	−0.852	−0.141	−0.358	−0.107	−0.464
0.0172	0.799	5.128	0.242	−2.058	3.076	−0.898	−0.146	−0.391	−0.026	−0.417
0.0180	0.811	5.286	0.235	−1.997	3.170	−0.946	−0.150	−0.424	0.077	−0.347

BDJ-type trial functions [Eq. (5.43)]; see Ref. 20. Corrections A and C have not yet been evaluated for mass 3, but B can be estimated by Eq. (6.56): $0.86(164/218)^3 \approx 0.39$ °K/atom at the equilibrium density $\rho = 0.0164$ Å^{-3}.

Two approximations in Ref. 12 and 14 which may be sources of error are (1) incorrect behavior of $g(r)$ for small r—as $\exp[(-d/r)^{10}]$ rather than the correct limiting form $\exp[-(d/r)^5]$ required by the inverse-twelfth-power term in the potential—and (2) use of the superposition approximation for $p^{(3)}$ in computing the mean kinetic energy of the boson solution Both 1 and 2 are discussed briefly in Chapter 6 following Eq. (6.43). Table 6-2 makes it clear that these errors are unappreciable at mass 4. However, at mass 3 significant differences appear in the numerical results obtained by Massey and Woo [12] and Schiff and Verlet [21]. At $\rho = 0.0141$ Å^{-3} the two procedures yield the results shown in Table 10-2.

TABLE 10-2

Reference	$E_0{}^{B}/N$ (°K)	$(E_0{}^{B} + E_0{}^{F})/N$ (°K)
12	−2.06	−0.20
21	−2.92	−1.27

It is not clear why errors introduced by approximations 1 and 2 should be insignificant at $m = 4$ and appreciable at $m = 3$, particularly since the two evaluations of $S(k)$ give almost identical results at both masses. As suggested in Chapter 6, the problem requires further investigation.

The Schiff–Verlet determination of $E_0{}^{B}$ brings the ground-state energy of the fermion spectrum including $\delta E_0^{(2)}$ down to about −1.6°K/atom, somewhat lower than the value −0.96°K/atom obtained by Brueckner and Gammel [15]. No firm conclusion can be drawn from the comparison, since different potentials were used in the two calculations. Corrections due to factors (noted in Section 6-7, parts A[16] and C[22]), which may amount to as much as −1°K/atom, are a legitimate part of $E_0{}^{B}$. Thus it appears possible that the method of correlated basis functions can account for the energy of the ground state of the fermion system within perhaps 0.5°K/atom of the experimental value. The three-particle polarization energy is a universal correction (necessary in all procedures).

The numerical evaluation of $f^{(1)}(\cos\theta)$ presents no difficulties. We follow the procedure described by Wu and Feenberg [5]. In evaluating $f^{(2)}(\cos\theta)$, the range of summation (or integration) is extended to include all A states, as is evident from the simple form of the limits on the summations over **p**, **q**, **k**, and ***l*** in Eqs. (10.20) and (10.29)–(10.30). Singularities occur in the integrands of the integral formulas as a result of zeros in the energy denominators. The integrals generated by the various sums over the interior and exterior of the Fermi sphere in Eqs. (10.20) and (10.29)–(10.30) are combined so that contributions from opposite sides of a singularity are paired off, leaving the principal value as the correct physical quantity

The geometrical constructions needed for the evaluation of the integrals defining $f^{(2)}(\cos\theta)$ resemble those used in the evaluation of the second-order energy $\delta E_0^{(2)}$, but are somewhat simpler because two of the wave vectors are fixed in magnitude ($h = h' = k_F$). Numerical results for the various components that make up $Nf^s(\cos\theta)/e_F$ and $Nf^a(\cos\theta)/e_F$ are listed in Table 10-3. The spin-independent (s) and spin-flip (a) compo-

TABLE 10-3

COMPONENTS OF THE SPIN-INDEPENDENT AND SPIN-FLIP INTERACTION FUNCTIONS AT $\rho = 0.0164$ Å^{-3}

$\cos\theta$	$Ng(\rho)/e_F$	$Nf^{(1)s}/e_F = Nf^{(1)a}/e_F$	$Nf^{(2)s}/e_F$	$Nf^{(2)a}/e_F$
−1.0	3.398	−0.533	−2.585	0.839
−0.8	3.398	−0.626	−1.548	0.709
−0.6	3.398	−0.702	−1.156	0.681
−0.4	3.398	−0.751	−0.936	0.640
−0.2	3.398	−0.767	−0.777	0.545
−0.0	3.398	−0.743	−0.625	0.415
0.2	3.398	−0.678	−0.410	0.219
0.4	3.398	−0.578	−0.329	0.110
0.6	3.398	−0.453	−0.232	0.035
0.8	3.398	−0.320	−0.142	0.012
1.0	3.398	−0.177	−0.095	−0.001

nents of $Nf(\cos\theta)/e_F$ appear in Table 10-4 and Figs. 10-2 and 10-3. The Legendre expansion coefficients for $Nf^{s(a)}/e_F$ and the associated scattering amplitudes are listed in Table 10-5 at the equilibrium density.

The total scattering amplitudes $A^{s(a)}(\theta, 0)$ are plotted in Fig. 10-4. These plots reveal a discrepancy in that the scattering amplitude for the parallel spin state $A^s(\theta, 0) + A^a(\theta, 0)$ does not vanish at $\cos\theta = 1$ as required by the exclusion principle. The dashed curves represent possible modifications which remove the discrepancy without producing noticeable

TABLE 10-4 SPIN-INDEPENDENT (s) AND SPIN-FLIP (a) COMPONENTS OF Nf/e_F

$\cos\theta$	$\rho = 0.0156$ Å^{-3}		$\rho = 0.0164$ Å^{-3}		$\rho = 0.0172$ Å^{-3}	
	Nf^s/e_F	Nf^a/e_F	Nf^s/e_F	Nf^a/e_F	Nf^s/e_F	Nf^a/e_F
−1.0	0.209	0.295	0.280	0.296	0.345	0.313
−0.8	0.904	0.084	1.224	0.088	1.524	0.089
−0.6	1.239	−0.020	1.540	−0.021	1.845	−0.017
−0.4	1.409	−0.111	1.710	−0.111	2.017	−0.110
−0.2	1.549	−0.218	1.854	−0.222	2.162	−0.222
0.0	1.721	−0.322	2.030	−0.328	2.343	−0.330
0.2	1.989	−0.451	2.308	−0.459	2.644	−0.464
0.4	2.268	−0.461	2.491	−0.468	2.826	−0.472
0.6	2.379	−0.416	2.712	−0.419	3.046	−0.419
0.8	2.598	−0.285	2.936	−0.288	3.281	−0.283
1.0	2.856	−0.179	3.126	−0.178	3.575	−0.174

TABLE 10-5 LEGENDRE EXPANSION COEFFICIENTS AT THE DENSITY $\rho = 0.0164$ atoms/Å^3

	L							
	0	1	2	3	4	5	6	7
F_L^s	6.938	3.841	−0.346	0.678	−0.614	0.387	−0.135	−0.001
A_L^s	0.874	1.684	−0.371	0.618	−0.659	0.374	−0.136	−0.001
F_L^a	−0.751	−0.989	0.859	0.331	0.097	−0.183	−0.013	0.019
A_L^a	−3.019	−1.475	0.733	0.316	0.096	−0.187	−0.013	0.019

changes in the calculated transport properties [because of the weighting factors $(\sin \frac{1}{2}\theta)^3$ and $(\sin \frac{1}{2}\theta)$ in the formulas for the transport coefficients]. Also, the resolution of $F^a(\cos \theta)$ into Legendre polynomials is not sensitive to the indicated degree of modification for $l \leq 3$. Presumably, the discrepancy is in part an artifact of the approximations introduced to make the calculation manageable and in part a result of

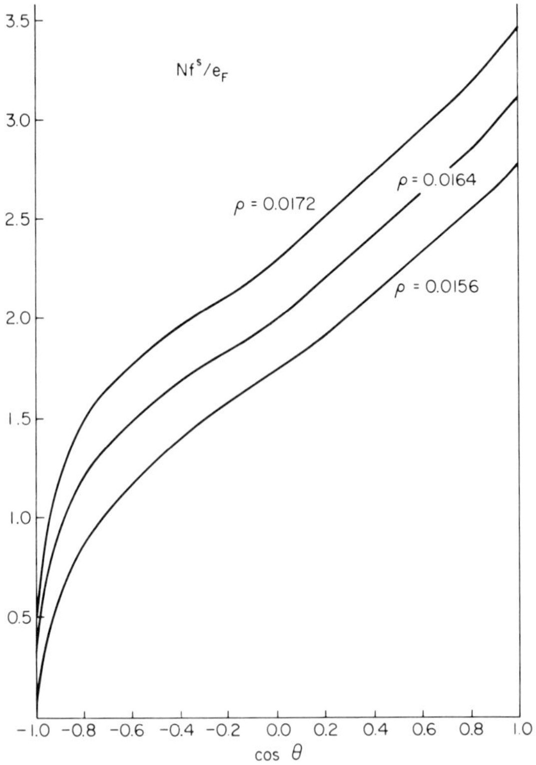

FIG. 10-2. Spin-independent (s) components of $Nf(\cos \theta)/e_F$.

accumulated error in the many arithmetical operations required to reduce the theory to numbers.

Numerical results for v_K, v_η, and v_D based on Eqs. (10.47) and (10.48) appear in Table 10-6.

Finally, ground-state and transport quantities are evaluated using only $E_a^{(0)}$ for the energies. These results appear in the last column of

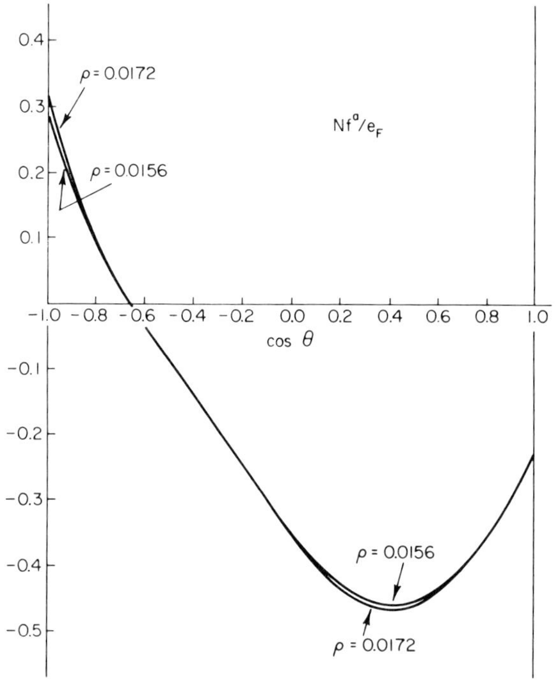

FIG. 10-3. Spin-flip (a) components of $Nf(\cos\theta)/e_F$.

TABLE 10-6

TRANSPORT PROBABILITY COEFFICIENTS

ρ (Å^{-3})	v_K	v_η	v_D
0.0156	7.6	2.35	15.4
0.0164	10.8	3.47	21.8
0.0172	25.0	8.5	52.1

Table 10-7. The great importance of the interaction and orthogonalization effects embodied in $\delta E_a^{(2)}$ is immediately apparent. Inclusion of $\delta E_a^{(2)}$ more than doubles the effective mass and brings the magnetic susceptibility down from the edge of ferromagnetism ($\chi \approx \infty$) to a moderately large positive value in semiquantitative agreement with experiment. When $f^{(2)}$ is neglected the result $F_0{}^a \approx -0.99$ and the associated very

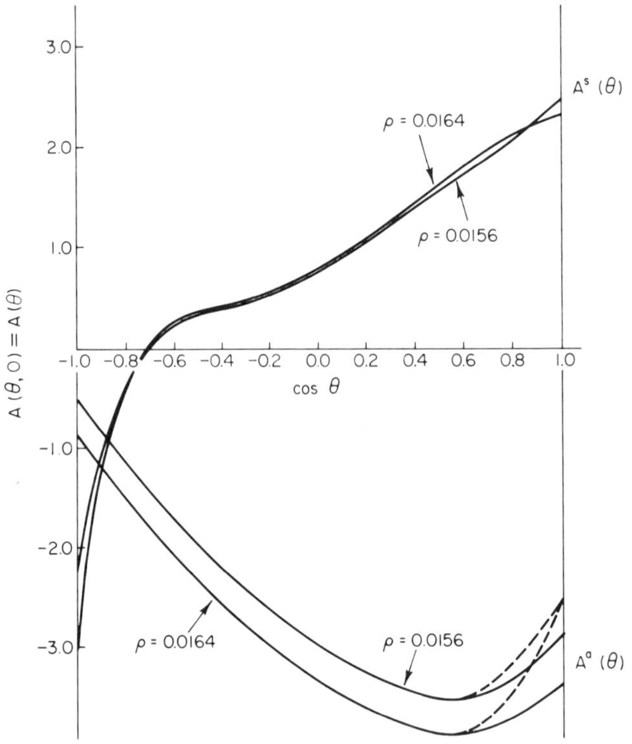

FIG. 10-4. Spin-independent (s) and spin-flip (a) scattering amplitudes.

large scattering amplitude $A_0{}^a$ has the consequence that the transport coefficients are too small by a factor of 10^{-3}. Also, the consistency condition $A^s(\theta=0)+A^a(\theta=0)=0$ required by the exclusion principle fails spectacularly. We interpret this failure as a sign that the diagonal matrix elements of H generated by correlated single-configuration states contain little information on the scattering and decay of quasiparticle excitations.

TABLE 10-7

EXPERIMENTAL AND CALCULATED PROPERTIES OF LIQUID ^{3}He

Physical quantity	Experiment[a]	Theory					
		Brueckner–Gammel	Woo	Tan			Derived from $E_a^{(0)}$
ρ (Å^{-3})	0.0164[b]	0.0136	0.0148	0.0156	0.0164	0.0172	0.0164
E/N (°K/atom)	−2.52	−0.96	−1.35	−0.49	−0.46	−0.42	−0.11
K (%/atm)	3.8	5.3	3.6[b]	4.8	3.9	3.2	3.55
c_1 (m/sec)	182.3	169.0	184.0[b]	164.0	178.0	191.0	188.0
χ/χ_0	11.1	12.0	13.9	7.8	9.2	13.4	2×10^2
m^*/m	2.82	1.84	—	2.18	2.28	2.48	1.11
$K_{\text{th.cond.}}\, T$(ergs/cm-sec)	33.0	—	—	64–86	45–60	18–24	10^{-1}
ηT^2 [P (°K)^2]	2.0	—	—	7.0–8.6	4.9–6.0	1.9–2.3	10^{-3}
$D_H T^2$ [10^{-6} cm^2(°K)^2/sec]	1.4	—	—	2.2–2.8	1.3–1.6	0.3–0.4	10^{-3}
c_0 (m/sec)	191.0	—	—	175.0	187.0	199.0	—

[a] J. C. Wheatley, "Quantum Fluids" (D. F. Brewer, ed.). North Holland, Amersterdam, 1966; *Phys Rev.* **165**, 304 (1968).
[b] At experimental equilibrium density.

The summand $f^{(2)}$ derived from $\delta E_a^{(2)}$ is able to supply this information because it is generated by linear combinations of correlated single-configuration states.

All the calculated physical quantities at three densities are listed in Table 10-7 together with experimental results and theoretical values obtained by Brueckner and Gammel [15] and Woo [13]. Since density is the relevant parameter, Tan's results at $\rho = 0.0164$ Å^{-3} should be compared with experiment, although his equilibrium density falls at $\rho = 0.0156$ Å^{-3}. I list Woo's results for compressibility and velocity of first sound at $\rho = 0.0164$ Å^{-3}. The significant features of the theoretical evaluation of magnetic susceptibility are that it is positive (paramagnetic) and large. The actual numerical values are probably highly sensitive to the approximations involved in all the calculations (see discussion by Woo [13]). The transport coefficients all vary rapidly with density; consequently, it is not surprising that the theoretical values from the corrected AK and Hone formulas agree with experiment at densities close to the equilibrium density.

The theory has been subjected to an additional test using the numerical information on m^*/m given in Table 10-7. The dependence of m^*/m on density is represented adequately by the formula

$$\begin{aligned} m^*/m &= 2.31 - 3.1[1 - (\rho/\rho_0)] \\ &\approx 2.31(\rho/\rho_0)^{4/3}, \qquad \rho_0 = 0.0164 \quad \text{Å}^{-3} \end{aligned} \tag{10.50}$$

within the probable uncertainty of the numerical evaluations. The power $\frac{4}{3}$ is of course without significance. With this information it is possible to estimate the thermal coefficient of volume expansion α. The theory [23] is based on the thermodynamic relation

$$\begin{aligned} \alpha &\equiv \frac{1}{\Omega}\left(\frac{\partial \Omega}{\partial T}\right)_{\mathrm{P}} = -\frac{\rho K_{\mathrm{T}}}{N}\left(\frac{\partial S}{\partial \rho}\right)_{\mathrm{T}} \\ &= -\frac{\rho}{Nmc^2}\left(\frac{\partial S}{\partial \rho}\right)_{\mathrm{T}} \end{aligned} \tag{10.51}$$

and the formula for the entropy

$$\begin{aligned} S(T, \rho) &= C_{\Omega}(T, \rho) \\ &= \frac{m^*}{m}\left(\frac{\rho_0}{\rho}\right)^{2/3} NK \frac{\pi^2}{2} \frac{KT}{e_{\mathrm{F}}(\rho_0)} \end{aligned} \tag{10.52}$$

Equations (10.42)–(10.44) yield

$$\begin{aligned}\alpha &= -\left[\rho\frac{\partial}{\partial\rho}\frac{m^*}{m} - \frac{2}{3}\frac{m^*}{m}\right]\left(\frac{\rho_0}{\rho}\right)^{2/3}\frac{\pi^2}{2}\frac{K}{mc^2}\frac{KT}{e_{\mathrm{F}}(\rho_0)} \\ &\approx -7.6\left(\frac{\rho}{\rho_0}\right)^{2/3}\frac{K}{mc^2}\frac{KT}{e_{\mathrm{F}}(\rho_0)} \\ &= -0.07T \quad (^\circ\mathrm{K})^{-1} \quad \text{at} \quad \rho = \rho_0 \end{aligned} \tag{10.53}$$

The most recent experimental evaluation [24] gives

$$(d\alpha/dT)_{T=0} \approx -0.16 \quad (^\circ\mathrm{K})^{-2}$$

The behavior of α as a function of density is dominated by the factor c^{-2}, which decreases rapidly as the pressure and density are raised. Consequently, α becomes smaller in magnitude as the density is raised (in qualitative agreement with the observations [24]).

References

1. L. D. Landau, *Zh. Eksperim. i. Teor. Fiz.* **30**, 1058 (1956); **32**, 59 (1957); **34**, 262 (1958) [English transls. (resp.): *Soviet Phys—JETP* **3**, 920 (1956/57); **5**, 101 (1957); **7**, 182 (1958).]
2. A. A. Abrikosov and I. M. Khalatnikov, *Repts. Progr. Phys.* **XXII**, 329 (1959) [The Physical Society, London.]
3. D. Pines and P. Nozieres, "The Theory of Quantum liquids." Benjamin, New York, 1966.
4. H. T. Tan, unpublished doctoral dissertation, Washington University, 1968; H. T. Tan and E. Feenberg, *Phys. Rev.* **176,** 360 (1968).
5. F. Y. Wu and E. Feenberg, *Phys. Rev.* **128**, 943 (1962).
6. D. Hone, *Phys. Rev.* **121**, 669 (1961).
7. G. Baym and C. Ebner, *Phys. Rev.* **164**, 235 (1967).
8. G. A. Brooker and J. Sykes, *Phys. Rev. Letters* **21**, 279 (1968).
9. K. S. Dy and C. J. Pethick, *Phys. Rev. Letters* **21**, 876 (1968).
10. H. H. Jensen, H. Smith, and J. W. Wilkins, *Phys. Letters* **27A**, 532 (1968).
11. V. J. Emery, *Phys. Rev.* **179**, 205 (1968).
12. W. E. Massey and C. W. Woo, *Phys. Rev.* **164**, 256 (1967).
13. C. W. Woo, *Phys. Rev.* **151**, 138 (1966).
14. W. E. Massey, *Phys. Rev.* **151**, A153 (1966).
15. K. A. Brueckner, and J. L. Gammel, *Phys. Rev.* **109**, 1040 (1958).
16. T. B. Davison, unpublished doctoral dissertation, Washington University, 1968.
17. B. M. Axelrod, *J. Chem. Phys.* **19**, 724 (1951).
18. A. Dalgarno and G. A. Victor, *Molec. Phys.* **10**, 333 (1966).
19. T. B. Davison and E. Feenberg, *Phys. Rev.* **178**, 306 (1969).
20. H. W. Jackson and E. Feenberg, *Ann. Phys.* (*N.Y.*) **15**, 266 (1961).
21. D. Schiff and L. Verlet, *Phys. Rev.* **160**, 208 (1967).
22. C. E. Campbell, private communication.
23. K. A. Brueckner and K. R. Atkins, *Phys. Rev. Letters* **1**, 315 (1958).
24. C. Boghasian, H. Meyer, and J. E. Rives, *Phys. Rev.* **146**, 110 (1966).

CHAPTER 11

Theory of a ^{3}He Atom in Liquid ^{4}He at $T=0$

11.1. STATEMENT OF THE PROBLEM

Interesting foreign objects in liquid ^{4}He include bubbles, electrons, positive ions, and ^{3}He atoms. The last is particularly interesting because it provides a physical realization of a nearly degenerate, weakly interacting fermion system. Much of the essential theory of the dilute solution of ^{3}He is based on the properties of the isolated ^{3}He atom in the liquid [1], [2]. These properties (separation energy, effective mass, and differential volume coefficient) are studied and evaluated numerically in this chapter based on a thesis by Davison [3], [4].

The Hamiltonian operator is

$$H = -\frac{\hbar^2}{2m_4}\sum_1^{N-1}\Delta_j - \frac{\hbar^2}{2m_3}\Delta_N + \sum_{i<j} v(r_{ij})$$
$$= H_0 + H_1 \qquad (11.1)$$

in which H_0 is the Hamiltonian for a system of N ^{4}He atoms and H_1 is the perturbation operator associated with the mass difference:

$$H_1 = -\tfrac{1}{2}\hbar^2[(1/m_3) - (1/m_4)]\,\Delta_N \qquad (11.2)$$

The physical problem requires a description of a state characterized by momentum $\hbar\mathbf{k}$, minimum energy, and absence of macroscopic mass flow. Similar terms characterize the problem of an elementary excitation in the pure boson liquid, and closely related methods of solution are available for both problems [5]–[7]. In the problem of the foreign atom suitable trial functions are generated by linear combinations of the normalized basis functions

$$
\begin{aligned}
|\mathbf{k}\rangle &= \psi_0{}^{\mathrm{B}} \exp i\mathbf{k} \cdot \mathbf{r}_N \\
|\mathbf{k}-\mathbf{k}', \mathbf{k}'\rangle &= \frac{1}{[NS(k')]^{1/2}} \psi_0{}^{\mathrm{B}}[\exp i(\mathbf{k}-\mathbf{k}') \cdot \mathbf{r}_N][\rho_{\mathbf{k}'} - S(k') \exp i\mathbf{k}' \cdot \mathbf{r}_N]
\end{aligned}
\tag{11.3}
$$

These basis functions differ among themselves in the partition of momentum between substrate and foreign particle; in $|\mathbf{k}\rangle$ all the momentum is carried by the foreign particle, and in $|\mathbf{k}-\mathbf{k}', \mathbf{k}'\rangle$ momentum $\hbar\mathbf{k}'$ is associated with elementary excitations in the substrate. The particular linear combination of elementary excitations and particle motion in $|\mathbf{k}-\mathbf{k}', \mathbf{k}'\rangle$ is determined by the requirement of orthogonality to $|\mathbf{k}\rangle$:

$$
\langle \mathbf{k}|1|\mathbf{k}-\mathbf{k}', \mathbf{k}'\rangle = 0, \qquad \mathbf{k} \text{ and } \mathbf{k}' \neq 0 \tag{11.4}
$$

The fact that $\langle \mathbf{k}-\mathbf{k}', \mathbf{k}'|1|\mathbf{k}-\mathbf{k}'', \mathbf{k}''\rangle$ does not vanish for $\mathbf{k}'' \neq \mathbf{k}'$ is not a source of difficulty, but would generate complications if the evaluation of the energy were carried beyond the second order of the perturbation procedure.

The Brillouin–Wigner perturbation formalism is used to compute the approximate eigenfunction

$$
\psi = |\mathbf{k}\rangle + \sum_{\mathbf{k}' \neq 0} \frac{|\mathbf{k}-\mathbf{k}', \mathbf{k}'\rangle\langle \mathbf{k}-\mathbf{k}', \mathbf{k}'|H|\mathbf{k}\rangle}{E(k) - \langle \mathbf{k}-\mathbf{k}', \mathbf{k}'|H|\mathbf{k}-\mathbf{k}', \mathbf{k}'\rangle} \tag{11.5}
$$

and the energy

$$
\begin{aligned}
E(k) &= E_0{}^{\mathrm{B}} + \mathscr{E}_1(k) + \mathscr{E}_2(k) + \cdots \\
\mathscr{E}_1(k) &= \langle \mathbf{k}|H - E_0{}^{\mathrm{B}}|\mathbf{k}\rangle \\
&= \frac{m_4 - m_3}{m_3 N} \langle 0|\mathrm{K.E.}|0\rangle + \frac{\hbar^2 k^2}{2m_3} \\
\mathscr{E}_2(k) &= \sum_{\mathbf{k}' \neq 0} \frac{|\langle \mathbf{k}-\mathbf{k}', \mathbf{k}'|H - E_0{}^{\mathrm{B}}|\mathbf{k}\rangle|^2}{\mathscr{E}_1(k) + \mathscr{E}_2(k) - \langle \mathbf{k}-\mathbf{k}', \mathbf{k}'|H - E_0{}^{\mathrm{B}}|\mathbf{k}-\mathbf{k}', \mathbf{k}'\rangle}
\end{aligned}
\tag{11.6}
$$

The energy formula has a simple interpretation. The first term $E_0{}^{\mathrm{B}}$, is the ground-state energy of the substrate, in which is included the foreign atom; the second term, $\mathscr{E}_1(k)$, is the first-order expectation energy; and the third, $\mathscr{E}_2(k)$, is the second-order energy generated by the flow in the substrate associated with the presence of the ^{3}He atom [6]. Since the trial functions are not eigenfunctions of H_0, the perturbation operator is $H - E_0{}^{\mathrm{B}}$ (and not just H_1). A third-order energy $\mathscr{E}_3(k, \rho)$ may not be negligible, but because of computational difficulties cannot be evaluated at the time of writing.

11.2. REDUCTION OF MATRIX ELEMENTS

The evaluation of matrix elements of (H_0) and (H_1) can be simplified by noting that

$$\langle 0|G^* H_0 F|0\rangle = E_0{}^{\mathrm{B}}\langle 0|G^* F|0\rangle + (\hbar^2/2m_4)\langle 0|\sum_1^N \boldsymbol{\nabla}_j G^* \cdot \boldsymbol{\nabla}_j F|0\rangle \quad (11.7)$$

$$-\langle 0|G^*\Delta_N F|0\rangle = \int (\boldsymbol{\nabla}_N \psi_0{}^{\mathrm{B}})^2 G^* F \, d\mathbf{r}_{1,2,\ldots,N} + \int (\psi_0{}^{\mathrm{B}})^2 [\boldsymbol{\nabla}_N G^* \cdot \boldsymbol{\nabla}_N F - \tfrac{1}{2}\Delta_N G^* F] \, d\mathbf{r}_{1,2,\ldots,N} \quad (11.8)$$

Thus, applying Eq. (11.7),

$$\begin{aligned} \langle \mathbf{k}|H_0 - E_0{}^{\mathrm{B}}|\mathbf{k}\rangle &= \frac{\hbar^2 k^2}{2m_4} \\ \langle \mathbf{k}-\mathbf{k}', \mathbf{k}'|H_0 - E_0{}^{\mathrm{B}}|\mathbf{k}-\mathbf{k}', \mathbf{k}'\rangle &= \frac{\hbar^2}{2m_4}(\mathbf{k}-\mathbf{k}')^2 + \frac{\hbar^2 k'^2}{2m_4 S(k')} + O\left(\frac{1}{N}\right) \\ \langle \mathbf{k}-\mathbf{k}', \mathbf{k}'|H_0 - E_0{}^{\mathrm{B}}|\mathbf{k}\rangle &= \frac{1}{[NS(k')]^{1/2}} \frac{\hbar^2 \mathbf{k}\cdot\mathbf{k}'}{2m_4}[1 - S(k')] \end{aligned} \quad (11.9)$$

The explicit formula for $\mathscr{E}_1$ is a special case of Eq. (11.7) with $G = F = \exp i\mathbf{k}\cdot\mathbf{r}_N$. To continue with applications of Eq. (11.7), let

$$\begin{aligned} G &= \exp i\mathbf{k}\cdot\mathbf{r}_N \\ F &= [\exp i(\mathbf{k}-\mathbf{k}')\cdot\mathbf{r}_N][\rho_{\mathbf{k}'} - S(k')\exp i\mathbf{k}'\cdot\mathbf{r}_N] \end{aligned} \quad (11.10)$$

Elementary reductions yield

$$\int (\psi_0{}^{\mathrm{B}})^2 [\nabla_N G^* \cdot \nabla_N F - \tfrac{1}{2} \Delta_N G^* F] \, d\mathbf{r}_{1,2,\ldots,N} = (\mathbf{k} \cdot \mathbf{k}' - \tfrac{1}{2} k'^2)[1 - S(k')] \tag{11.11}$$

$$\int (\psi_0{}^{\mathrm{B}})^2 [\nabla_N F^* \cdot \nabla_N F - \tfrac{1}{2} \Delta_N F^* F] \, d\mathbf{r}_{1,2,\ldots,N} = (\mathbf{k} - \mathbf{k}')^2 \tag{11.12}$$

Next

$$\begin{aligned} \int (\nabla_N \psi_0{}^{\mathrm{B}})^2 F^* F \, d\mathbf{r}_{1,2,\ldots,N} &= \int |\nabla_N \psi_0{}^{\mathrm{B}}|^2 |\rho_{\mathbf{k}'}|^2 \, d\mathbf{r}_{1,2,\ldots,N} + O(N^0) \\ &= NS(k') \int |\nabla_N \psi_0{}^{\mathrm{B}}|^2 \, d\mathbf{r}_{1,2,\ldots,N} + O(N^0) \end{aligned} \tag{11.13}$$

Equation (11.13) requires some explanation. The first statement follows immediately from the explicit formula for F^*F; the second is based on the intuitive argument that the two-particle distribution function generated by integrating $|\nabla_N \psi_0{}^{\mathrm{B}}|^2$ over all coordinates except $\mathbf{r}_i$ and $\mathbf{r}_j$ differs little from the true radial distribution function $g(r_{ij})$ defined by $(\psi_0{}^{\mathrm{B}})^2$ (for all pairs i and j even including N) except for a normalization factor. An explicit evaluation of the integral using the BDJ form for $\psi_0{}^{\mathrm{B}}$ yields the same result [3].

One summand of $\langle \mathbf{k} - \mathbf{k}', \mathbf{k}' | H - E_0{}^{\mathrm{B}} | \mathbf{k} \rangle$ is given by Eq. (11.9); the remaining summand $\langle \mathbf{k} - \mathbf{k}', \mathbf{k}' | H_1 | \mathbf{k} \rangle$ can be estimated by introducing the BDJ form for $\psi_0{}^{\mathrm{B}}$ [Eqs. (2.12), (5.3)]. Then

$$\begin{aligned} &\int |\nabla_N \psi_0{}^{\mathrm{B}}|^2 G^* F \, d\mathbf{r}_{1,2,\ldots,N} \\ &\qquad \approx -\tfrac{1}{4}(N-1) \int (\psi_0{}^{\mathrm{B}})^2 \nabla_N \cdot [G^* F \nabla_N) u(r_{1N})] \, d\mathbf{r}_{1,2,\ldots,N} \end{aligned} \tag{11.14}$$

The right-hand member of Eq. (11.14) is easily expressed in terms of the two- and three-particle distribution function generated by $\psi_0{}^{\mathrm{B}}$. One component in $p^{(3)}(1, 2, N)$ can be eliminated by using the vector form of the BBGKY equation [Eq. (2.33)], with the result

$$\begin{aligned} \langle \mathbf{k} - \mathbf{k}', \mathbf{k}' | H_1 | \mathbf{k} \rangle = \frac{m_4 - m_3}{m_3 [NS(k')]^{1/2}} \frac{\hbar^2}{2m_4} \Big\{ &[1 - S(k')](\mathbf{k} \cdot \mathbf{k}' - \tfrac{1}{4} k'^2) \\ &- \tfrac{1}{4} \rho \int (\exp i\mathbf{k}' \cdot \mathbf{r}) g(r) \, \Delta u \, d\mathbf{r} \\ &- \frac{1}{4N} \int \{ p^{(3)}(1, 2, 3) - \rho^3 g(r_{12}) g(r_{13}) \} (\exp i\mathbf{k}' \cdot \mathbf{r}_{12}) \\ &\times \Delta_1 u(r_{13}) \, d\mathbf{r}_{1,2,3} \Big\} \end{aligned} \tag{11.15}$$

In the multiple integral in Eq. (11.15) the factor $\Delta_1 u(r_{13})$ ensures that the integrand is large only when points 1 and 3 are not far apart. The remaining factor in the integrand vanishes if point 2 is far from point 1. These properties ensure that the multiple integral is a continuous function of k' at $k' = 0$, where it has the value

$$-(1/4N) \int [(N-2)\rho^2 g(r_{13}) - (N-1)\rho^2 g(r_{13})]\, \Delta_1 u(r_{13})\, d\mathbf{r}_3 = \tfrac{1}{4}\rho \int g\, \Delta u\, d\mathbf{r}$$

Thus the integral terms in Eq. (11.15) cancel at $\mathbf{k}' = 0$ and the complete matrix element vanishes. The preceding statement is a consequence of the sequential relation connecting $p^{(2)}(13)$ and $p^{(3)}(1, 2, 3)$; to extend the evaluation to $k' \neq 0$, we need an approximate form for $p^{(3)}$ which contains $g(r_{13})$ as a factor and satisfies the sequential relation when integrated over point 2. These conditions are met by the mixed form

$$\hat{p}(13|2) = \rho^3 g(r_{13}) \left[1 + h_{12} + h_{23} + h_{12} h_{23} + \rho \int h_{14} h_{24} h_{34}\, d\mathbf{r}_4 \right] \tag{11.16}$$

taken from Chapter 2, Appendix 2-A. Inserting Eq. (11.16) for $\hat{p}(13|2)$ in Eq. (11.15), the integration over coordinate $\mathbf{r}_2$ can be completed, leaving finally

$$\begin{aligned} \langle \mathbf{k} - \mathbf{k}', \mathbf{k}' | H_1 | \mathbf{k} \rangle \approx{}& \frac{m_4 - m_3}{m_3 [N S(k')]^{1/2}} \frac{\hbar^2}{2m_4} \\ &\times \left\{ [1 - S(k')] \left(\mathbf{k} \cdot \mathbf{k}' - \frac{1}{4} k'^2 \right) \right. \\ &- \frac{1}{4} S(k') \rho \int (\exp i\mathbf{k} \cdot \mathbf{r}) g(r)\, \Delta u(r)\, d\mathbf{r} \\ &- S(k') \frac{1}{4(2\pi)^3} \int [S(k'') - 1][S(|\mathbf{k}' + \mathbf{k}''|) - 1] \\ &\left. \times (\exp i\mathbf{k}'' \cdot \mathbf{r}) g(r)\, \Delta u(r)\, d\mathbf{r}\, d\mathbf{k}'' \right\} \end{aligned} \tag{11.17}$$

The bits and pieces in Eqs. (11.6), (11.13), and (11.17) add up to the complete matrix elements

$$\begin{aligned} \langle \mathbf{k} - \mathbf{k}', \mathbf{k}' | H - E_0{}^{\mathrm{B}} | \mathbf{k} - \mathbf{k}', \mathbf{k}' \rangle ={}& \frac{\hbar^2}{2m_3} (\mathbf{k} - \mathbf{k}')^2 + \frac{\hbar^2 k'^2}{2m_4 S(k')} \\ &+ \frac{m_4 - m_3}{m_3} \frac{1}{N} \langle 0 | \mathrm{K.E.} | 0 \rangle + O\left(\frac{1}{N} \right) \end{aligned} \tag{11.18}$$

$$\begin{aligned}
&\langle \mathbf{k}-\mathbf{k}', \mathbf{k}'|H - E_0{}^{\mathrm{B}}|\mathbf{k}\rangle \\
&\quad \approx \frac{\hbar^2}{2m_3[NS(k')]^{1/2}} \Bigg\{[1 - S(k')]\left(k \cdot k' - \frac{m_4 - m_3}{4m_4} k'^2\right) \\
&\quad - \frac{m_4 - m_3}{m_4} \pi S(k')\rho \int_0^\infty \frac{\sin k'r}{k'r} g(r)\, \Delta u(r) r^2\, dr \\
&\quad - \frac{m_4 - m_3}{m_4} \frac{1}{8\pi^2} \int [S(k'') - 1][S(|k' + k''|) - 1] \\
&\quad \times \int_0^\infty \frac{\sin k''r}{k''r} g(r)\, \Delta u(r) r^2\, dr\, \mathbf{dk}''\Bigg\}
\end{aligned} \tag{11.19}$$

These results permit writing the second-order energy in the form

$$\mathscr{E}_2(k, \rho) = \frac{\hbar^2}{2m_4} Y(k, \rho)$$

(11.20)

$$Y(k, \rho) = \frac{1}{4\pi^2 \rho} \int_0^\infty k'^2\, dk' \int_{-1}^{1} \frac{N|\langle \mathbf{k}-\mathbf{k}', \mathbf{k}'|(2m_4/\hbar^2)H|\mathbf{k}\rangle|^2\, dz}{Y(k, \rho) + \frac{4}{3}(2kk'z - k'^2) - [k'^2/S(k')]}$$

Here $z = \cos(\mathbf{k}, \mathbf{k}')$. Equation (11.19) gives $|\langle \mathbf{k}-\mathbf{k}', \mathbf{k}'|H|\mathbf{k}\rangle|^2$ as a quadratic polynomial in z; consequently, the integration over z can be carried through analytically, leaving the equation in the form of a nonlinear, one-dimensional integral equation for the unknown function $Y(k, \rho)$. A solution is found by iteration starting from a suitable zeroth-order approximation.

Davison's thesis and reference 4 contain numerical results based on several recent evaluations of the binding energy, mean kinetic energy, and liquid structure function of the ^{4}He liquid [8]–[10]. These evaluations employ an earlier (and presumably less accurate) estimate of the interaction matrix element based on the Kirkwood superposition approximation for $p^{(3)}$. In the following discussion one set of theoretical estimates (based on $E_0{}^{\mathrm{B}}$, $\langle 0|\text{K.E.}|0\rangle$, and $S(k)$ determined by Massey and Woo [10] is sufficient to bring out the significance of second-order contributions to the various physical quantities.

11.3. NUMERICAL EVALUATION OF MATRIX ELEMENTS AND ENERGY

The separation energy $B_\rho(k, \rho)$ is defined as the energy required to remove a ^{3}He atom from the solution while holding the density constant. The explicit formula is

$$\begin{aligned} -B_\rho(k, \rho) &= E(k, \rho) - \frac{N-1}{N} E_0{}^{\mathrm{B}}(\rho) \\ &\approx \frac{1}{N} E_0{}^{\mathrm{B}}(\rho) + \mathscr{E}_1(k, \rho) + \mathscr{E}_2(k, \rho) \\ &= \frac{1}{N}\left[E_0{}^{\mathrm{B}}(\rho) + \frac{1}{3}\langle 0|\mathrm{K.E.}|0\rangle\right] + \frac{\hbar^2 k^2}{2m_3} + \mathscr{E}_2(k, \rho) \end{aligned} \tag{11.21}$$

Available numerical results for the factor in brackets at $\rho = \rho_0 = 0.0218$ Å^{-3} and $\rho = 0.9\rho_0$ appear in Table 6-2. The table includes energies computed by (1) Schiff and Verlet [11] using the method of molecular dynamics on a finite system (864 particles), and (2) McMillan [12] using a Monte Carlo integration procedure for a finite system (108 particles). The de Boer–Michels potential is common to all these calculations. Additional results covering the density range of the ^{4}He liquid appear in Table 6-3. Table 11-1 exhibits numerical results for the first- and second-order components of $B_\rho(0, \rho)$.

The measured separation energy at the equilibrium density ($\rho = 0.0218$ Å^{-3}) is $B_{\mathrm{exp}} = 2.76$ °K [13]. In the theoretical first order, two large terms of opposite sign nearly cancel, greatly enhancing the relative importance of the second-order energy $\mathscr{E}_2$. Explicitly,

$$B_\rho(0, \rho) = (5.97 - \tfrac{1}{3}14.06) + 0.11 = 1.39 \quad {}^\circ\mathrm{K/atom} \tag{11.22}$$

The numbers in the last column of Table 6-2 illustrate the illusory improvement in the theoretical separation energy when it is computed at a density below the experimental equilibrium density. In general, comparisons of experimental and theoretical quantities should be made at the same density. The equilibrium energy is, of course, an exception just because it is an extreme value (as a function of density).

The discrepancy between 2.76 °K/atom (experimental [13]) and 1.39 °K/atom (theoretical [3]) may be correlated with the fact that the calculated energy per particle at the equilibrium density falls short of the experimental

TABLE 11-1

ENERGY QUANTITIES FROM THE DE BOER–MICHELS POTENTIAL (in °K/atom)

$\rho(\text{Å}^{-3})$	$(1/N)\langle 0\|\text{K.E.}\|0\rangle$	$E_0{}^{\text{B}}/N$	$(E_0{}^{\text{B}} + \frac{1}{3}\langle 0\|\text{K.E.}\|0\rangle)/N$	$\mathscr{E}_2(0, \rho)$	$B_\rho(0, \rho)$
0.0218	14.06	−5.97	−1.28	−0.108	1.39
0.0226	14.98	−6.03	−1.03	−0.120	1.15
0.0234	15.88	−6.04	−0.75	−0.131	0.88
0.0242	16.85	−6.00	−0.38	−0.141	0.51
0.0250	17.76	−5.90	−0.02	−0.150	0.13
0.0258	18.70	−5.72	−0.51	−0.161	−0.36

value by close to -1.15 °K/atom. It is tempting to consider that an improved description of the ground state will lower the energy substantially with relatively little increase in the kinetic energy. In a similar optimistic spirit, Eq. (11.21) can be treated as very nearly exact (at $k = 0$) and used to evaluate the mean kinetic energy at the equilibrium density in terms of measured quantities $[E_0{}^{\mathrm{B}} = -7.20,\ B_\rho(0, \rho) = 2.76]$ and the computed value of $\mathscr{E}_2(0, \rho)$:

$$(1/N)\langle 0|\mathrm{K.E.}|0\rangle \approx 3[-2.76 + 7.20 + 0.11] \\ = 13.65 \quad ^\circ\mathrm{K/atom} \qquad \text{at} \quad \rho = 0.0218 \quad \text{Å}^{-3} \tag{11.23}$$

slightly smaller than the theoretical estimates in Table 6-2.

11.4. EFFECTIVE MASS

The concept of effective mass is based on the working hypothesis that $\mathscr{E}(k, \rho)$ is a quadratic function of k. In fact, the exact numerical values of $\mathscr{E}_2(k, \rho)$ are well represented by a quadratic formula with errors of about 1% in the range $0 < k \leq 1$ Å^{-1}. I write

$$\mathscr{E}(k, \rho) = \mathscr{E}_1(k, \rho) + \mathscr{E}_2(k, \rho) \approx \mathscr{E}(0, \rho) + (\hbar^2 k^2 / 2m^*) \tag{11.24}$$

Numerical values of m^*/m as given in Table 11-2. Specific-heat measurements yield $m^*/m_3 \approx 2.4$ at the equilibrium density [14]. The parameter m^* is the effective mass of the quasiparticle moving freely through the substrate (replacing the actual fermion, which interacts strongly with the substrate).

TABLE 11-2

EFFECTIVE MASS AND DIFFERENTIAL VOLUME COEFFICIENT OF A ^{3}He ATOM IN LIQUID ^{4}He

ρ (Å^{-3})	m^*/m_3	$\alpha_1(\rho)$	$\alpha_2(\rho)$	$\alpha(\rho)$
0.0218	1.81	0.309	-0.0127	0.297
0.0226	1.89	0.264	-0.0099	0.254
0.0234	1.99	0.228	-0.0076	0.220
0.0242	2.08	0.200	-0.0058	0.194
0.0250	2.19	0.177	0.0052	0.172
0.0258	2.30	0.158	0.0046	0.154

Theory and experiment would agree if the coefficient of $-k^2$ in $\mathscr{E}_2(k, \rho)$ were 30% larger than the actual computed coefficient. In any case, the extremum property of H for fixed momentum guarantees that an improved description of the system in the state of minimum energy with momentum $\hbar\mathbf{k}$ will produce a larger coefficient of $-k^2$ in $\mathscr{E}_2(k, \rho)$ and a larger effective mass.

11.5. THE DIFFERENTIAL VOLUME COEFFICIENT

Consider a solution of ^{3}He in liquid ^{4}He at the concentration x ($x = N_3/N_3 + N_4) \ll 1$). The differential volume coefficient $\alpha(\rho)$represents the relative increase in volume when a ^{4}He atom is replaced by ^{3}He (at constant pressure and temperature). The volume of the dilute solution then exceeds the volume of pure liquid ^{4}He by the amount

$$\delta\Omega = \Omega\alpha(\rho)x \tag{11.25}$$

In particular, for a solution containing one ^{3}He atom

$$\delta\Omega = (1/\rho)\alpha(\rho) \tag{11.26}$$

The theoretical evaluation of $\alpha(\rho)$ at $T=0$ is based on the formula for the energy when the concentration is low:

$$E(x, \rho) = E_0{}^{\mathrm{B}}(\rho) + xN\mathscr{E}(0, \rho) \tag{11.27}$$

Let $P(\rho)$ and $P'(\rho)$ represent the pressures in the pure liquid and the solution, respectively, at constant volume. Equation (11.27) yields

$$(P' - P)\Omega = xN\rho\; \partial\mathscr{E}(0, \rho)/\partial\rho \tag{11.28}$$

The relaxation to volume $\Omega + \delta\Omega$ reduces the pressure to P; thus

$$\begin{aligned} P' - P &= -\delta P \\ &= -[\partial^2 E(x, \rho)/\partial\Omega^2]\,\delta\Omega \\ &= \delta\Omega/\Omega K_{\mathrm{T}} \end{aligned} \tag{11.29}$$

in which $K_T(\rho)$ is the isothermal compressibility of the ^{4}He liquid. Equations (11.25), (11.27), and (11.29) give Baym's formula [1], [2]

$$\alpha(\rho) = (\rho/m_4 c^2)\, \delta\mathscr{E}(0, \rho)/\partial\rho \tag{11.30}$$

which may be resolved into two summands

$$\begin{aligned} \alpha_1(\rho) &= \frac{\rho}{3m_4 c^2} \frac{\partial}{\delta\rho} \langle 0|\text{K.E.}|0\rangle \\ \alpha_2(\rho) &= \frac{\rho}{m_4 c^2} \frac{\partial}{\delta\rho} \mathscr{E}_2(0, \rho) \end{aligned} \tag{11.31}$$

In the reduction of the theory to numbers, the velocity of sound $c(\rho)$ may be taken from experiment or derived from the theoretical evaluation of $E_0{}^B(\rho)$. The second procedure would be meaningful if the theoretical energy coincided closely with the experimental energy curve. However, since the calculations with the de Boer–Michels parameters have not yet achieved such accuracy (a discrepancy of 16% in the computed energy), the experimental velocity of sound is used in computing the numbers exhibited in Table 11-2.

The experimental determination by Kerr [15] gives $\alpha \approx 0.28$ at the equilibrium density. Baym, Bardeen, and Pines [2] obtain $\alpha \approx 0.275$ from the effective interaction between ^{3}He atoms in solution. The fact that the theoretical estimate (0.297) is too large agrees with expectations that the approximate trial functions used to describe the ground state become increasingly inaccurate as ρ increases, resulting in an associated excessive rate of increase of $\langle 0|\text{K.E.}|0\rangle$ with increasing density.

The unexpected result that α_2 is almost negligible must be stressed. This means that the measured $\alpha(\rho)$ provides direct and fairly accurate information on the mean kinetic energy of the ^{4}He liquid as a function of density.

The extension of this analysis to a system of two ^{3}He atoms in the ^{4}He liquid should determine the interaction operator between ^{3}He atoms in solution. In summary, the comparison of theory and experiment reveals an interesting pattern of partial agreement and meaningful disagreement. It is clear that improvements are needed in the theory of the ^{4}He liquid, and probably also in the evaluation of $\mathscr{E}_2(k, \rho)$. It is also necessary to again state explicitly that no objective grounds are known for supposing that the third-order energy $\mathscr{E}_3(k, \rho)$ is negligible.

One promising current development may be mentioned. Massey, Tan and Woo [16] have initiated a program for the study of dilute solutions of ^{3}He in liquid ^{4}He based on an asymmetrical correlation factor $\psi_0{}^{\mathrm{B}}(\mathbf{r}_1, \mathbf{r}_2, \ldots, \mathbf{r}_{N_4}; \mathbf{r}_{N_4+1}, \ldots, \mathbf{r}_{N_4+N_3})$ characterized by the statement that it is the ground-state solution of the Schrödinger equation (with both sets of particles treated as spinless bosons). This procedure has the advantage of incorporating a large part of the physics of the problem into the eigenvalue $E_0{}^{\mathrm{B}}(N_4, N_3)$ and the associated radial distribution functions $g^{44}(r)$, $g^{43}(r)$, and $g^{33}(r)$. All matrix elements of H can be expressed directly in terms of the distribution functions generated by $\psi_0{}^{\mathrm{B}}$.

References

1. G. Baym, *Phys. Rev. Letters* **17**, 952 (1966).
2. J. Bardeen, G. Baym, and D. Pines, *Phys. Rev.* **156**, 207 (1967).
3. T. B. Davison, unpublished doctoral dissertation, Washington University, 1967.
4. T. B. Davison and E. Feenberg, *Phys. Rev.* 178, 306 (1969).
5. R. P. Feynman, *Phys. Rev.* **94**, 262 (1954).
6. R. P. Feynman and M. Cohen, *Phys. Rev.* **102**, 1189 (1956).
7. H. W. Jackson and E. Feenberg, *Rev. Mod. Phys.* **34**, 686 (1962).
8. W. E. Massey, *Phys. Rev.* **151**, A153 (1966).
9. D. K. Lee, unpublished doctoral dissertation, Washington University, 1966; *Phys. Rev.* **162**, 134 (1967).
10. W. E. Massey and C-W. Woo, *Phys. Rev.* **164**, 256 (1967).
11. D. Schiff and L. Verlet, *Phys. Rev.* **160**, 208 (1967).
12. W. L. McMillan, *Phys. Rev.* **138**, A442 (1965).
13. E. M. Ifft, D. O. Edwards, R. E. Sarwinski, and M. M. Skertic, *Phys. Rev. Letters*, **19**, 831 (1968).
14. A. C. Anderson, D. O. Edwards, W. R. Roach, R. E. Sarwinski, and J. C. Wheatley, *Phys. Rev. Letters* **17**, 367 (1966).
15. E. C. Kerr, *In* "Proceedings of the Fifth International Conference on Low Temperature Physics and Chemistry," p. 160. University of Wisconsin Press, Madison, Wisconsin, 1958.
16. C.W. Woo, H.T. Tan and W. E. Massey, *Phys. Rev. Letters* **22**, 278, (1969); extended treatment to appear in *Phys. Rev.*

Author Index

Numbers in parentheses are reference numbers and indicate that an author's work is referred to, although his name is not cited in the text. Numbers in italics show the page on which the complete reference is listed.

Subject Index

PURE AND APPLIED PHYSICS

A Series of Monographs and Textbooks

Consulting Editors

H. S. W. Massey
University College, London, England

Keith A. Brueckner
University of California, San Diego
La Jolla, California

1. F. H. Field and J. L. Franklin, Electron Impact Phenomena and the Properties of Gaseous Ions.
2. H. Kopfermann, Nuclear Moments, English Version Prepared from the Second German Edition by E. E. Schneider.
3. Walter E. Thirring, Principles of Quantum Electrodynamics. Translated from the German by J. Bernstein. With Corrections and Additions by Walter E. Thirring.
4. U. Fano and G. Racah, Irreducible Tensorial Sets.
5. E. P. Wigner, Group Theory and Its Application to the Quantum Mechanics of Atomic Spectra. Expanded and Improved Edition. Translated from the German by J. J. Griffin.
6. J. Irving and N. Mullineux, Mathematics in Physics and Engineering.
7. Karl F. Herzfeld and Theodore A. Litovitz, Absorption and Dispersion of Ultrasonic Waves.
8. Leon Brillouin, Wave Propagation and Group Velocity.
9. Fay Ajzenberg-Selove (ed.), Nuclear Spectroscopy. Parts A and B.
10. D. R. Bates (ed.), Quantum Theory. In three volumes.
11. D. J. Thouless, The Quantum Mechanics of Many-Body Systems.
12. W. S. C. Williams, An Introduction to Elementary Particles.
13. D. R. Bates (ed.), Atomic and Molecular Processes.
14. Amos de-Shalit and Igal Talmi, Nuclear Shell Theory.
15. Walter H. Barkas. Nuclear Research Emulsions. Part I.
    Nuclear Research Emulsions. Part II. *In preparation*
16. Joseph Callaway, Energy Band Theory.
17. John M. Blatt, Theory of Superconductivity.
18. F. A. Kaempffer, Concepts in Quantum Mechanics.
19. R. E. Burgess (ed.), Fluctuation Phenomena in Solids.
20. J. M. Daniels, Oriented Nuclei: Polarized Targets and Beams.
21. R. H. Huddlestone and S. L. Leonard (eds.), Plasma Diagnostic Techniques.
22. Amnon Katz, Classical Mechanics, Quantum Mechanics, Field Theory.
23. Warren P. Mason, Crystal Physics in Interaction Processes.
24. F. A. Berezin, The Method of Second Quantization.
25. E. H. S. Burhop (ed.), High Energy Physics. In four volumes.

26. L. S. Rodberg and R. M. Thaler, Introduction to the Quantum Theory of Scattering.

27. R. P. Shutt (ed.), Bubble and Spark Chambers. In two volumes.

28. Geoffrey V. Marr, Photoionization Processes in Gases.

29. J. P. Davidson, Collective Models of the Nucleus.

30. Sydney Geltman, Topics in Atomic Collision Theory.

31. Eugene Feenberg, Theory of Quantum Fluids.

32. Robert T. Beyer and Shephen V. Letcher, Physical Ultrasonics.

In preparation

J. Killingbeck and G. H. A. Cole, Physical Applications of Mathematical Techniques.